McDONNELL ENGINEERING
Steam Turbine
Application & Field Engineering
1014 5th Ave West
Seattle, WA. 98119 USA

INTRODUCTION TO
STAINLESS STEELS

3rd Edition

Jonathan Beddoes, Carleton University
J. Gordon Parr

ASM INTERNATIONAL

The Materials
Information Society

First printing, June 1999

Great care is taken in the compilation and production of this Volume, but it should be made clear that NO WARRANTIES, EXPRESS OR IMPLIED, INCLUDING, WITHOUT LIMITATION, WARRANTIES OF MERCHANTABILITY OR FITNESS FOR A PARTICULAR PURPOSE, ARE GIVEN IN CONNECTION WITH THIS PUBLICATION. Although this information is believed to be accurate by ASM, ASM cannot guarantee that favorable results will be obtained from the use of this publication alone. This publication is intended for use by persons having technical skill, at their sole discretion and risk. Since the conditions of product or material use are outside of ASM's control, ASM assumes no liability or obligation in connection with any use of this information. No claim of any kind, whether as to products or information in this publication, and whether or not based on negligence, shall be greater in amount than the purchase price of this product or publication in respect of which damages are claimed. THE REMEDY HEREBY PROVIDED SHALL BE THE EXCLUSIVE AND SOLE REMEDY OF BUYER, AND IN NO EVENT SHALL EITHER PARTY BE LIABLE FOR SPECIAL, INDIRECT OR CONSEQUENTIAL DAMAGES WHETHER OR NOT CAUSED BY OR RESULTING FROM THE NEGLIGENCE OF SUCH PARTY. As with any material, evaluation of the material under end-use conditions prior to specification is essential. Therefore, specific testing under actual conditions is recommended.

Nothing contained in this book shall be construed as a grant of any right of manufacture, sale, use, or reproduction, in connection with any method, process, apparatus, product, composition, or system, whether or not covered by letters patent, copyright, or trademark, and nothing contained in this book shall be construed as a defense against any alleged infringement of letters patent, copyright, or trademark, or as a defense against liability for such infringement.

Comments, criticisms, and suggestions are invited, and should be forwarded to ASM International.

Library of Congress Cataloging-in-Publication Data

Jonathan Beddoes
J. Gordon Parr
Introduction to Stainless Steels
Includes bibliographical references and index.
I. Title
TA169.5.T56   1998   620'.00452-dc21   98-29456

ISBN: 0-87170-673-3
SAN: 204-7586

ASM International®
Materials Park, OH 44073-0002

Printed in the United States of America

Contents

Preface

This book is intended as an introduction. It is a handshake that is firm in its resolution but not prolonged. We hope that the stranger will find conviction in its grasp, while anyone who has already hobnobbed with the metallurgical family will enjoy this new acquaintance.

We are not the first to observe that while an introductory text must have no less integrity than an advanced treatise, it obviously cannot assume the language, the derivations, the premises, perhaps even the dogma, which an advanced work takes for granted. Consequently, the authors find themselves questioning their own assumptions as they try to find explanations that are straightforward while correct and cogent. Therefore, although this book does not pretend to cover the extensive technology of its subject, it does presume to give a fair and honest fistful in its introductory handshake.

The more comprehensive texts from which we have drawn include *Stainless Steels*, Les Editions de Physique Les Ulis, 1993; Sedriks' *Corrosion of Stainless Steels,* John Wiley & Sons, Inc., 1996, and several *ASM Handbooks,* particularly the *ASM Specialty Handbook: Stainless Steels,* 1994. If you seek original sources (for we have not attempted such a catalog), these three texts should more than satisfy you in their plenitude. We began by looking at *An Introduction to Stainless Steel* by Parr and Hanson, American Society for Metals, 1965, and its revision, *Stainless Steel,* by Lula in 1986. Although we have been guided by their outline and initially thought we might simply revise and supplement, this presentation is entirely new.

Commercially supported institutions have been generous in their response to our requests. The Nickel Development Institute's substantial arsenal of material relating to the nickel-bearing stainless steels has been of immense help, and we are particularly indebted to the institute consultant Jack F. McGurn. The International Chromium Development Association made a valuable supplement to our holdings, both in print and especially in videos that deal with ferritic stainless steels. The Specialty Steel Industry of North America has been extremely helpful, too. Several companies involved with stainless steel have provided valuable information, including Atlas Steels, Bekintex, Cromweld, the Hazelett Strip Casting Corporation (through Wojtek Szczypiorski), Inco (through Mark Parker), Lukens, and Terray Corporation. These and other organizations, including publishers, that have given us permission to reproduce their material, have been acknowledged in the text.

Colleagues have been generous as we elicited their views. While we do not want to implicate them in any way, our thanks go to Dr. Jack Cahoon, Norman G. Eley, Kelvin Leddy, and Dr. Walter S. Owen. There may be others who did not realize that we were picking their brains.

Our thanks are extended to Veronica Flint at ASM International for her cheerful support and encouragement.

Very special thanks go to Dr. Malcolm J. Bibby, Dean, Faculty of Engineering, Carleton University, for he introduced us to each other. He anticipated this introductory text, but did not know that he had initiated a cordial partnership and a warm friendship between the authors.

We apologize for any omissions, anticipate gentle reminders, and promise that our oversights will be emended in the next edition.

Jonathan Beddoes
J. Gordon Parr

Technical Books Committee

A Review of Stainless Steels: What They Are; What They Do

1.1 Introduction

Most useful metals and alloys do not corrode in pure, dry air at atmospheric temperature. Commercial plain-carbon structural steels, for instance, do not rust away or develop corrosion pits if they are kept in a dessicator. Other useful metals do corrode but only to such a minute extent that the use of the word corrode is probably not correct. These metals react with the oxygen of the air to form an invisible, passive layer on or at their surface. A useful hypothesis is that the metal surface becomes enveloped in a molecularly thin, transparent oxidic coating, which not only provides protection from the environment but is self-healing should it be damaged. Indeed, if the protective layer does not re-form, then the underlying metal is attacked. It corrodes.

Practical atmospheres are not dessicator-dry; the environment around structural materials and metal goods is usually wet or moist and contaminated. Consequently, most engineering metals and alloys are susceptible to corrosive attack. Under these circumstances, unprotected plain-carbon steels corrode, as do the low-alloy steels; but the stainless steels generally do not because their chromium content causes the formation of that important, protective, passive layer. They do not discolor in a normal atmospheric environment, nor are they attacked by dilute nitric acid, which is commonly used as an etchant in the preparation of metallographic specimens. They were said, therefore, not to stain and so became known as stainless steels. It is a happy description: not only are its alliterative sibilants poetically attractive, it gives a practical impression of usefulness.

When the first stainless steels were developed in the early 1900s (that interesting story is reviewed in Chapter 2), the range of corrosion-resistant expectations was far less extensive than it is today; the simple stainless steels of the time justified their broad characterization. As we come to consider the contemporary usefulness of stainless steels, we have to remember that when they were first nudged into service, there was little demand for engineering materials that withstood temperatures far above atmospheric. The subsequent appreciation that the stainless steels had better high-temperature mechanical properties than did other steels, coupled with their corrosion resistance, was of enormous consequence. It spurred not only alloy development but industrial expectations and demands.

Improvements and refinements were made—and are still being made—to an increasing range of alloys, each of which has necessarily become more specific in its application. The developments relate not only to chemical composition, vitally important though that is. Heat-treatments, fabrication techniques, the steelmaking process and its control have all contributed to the development of an arsenal of stainless iron-base alloys whose usefulness far outruns the initial expectations that, in retrospect, seem so modest.

Martensitic stainless steels may have yield strengths as high as 1800 MPa (260 ksi). Even higher strengths are obtainable by heavily cold working the high-manganese, high-nitrogen austenitic alloys. Some stainless steels may be used at temperatures in excess of 1100 °C (2010 °F); some retain their toughness when they are cooled to very low temperatures only slightly above absolute zero. All have specific features of resistance to corrosion, although (we may as well warn you of this at the outset) none is universally applicable.

The stainless steels are fabricated into a myriad of functional shapes. The list of possible shaping processes covers the gamut. There are good casting alloys, but forged or rolled products, especially sheet, account for a far greater tonnage. Bar can be rolled or extruded and drawn to wire; slabs are rolled to plate or to sheet that may be bent, deep-drawn, or spun. Tube and pipe may be made by seamless or welding processes. Powder metallurgy techniques have their special applications. Some alloys are designed for easy machinability; most can be soldered, brazed, welded, or glued. Hard surfaces may be applied to stainless steel in many ways including, most recently, plasma-arc transfer. Stainless may form the surface of other metals, most commonly by cladding, so that the attractive surface qualities of stainless are combined with the mechanical properties of a cheaper substratum.

1.2 Stainless Steel Production

Table 1.1 summarizes the world production of stainless steel. Consumption in many countries is shown in Table 1.2. Stainless steel producers review per capita consumption shown in Table 1.3 with cautious optimism as they contemplate projections for the rest of the world implied by the figures for Taiwan, South Korea, and Hong Kong. However, analysts remind us that enterprises that require a high stainless steel consumption are not priorities in the Third World; therefore, immediate dramatic increases are not expected there. The comparatively low figures of consumption in North America and much of Europe arise because the principal industries that consume stainless steel, such as manufacturing and construction, now repre-

Table 1.1   World production of stainless steel

| | Stainless steel production, 1000 tonnes liquid metal | | | | | | | | | |
	1987	1988	1989	1990	1991	1992	1993	1994	1995	1996
Western Europe										
Austria	54	67	65	49	36	30	26	32	34	...
Belgium	182	264	337	372	360	445	435	520	622	577
Finland	189	206	192	226	258	322	371	426	431	462
France	700	781	727	797	772	814	786	919	980	972
Germany	957	1,187	1,169	1,146	1,154	1,163	1,194	1,419	1,490	1,280
Italy	547	629	619	574	606	645	720	854	1,017	862
Spain	320	426	367	461	454	483	560	652	765	841
Sweden	455	482	457	471	429	483	554	602	618	586
United Kingdom	393	428	380	388	374	388	433	531	548	557
Other Europe	35	35	30	31	20	10	16	25	42	112
Total	3,832	4,505	4,343	4,515	4,463	4,783	5,095	5,980	6,547	6,249
Africa										
South Africa	120	122	112	118	120	150	168	181	260	334
Asia										
India	162	176	188	220	265	245	292	400	560	600
Japan(a)	2,722	3,160	3,134	3,130	3,357	3,148	3,213	3,449	3,925	3,891
South Korea	40	80	180	360	430	489	550	626	704	839
Taiwan	131	139	140	150	157	162	154	265	498	712
Total	3,055	3,555	3,642	3,860	4,209	4,044	4,209	4,740	5,687	6,042
Americas										
Brazil	192	188	196	186	190	185	211	239	237	226
Canada	82	127	154	145	150	162	185	182	193	185
U.S.A.	1,836	1,996	1,748	1,851	1,708	1,808	1,774	1,835	2,055	1,870
Total	2,110	2,311	2,098	2,182	2,048	2,155	2,170	2,256	2,485	2,281

(continued)

(a) HR production converted on a 90% basis. Source: *Inco World Stainless Steel Statistics*, 1997

Table 1.1 (continued)

	Stainless steel production, 1000 tonnes liquid metal									
	1987	1988	1989	1990	1991	1992	1993	1994	1995	1996
Other countries										
Australia	45	34	...	...	...	...	...	...	...	...
Others	20	...	...	...	...	...	...	...	...	...
Total	65	34	0	0	0	0	0	0	0	0
Subtotal	**9,182**	**10,527**	**10,195**	**10,675**	**10,840**	**11,132**	**11,642**	**13,157**	**14,979**	**14,906**
Austenitic share	74.8%	75.1%	74.5%	75.0%	74.5%	74.0%	75.0%	75.0%	76.2%	76.0%
Commonwealth of Independent States	2,000	2,270	2,140	1,790	1,600	1,260	550	288	200	330
Eastern Europe	185	·200	210	140	140	100	100	50	40	67
People's Republic of China	220	240	250	240	260	250	319	325	380	270
World total	**11,587**	**13,237**	**12,795**	**12,845**	**12,840**	**12,742**	**12,611**	**13,820**	**15,599**	**15,573**

(a) HR production converted on a 90% basis. Source: *Inco World Stainless Steel Statistics*, 1997

Table 1.2 World consumption of stainless steel

	Stainless steel consumption, 1000 tonnes									
	1987	1988	1989	1990	1991	1992	1993	1994	1995	1996
Western Europe										
France	315	365	335	380	400	408	340	440	518	413
Germany	770	830	814	900	935	975	915	960	1,093	1,061
Italy	505	540	565	524	570	609	638	900	1,031	988
Spain	120	177	142	220	200	197	200	150	266	273
United Kingdom	243	298	260	300	255	308	302	330	310	291
Other Europe	527	650	589	591	615	628	575	750	721	672
Total	2,480	2,860	2,705	2,915	2,975	3,125	2,970	3,530	3,939	3,698
Asia										
Japan	1,480	1,870	1,914	1,836	1,985	1,760	1,750	1,837	2,045	2,105
Americas										
U.S.A.	1,411	1,577	1,467	1,537	1,479	1,612	1,742	1,960	2,015	2,088
Other countries	1,490	1,720	1,656	1,980	1,983	2,075	2,228	2,618	3,214	3,287
Subtotal	**6,861**	**8,027**	**7,742**	**8,268**	**8,422**	**8,572**	**8,690**	**9,945**	**11,213**	**11,178**
Commonwealth of Independent States	1,250	1,300	1,300	1,210	1,100	865	380	200	162	158
Eastern Europe	175	190	210	180	140	125	125	90	120	140
People's Republic of China	210	290	260	185	325	470	649	631	717	941
World total	**8,496**	**9,807**	**9,512**	**9,843**	**9,987**	**10,032**	**9,844**	**10,866**	**12,212**	**12,417**

U.S. apparent consumption figures revised to exclude imports of intermediate products. Source: *Inco World Stainless Steel Statistics*, 1997

Table 1.3   Consumption of stainless steel per capita

	GDP, US $95 Bn nominal	Stainless consumption, 1000 tonnes	Population, millions	GDP, $1000 per capita	Stainless consumption, kg per capita
Japan	4,599	2,105	126	36.6	16.7
Germany	2,213	1,061	82	27.0	13.0
U.S.A.	7,576	2,088	267	28.4	7.8
France	1,540	413	58	26.4	7.1
Hong Kong	155	137	6	24.5	21.7
Canada	587	158	30	19.6	5.3
Italy	1,215	988	57	21.2	17.2
United Kingdom	1,150	291	58	19.7	5.0
Spain	581	273	39	14.8	6.9
Taiwan	273	728	21	12.8	34.2
South Korea	485	725	46	10.7	15.9
Brazil	688	164	156	4.4	1.1
South Africa	127	114	41	3.1	2.8
Thailand	184	155	59	3.1	2.6
Mexico	279	79	91	3.1	0.9
China	673	941	1,240	0.5	0.8
India	294	500	936	0.3	0.5
Total	22,619	10,920	3,313	6.8	3.3
Total without China and India	21,652	9,479	1,137	19.0	8.3

GDP, gross domestic product. Source: *Inco World Stainless Steel Statistics*, 1997

sent a much smaller share of the overall economy. However, world growth is anticipated. Many producers are increasing their melting capacities; new rolling mills are being built for the production of cold-rolled products, which as Table 1.4 shows, represents the largest single use of stainless.

1.3 Stainless Steel Prices

Stainless is one of the commodities described as specialty steels. Figure 1.1 shows where its price range fits compared to others in that group. The range is wide: 70 cents per pound at the low end; four dollars per pound at the top. The low figure is for the ferritic stainless steels, which contain no nickel. Table 1.1 shows that these represent about 25% of world production of stainless. The top end represents the highly alloyed stainless steels, whose total alloy content and iron content are fairly equal. Prices change very quickly—not because the cost of production changes very much over that time span, but because demand and availability do. However, we must try to offer some perspective. In January 1997 when Fig. 1.1 was published, the cost of cold-rolled steel sheet was 23.5 cents per pound. If it were to be

Table 1.4　1996 Consumption of stainless steel by product group

| | Product group, 1000 tonnes | | | | | |
	Hot-rolled plate and sheet	Cold-rolled sheet and strip	Bars, hot rolled and cold finished	Wire products	Semis	Total
Western Europe						
France	60	225	45	50	33	413
Germany	180	665	66	50	100	1,061
Italy	187	536	70	80	115	988
Spain	35	150	28	30	30	273
United Kingdom	68	174	20	11	18	291
Other Europe	150	424	26	52	20	672
Total	680	2,174	255	273	316	3,698
North America						
Canada	28	93	20	8	9	158
U.S.A.	344	1,381	227	42	94	2,088
Total	372	1,474	247	50	103	2,246
Latin America						
Brazil	29	101	20	2	12	164
Mexico	5	68	3	2	1	79
Other Latin America	7	38	7	2	3	57
Total	41	207	30	6	16	300
Asia						
Hong Kong	12	104	13	6	2	137
India	60	232	65	78	65	500
Indonesia	18	65	14	1	1	99
Japan	661	1,032	116	204	92	2,105
Malaysia	17	32	4	17	...	70
Philippines	4	21	2	4	...	31
Singapore	9	61	29	3	...	102
South Korea	159	450	24	84	8	725
Taiwan	152	450	9	104	13	728
Thailand	13	129	12	...	1	155
Total	1,105	2,576	288	501	182	4,652
Total Australasia	9	47	5	5	...	66
Africa						
South Africa	30	80	3	1	...	114
Other Africa	5	20	3	1	...	29
Total	35	100	6	2	0	143
Total Middle East	8	55	7	3	...	73
Total Western World	**2,250**	**6,633**	**838**	**840**	**617**	**11,178**
C.I.S. Commonwealth of Independent States	48	40	20	30	20	158
Eastern Europe	35	46	23	13	23	140
People's Republic of China	148	678	70	25	20	941
World total	**2,481**	**7,397**	**951**	**908**	**680**	**12,417**

Apparent consumption figures based on published information and on discussions with the industry. Source: *Inco World Stainless Steel Statistics*, 1997

protected from atmospheric corrosion, it would have to be painted. Galvanized steel sheet (a possible alternative, without painting) was about 30 cents per pound. Ferritic stainless steel (that is, nickel-free) was about 70 cents per pound. The basic 18-8 chromium-nickel austenitic stainless, cold-rolled steel cost roughly $1.50 per pound.

1.4 Classification of Stainless Steels

There are about two hundred commercially available stainless steel compositions, each with properties that are influenced by heat treatment and the manner of fabrication. This profusion has two sides to its coin: one side encourages us by suggesting that there is a specific alloy to do exactly what we want; the other side frightens us with the many factors that should influence our selection.

That steel should be stainless at all requires that it contain a minimum chromium content. If the iron were pure (in which case, the meticulous reader might insist that we are not writing of steels), the addition of 11% Cr

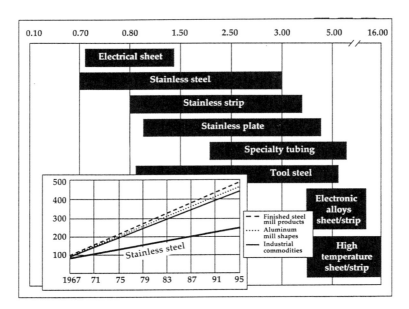

Fig. 1.1 Price ranges for specialty steel alloys, in dollars per pound. Price trends for stainless steel compared with other materials, inset

would ensure passivity in normal atmospheric environments; that is, in those fairly benign atmospheres which we would like to believe surround our homes.

When carbon is introduced to the steel, more chromium is needed. It is fair to assert that any steel called stainless must have at least 11% Cr in its composition. It may have more, much more. Indeed, some stainless steels have a chromium content as high as 30%, and many of the most popular varieties contain substantial quantities of nickel, as well as a generous handful of other effective elements.

Convention would have us agree that when the iron content itself falls below 50%, the alloy cannot reasonably be called a steel. At this juncture, we are confronted with exotic alloys rich in chromium, nickel, cobalt, and tungsten, with a diversity of applications generally involving very high temperatures or extremely critical corrosive conditions. Their categorization is complex—a fact that should offer some consolation as we move into the comparatively simple beginnings of a classification of stainless steels.

1.4.1 Ferritic Stainless Steels

This class gets its name because the crystal structure of the steel (which we run over lightly in Chapter 3) is the same as that of iron at room temperature. Unlike the austenitic stainless steels, which are introduced in section 1.4.3, the ferritic grades are magnetic until they are heated to their Curie point, approximately 750 °C (1380 °F). Their corrosion resistance is imparted by nothing more than a chromium content as low as 11.5% (a little more than the critical 11%, which we have quoted, because of a necessary carbon content). Although small alloy additions may be made for reasons that are described later, many ferritics are substantially the binary alloy. Hence, they obviously have an economic appeal.

However, because ferritic stainless steels were more difficult to shape and to weld than the austenitic steels were, they were used in comparatively small quantities until about 1960. At that time, the needs of the automotive industry and perhaps the expectations of its customers called for more stainless, initially for trim and then for mufflers. Assembly line techniques were designed to effectively form and weld ferritic grades. Then, with improved steelmaking processes, carbon and nitrogen values were reduced, which in turn permitted a lower chromium content. It was a win/win situation: both fabricability and affordability were improved to an extent that brought the ferritic stainless steels into a new prominence. Their application where the time-honored austenitic stainless steels were used is not insignificant. But their greater use appears to be where mild steel can now be economically replaced. We describe some of their applications in later chapters (especially in Chapter 11), and their substantial use in automotive exhaust systems is discussed in section 11.3.1.

1.4.2 Martensitic Stainless Steels

The heat treatment of steels is a fascinating chapter in metallurgical history, for although the greatest tonnage of steels—the structural steels—is not quenched and tempered, our reliance on quenching and tempering to produce the tools for shaping metals is immense.

The heat treatment of steels to improve their strength usually requires adding alloying elements to the basic ingredients—iron, carbon, and manganese. This also increases hardenability so that a greater thickness of material will be affected by the quenching process. Of necessity, stainless steels contain a substantial amount of one alloying element that increases hardenability: chromium. But were they to contain no carbon, the quench at any depth would not cause any hardening. Consequently, while the ferritic grades purposely hold the carbon content to low values, the martensitic grades must adjust the carbon content upwards so that a required hardness (and the associated mechanical properties) is attained. Chromium at 11% or more will assure us of hardenability. Generally, this chromium level, together with the effect of other elements that are purposely or inevitably present, will give such a highly hardenable alloy that cooling in air presents a sufficient quenching speed. Possibly, but not often, the more rapid rate of oil quenching is required.

The strengthening of any alloy, ferrous or nonferrous, can be expected to have a downside. Most obviously, in iron alloys, ductility diminishes as strength increases; in copper alloys, electrical conductivity suffers. All metals and alloys become more difficult to form and to join as strength is improved. So far as corrosion resistance is concerned, if there are exceptions to this perverse Murphy's law—which tells us that as strength increases we should anticipate a reciprocity of problems—the martensitic stainless steels are not among them. As we increase their strength, their susceptibility to corrosion increases. There are other difficulties too, but we reserve these delights for Chapter 4.

1.4.3 Austenitic Stainless Steels

Austenite is the high-temperature form of iron, which exists between 910 and 1400 °C (1670 and 2550 °F). If the name austenite is to be justified, the iron must contain carbon in some small amount, or else the correct name is simply gamma-iron. Austenite is nonmagnetic and can be retained at room temperature by the addition of appropriate alloying elements of which nickel is the most common. Manganese and nitrogen were recognized as austenitizers in the 1930s and present a class of austenitic stainless steels that justifies separate consideration.

The granddaddy of the austenitic stainless steels is called 18-8. Eighteen percent chromium provides basic corrosion resistance; basic, we say, because while the added 8% Ni has the primary purpose of retaining the austenitic structure at room temperature, it also reduces corrodibility in several environments. The austenitic class, based on the 80 year old 18-8 recipe, is the largest family and most used of stainless steels. Its chromium and nickel contents can be increased to improve corrosion resistance and high-temperature mechanical properties; and many alloy additions, not so baffling as they might at first appear, have specific purposes, which are the subject of later chapters.

1.4.4 Manganese-Nitrogen Substituted Austenitic Stainless Steels

Most probably, nothing more than caution delayed the acceptance of these steels, which, although they were developed in the 1930s, only became prominent as a result of the nickel shortage during the Korean War from 1950 to 1953. Briefly, manganese and nitrogen were partially substituted for nickel as an austenitizer and were more economical. Careful control of the nitrogen content is imperative; consequently, this class of stainless has become much more feasible since the advent of argon oxygen decarburization (AOD) in the steelmaking process. As we shall see later, manganese-nitrogen alloys have been developed that do more than simply substitute for nickel.

1.4.5 Precipitation-Strengthened Stainless Steels

The phenomenon of strengthening a material by encouraging an intermetallic compound to precipitate from solid solution but not quite letting it form into coherent globs became a subject of intensive speculation and research with the advent of duralumin (an aluminum alloy) in the 1920s. Since then, the applicability of precipitation hardening to many alloy systems has been generously and successfully exploited, especially in austenitic and martensitic stainless steels. A further possibility arises when precipitation hardening follows the production of metastable austenite. The metal is shaped in the austenitic condition when it is most ductile; subsequent heat treatment develops the double enhancement of strength by martensite formation and precipitation hardening.

1.4.6 Duplex Stainless Steels

As the name suggests, the duplex steels have a constitution that contains both ferrite and austenite. Their properties combine both the good and the less satisfactory of each class, but they may offer an optimal choice where a compromise must be made between corrosion resistance (especially to stress-corrosion cracking) and strength. The duplex alloys are interesting too because they can exhibit the phenomenon of superplasticity, which occurs under tensile stress when plastic deformation is spread out rather than localized.

1.4.7 Austenitic Transformation Induced Plasticity (TRIP) Steels

These are mentioned only because the early steels that exploited this phenomenon (which gives high strength with good ductility) had a composition that was stainless. Their cost (and possibly the sophistication of the necessary thermomechanical treatment) put them into a category of academic interest. More recently, much more economical, low-alloy steels have been developed to justify a commercial interest.

1.4.8 Stainless-Clad Steels

The possible combinations are enormous as one contemplates the mechanical properties offered by a relatively cheap substratum combined with the corrosion protection of a stainless steel surface selected for specific environmental conditions. Such prospects of potential economies were recognized more than 50 years ago. But, as always, it is not quite so simple. First, the desired combination is not always a mill run: you cannot get a meager few pounds of the stuff. Second, if you choose to make the cladding by weld deposition, there are problems of carbon transfer as well as differential thermal expansion. For a small application, a plate of solid stainless may be as satisfactory–and cheaper!

1.4.9 Cast Stainless Steels

Stainless steels can be classified in the same way that wrought alloys are: ferritic, martensitic, and so on. Castings can be made of any of them, if necessary. However, the designations given to cast alloys differ from those given to wrought alloys. The respective institutions responsible for these matters have their own thoughts. Otherwise, at this point, we should warn that while the composition of wrought austenitic alloys avoids the presence of any ferrite, which detracts from workability, austenitic alloy castings (fearless of being worked) can, in fact, be duplex. To be truly austenitic, cast alloys contain substantially more nickel and carbon than their wrought counterparts (see section 9.2).

1.4.10 Designations

It might be worse! There is, at least, some conformity between the tags given to stainless steels by all the institutions that have an interest in the matter. That is more than one can say about prescription drugs! More importantly, the tags of wrought alloys relate closely to the generic classes just outlined.

It is simplest to start with the specifications set down for wrought alloys by the American Iron and Steel Institute (AISI). Each of these prescribes a chemical composition with a three-digit number. To make life easier for us, all the nickel-containing austenitic alloys begin with the number 3; the manganese/nitrogen austenitic alloys begin with 2. So far, so good. However, the three-digit numbers that begin with a 4 include both ferritic and martensite alloys. Precipitation-hardening grades begin with 6. The manufacturers can help us if they add 'PH' to the approximate chemistry of their product (e.g., 17-7 PH), or they can confuse us when they do not (e.g., 'Custom 450' [The Carpenter Technology Corporation, Reading, PA]). What is more, many nickel-base alloys also have a three-digit number beginning with 6. Letters may be added to the numeric designation: for instance, 'L' for low-carbon and Se for a machinable grade containing selenium.

The Society of Automotive Engineers (SAE) conforms to AISI compositional specifications, and generally, the American Society for Testing and

Materials (ASTM) goes along with all those compositional recipes as it adds its own requirements for mechanical properties. This, after all, is ASTM's business. It is concerned with an adherence to the properties that are developed by materials, and its specifications must reflect that concern.

Happily, the subsequent introduction of what is optimistically called the Unified Numbering System (UNS), developed jointly by ASTM and SAE, retains the AISI nomenclature in the first three digits of its six character (five digit) designations. There seems to be general approval that unless a person wishes to put memory to the test, those three digits are enough. In Appendix 3, we make our best effort to present a correlation.

So much for wrought alloys. Although cast alloys may share compositional requirements with wrought alloys, they do not have similar designations. The ACI (formerly The Alloy Casting Institute, now The High Alloy Product Group of the Steel Founders' Society of America) gives a prefix H or C, depending upon the expectation of an alloy to be heat resistant or corrosion resistant. The ASTM has its own designations for most of the alloys within the ACI register. In Chapter 8, useful correlations are made for cast alloys.

1.5 Properties of Stainless Steels

Later chapters deal in some detail with each of the grades of stainless. This section presents a general view, to give an idea of the panorama—its extent, its limits. Before deciding how a stainless steel can be selected from its extensive arsenal, one must come to grips with three property categories, each of which affects the ultimate decision. Each property, namely physical, mechanical, and chemical, is related to and interacts with the others.

1.5.1 Chemical Properties

Perhaps this category is the most complicated of all. As far as we are concerned, this pertains almost exclusively to corrosion resistance. Therefore, we can avoid a lot of chemistry that we have been loath to learn. Unfortunately, however, while engineering design may be substantially based upon measured physical and mechanical properties, no chemical equation—or simple corrosion test—offers the same level of predictability.

Hence, while knowledge of corrosion principles is vitally important to the sensible selection and application of stainless steels, we must rely heavily on recorded experience.

1.5.2 Physical Properties

Of the many physical properties attached to any substance, we limit concern to only a few: specific gravity, electrical conductivity, magnetic susceptibility, and thermal conductivity. These rarely head the order of priorities but have a secondary importance. On some special occasions, we must not overlook physical properties that affect the behavior of materials in nuclear reactors.

1.5.3 Mechanical Properties

Mechanical properties include, obviously, the strength of our materials. At the top of the list is usually the ultimate tensile strength that tells us, too late, when a material breaks in tension. More important is the strength that can be sustained before the material yields and will not return to its original shape. Theoretically, this is the elastic limit. From a practical point of view, it is the yield strength, which is arbitrarily—but fairly consistently—defined as the stress that can be tolerated at a given small, specified amount of plastic elongation. It is slightly above the elastic limit. Whether designers base their structural requirements on ultimate tensile strength or yield strength, they always apply a substantial safety factor. This is especially important when the structure is subject to the prospect of failure by fatigue through cyclic loading. While the calculation of stresses in the most complicated shapes is the joy of design engineers, the distribution of stresses in the vicinity of joints, whether these are made by mechanical fasteners or by welding, is less precise. It must be arbitrarily accommodated by a safety factor.

That quality called toughness is no less important. It involves both ductility and strength and is a measure of the ability of a material to absorb energy. In more practical terms, toughness pertains to resistance of a material to fracture when stress concentrates—as it inevitably does—at a notch. The notch may be observable—a crack, an abrupt change of section, a weld interface—or it may be microscopically small, created perhaps by a brittle constituent at a grain boundary. Inevitably, almost every stress-bearing structure will contain notches of one sort or another; consequently, toughness is an important engineering parameter.

Most properties of alloys—physical, mechanical, or chemical—can be changed to a useful extent by altering composition, heat-treatment, working, and fabrication. Given the basic requirements of a stainless steel (i.e., that it should be corrosion resistant under particular, prescribed circumstances of environment and stress), the name of the game is simply to make those adjustments that are available to us so that the best possible combination of properties is achieved. But there are some properties that cannot be changed, or only marginally so. It is well to acknowledge these at the outset.

Among the chemical properties of stainless steels that pertain to corrosion resistance is the realization that nothing less than 11% Cr will work.

Among the physical properties, nothing will have appreciable effect on the specific gravity of alloys within the commercial grades. In the stainless steels, depending upon the alloying additions, specific gravity can vary from approximately 7.7 to 8.0. Hence when we deal with strength to weight ratios, the weight portion of the ratio is not a significant variable.

Arguably, elastic modulus is included among mechanical, rather than physical, properties. And while enormous ranges of strength, ductility, and toughness are encompassed by the stainless steels, all of them have roughly the same modulus of elasticity regardless of how they are alloyed, worked, or heat treated. That is, when loads do not exceed the elastic limit, all of them will stretch or bend, elastically, to the same extent under a given load. With very few exceptions, nothing can be done to any alloy of iron that changes its elastic constant in tension (Young's modulus) by more than a few percentage points from approximately 196 GPa. The stainless steels at room temperature do not go below 190 GPa and rarely rise above 200 GPa.

We digress for a moment to make a useful generalization. The elastic modulus of a metal and its alloys is usually related to the melting temperature of the parent; alloying elements have little influence. For instance, engineering alloys of aluminum are stuck with an elastic modulus in tension around 69 GPa, bronzes and brasses around 110 GPa. Nickel is something of a loose cannon, because its alloys range between 130 and 190 GPa. The refractory metal, tungsten, is up at 345 GPa while lead alloys rarely go above 30 GPa. There is a relationship—albeit subject to vagaries and not susceptible to a hard mathematical formula—between elastic modulus, melting temperature, and hardness of the parent metal of any alloy system.

You may (or may not) want to scratch your heads about rationalizing that one. It is worth remembering that however a stainless steel is alloyed, heat treated, worked, and fabricated, and while all other mechanical properties can be changed enormously, nothing will change elastic modulus very much.

Having dealt with the unchangeable in this broad, preliminary swing at properties, we now strike out at the most significant ones that characterize the three principal classes of stainless steels: ferritic, austenitic, and martensitic. Generalizations about the other groups already mentioned would be hazardous and they are dealt with specifically in later sections.

1.5.4 Ferritic Stainless Steels

Where tonnage quantities are required of a stainless steel that can be formed under the controlled, reproducible conditions of an assembly line, the low-chromium ferritics are attractive because they are the cheapest. While chromium levels higher than 11% are used in specific corrosive environments (especially the superferritics), the so-called utility stainless steels, based upon AISI 409, currently represent by far the greatest usage of ferritics. These steels, used mainly for exhaust systems in cars and trucks, account for about two-thirds of ferritic consumption in the United States. They are increasingly used in transport equipment, for architectural purposes, and in industrial applications, where they win out over mild steel in the long haul. Unlike the austenitic stainless steels, ferritic grades are generally (but not always) resistant to stress-corrosion cracking in chloride solutions as long as unwanted alloying elements are avoided. These elements—particularly nickel and copper—can interfere if scrap is not carefully sorted prior to steelmaking. Ferritic steels cannot be strengthened by heat treatment, and the extent of strengthening by cold working is so limited that this technique is not very often used.

1.5.5 Austenitic Stainless Steels

Like the ferritic class, austenitic stainless steels cannot be strengthened by heat treatment. They are much more susceptible to strengthening by cold working, and, to put it in a general way, they have a reputation of being easier to deal with than the ferritics. Perhaps this is because of a longer experience with them than with the newer low-carbon, low-nitrogen ferritics, whose recent chemistry has improved weldability. In some environments, the nickel content of austenitic stainless steels enhances corrosion resistance, which may be further improved by other alloying additions. However, the 18-8s are highly susceptible to chloride stress-corrosion cracking, which can only be mitigated at such very high nickel levels that the alloy contains as much nickel as iron.

Associated with their work-hardenability, special austenitic grades have been developed to withstand erosion and galling.

Across the world, about three-quarters of the stainless steel consumed is austenitic—most of it 18-8 or near relatives and much of that in the form of cold-rolled sheet.

In these preliminary generalizations, it is safe to say that the manganese-nitrogen substituted austenitic stainless steels fall within the roughly marked property boundaries just reviewed. Noteworthy exceptions are that their yield strengths are higher both in the annealed and cold-worked conditions and they maintain toughness at high strength levels.

1.5.6 Martensitic Stainless Steels

Martensitic stainless steels once offered the only means of attaining high strength in stainless steels other than in severely worked austenitic sheet or wire. Martensitic stainless steels are still very important, of course, especially where high hardness is required. But one can now weigh their potential against the possibility of using duplex or precipitation-hardened alloys.

At a carbon level that will confer strength by heat treatment, chromium content must be taken above a threshold of 11% if corrosion resistance is to be satisfactory. Consequently, the working member of the martensitic class, 410, has a composition about 12.5% Cr and 0.15% C. Steels with higher carbon levels are used where greater hardness and strength are required, so they must contain more chromium. Cutlery grades, for example, will characteristically have 0.75% C for hardness with 18% Cr to ensure that the steel is, indeed, stainless.

1.6 Selection of Stainless Steels

The first edition of this book was published in 1965 when the publisher was the American Society for Metals. The current name of the organization, ASM International, suggests a worldwide territory. Its subtitle, "The Materials Information Society," reminds us that metals are but part of a wider territory that has no geographic bounds.

In 1965, to offer a few examples, vacuum deposition of metal on plastics was not a commercially viable alternative to electroplated die castings; fiber reinforcement was a laboratory curiosity; ceramics involved mainly cups and saucers, toilet bowls, and spark-plugs; adhesive bonding was for the home workshop. Today, the range from which a material can be selected has exploded beyond those limits which can be reasonably comprehended by any person, or even by teams of people who are called upon to specify a material for a job.

Should it be a metal? Would a plastic serve and be more economical? Given the new availability of materials, have the designers redesigned with the knowledge of new opportunities? Have they overlooked old ones? If designers and materials people can get together, will they reflect a concern for conservation and a thoughtfulness about the environment? That is another book, which we are not about to write!

1.6.1 Life Cycle Costing (LCC)

This sort of computation to find what is cheapest in the long haul was probably applied by rule of thumb in the days when a plant manager might be heard to mutter, "The heck with it! If we let it corrode, we'll save money!" Today, like so many rules of thumb, intuition has grown into an inexact science.

The idea of LCC is simple enough. But its thorough application involves a daunting number of variables that, although quickly consumed by computers, are difficult to define and, once defined, are hard to quantify. The principle is that capital costs are set against the long-term operating costs. The initial capital costs for each likely contender should take into account not only the cost of the thing itself but also such items as the price of redesign, the retraining of employees, and ancillary equipment. The long-term operating costs will not only accommodate replacement costs but also downtime, adjustments to insurance premiums, and changes in productivity.

To be successful, LCC must begin with an itemization of every possible element involved in the initial expenditure in the eventual operating costs, allowing, as far as it can, for changing parameters during the life of the system, such as interest rates, wages, and government regulations. Perhaps, to be on the safe side, the cost of such a computation itself should be included. Computer programs are available to help one through the intricacies of LCC. We have enjoyed reviewing the prospects offered by a program made available on diskette by The Specialty Steel Industry of North America (Washington, D.C.).

Very often, and frequently with justification, the selection of a material depends on previous experience. But while this may be prudent, it is not always appropriate to suppose that what worked best last time is the best choice today. The pot of materials should be stirred, tasted—perhaps tested—to see if there are ingredients that might have been overlooked or, perhaps, were not even available. Some readers recall when dashboards were, indeed, boards, radios had tubes, and kitchen sinks were porcelain. More readers recall that beer cans were always of tinplate; gin bottles were not plastic. Car mufflers were never stainless. New choices are an inevitable part of any evolution.

A fair approach, if one is basing a choice on previous experience, is to ask in what ways the material was deficient or, if not deficient, in what ways performance could be improved by a different selection. Here, LCC comes into play. If this leads to the confirmation of a previous disposition to stainless steel, then it would be wise to reconsider that particular grade in the light of new grades that have come on the market.

If stainless steel is the apparent successor to some other material, metallic or nonmetallic, the question arises where to start. The answer to that used to be simpler than it is today: "Try 18-8 and go from there! Start with 304." The qualification might have been made that if high strength were needed, a martensitic stainless rather than an austenitic was obviously required. And a most important caution should have been added, that if the circumstances might induce stress-corrosion cracking, consider a ferritic grade.

More recently, two codicils must be made; both pertain to economy. First, the manganese-nitrogen substituted austenitic grades can offer a cheaper answer—higher strength, lower cost. Second, the nickel-free, low-chromium ferritics are reliable and much easier to handle than they used to be, on account of their low carbon and nitrogen values. These "utility stainless steels" are called by their promoters "the poor man's stainless."

Further generalizations fail us. We suggest that you write down in order of priority, on the left-hand side of a page, those particular properties sought. The list probably begins with corrosion resistance in a defined environment, moves into particular mechanical properties, and fades out with magnetic hysteresis. Give each property a number that is in rough proportion to its importance. Then, to the right of this list, enter the classes of stainless steel that will accommodate each requirement.

Of course, some will be more and some will be less accommodating, so one can write in a number that represents the extent of the match. There follows a simple arithmetic and, finally, the selection of a particular alloy within the winning grade. Well, not finally. It is wise to go through two more exercises: iterate LCC and check around once more to discover if your choice has been used under similar circumstances.

1.7 Review of the Applications of Stainless Steels

It would be much more exciting to make predictions about where stainless steels have yet to be applied. However, we must be content with a review of current applications. At this juncture, the review is very brief, because Chapter 11 gives a richer survey and then deals with some specific applications. These have been selected because each has its special importance and, can lead to further possibilities.

The chemical industry draws upon the greatest variety of stainless steels and, when it is added to the power generation industry, represents the greatest single consumption. This isn't surprising. After all, these are industries whose success depends upon an output of tonnage or wattage through machinery that operates under corrosive conditions, often at elevated temperatures, and not infrequently calling for demanding mechanical properties.

The earliest use of stainless, cutlery, is now encompassed in the broader spectrum of kitchen equipment: saucepans, sinks, dishwashers. Putting into this arena the use of stainless in food-processing equipment, the sanitary needs of hospitals, and the equipment used in commercial laundries and laundrettes, raises not only a respectable tonnage but also intrudes into a large number of the stainless grades.

In the transportation industry, stainless applications were limited mainly to the ferritic grades for trim. Then, the austenitic grades, the 18-8s, and subsequently the manganese-nitrogen species strengthened by cold working presented attractive strength to weight ratios for corrosion-resistant bodywork in railroad cars and coaches. Seagoing tankers transporting chemical products always rely on stainless. The alloys resist light abrasion; their "slidability" reduces the amount of material that sticks to them during dumping. Largely as a result of the use of low-carbon ferritic stainless steels in automotive exhaust systems, U.S. consumption of one particular grade of ferrite (AISI 409) is now second only to that of the 18-8s.

A realization that stainless grades are more fire resistant than mild steel and, because they need no protective coating, do not present a danger of toxic fumes in the event of fire has led to their increased use in mundane structural applications: stairways, floor gratings, firewalls, and tunnel linings.

Once a sort of show-off in architectural design, the 18-8s quickly became recognized as a wise economic investment. Today, they are complemented by the nickel-free ferritics. In office interiors and furniture, stainless steel has found a utilitarian place: it stays clean, does not scuff, and is cost efficient. Those who complain that despite all of its qualities stainless steel shows finger marks should try a soft cloth moistened with lemon oil—applied, of course, to the stainless steel.

A Short History of Stainless Steels

After the principal elements are introduced, they will be fused into a very brief historical account of the discovery and development of stainless steels.

2.1 The Essential Elements

Obviously iron is essential! In this connection, it is interesting to note that the first iron used on earth (long before it was *made* on earth) was meteoric iron, which generally contains substantial amounts of nickel. It has been suggested that the composition of meteoric iron might possibly be affected as meteors speed through the earth's atmosphere. Probably, ancient artifacts made of meteorites whose nickel content was low have corroded away and are not available for our analysis. In any event, it seems that the iron of prehistoric times was of meteoric origin and contained nickel—as much as 30% but usually between 7 and 15%.

It was not until about 1400 B.C. that iron was made by smelting. Although its minerals are much more widespread than copper minerals, iron's higher melting temperature confounded the early smiths, whose livelihood depended on the more easily liquefied bronzes. Indeed, for almost 3000 years following its first manufacture, iron was but a pasty stuff. It was hammered to squeeze out the slag and shaped to make quite small pieces, usually weapons. This material is what we know as wrought iron. It could only be alloyed by the solid diffusion of carbon from the charcoal fires in which it was heated as it was hammered into shape. Heat treatment of this carburized iron was known to the Romans.

Then, in approximately A.D. 1400, liquid iron was produced in primitive shaft furnaces whose size and efficiency substantially increased when, in the first half of the 18th century, coke replaced the charcoal of an earlier burden. In the beginning, this liquid iron was cast into useful shapes, but it became the starting material for the production of bulk quantities of wrought iron from which beams, plate, and rail were made and whose properties were more versatile than those of the cast material.

Following many smaller-scale attempts involving obfuscating patents, bankruptcies, and other disasters, the conversion of liquid iron into steel was realized on a large scale by Henry Bessemer in the United Kingdom and William Kelly in the United States. The principle is simple enough: air blown through liquid iron lowered the carbon content by oxidation to the values that match steel's prescription. Attendant requirements and problems need not concern us here, because they were resolved by refinements of processing. In the 1870s, most of the world's steel was made by the converter process of Henry Bessemer or the pneumatic process of William Kelly.

However, by the end of the 19th century, the converter was on the decline, and the open-hearth process of steelmaking, which had been introduced about 1870, had gained ascendancy. This process was gentler, more readily controllable; the removal of carbon was not effected by a cruel blast of air but by the more subtle effects of oxidizing fluxes on the metal surface. Nitrogen, inevitably introduced in converter practice, was much reduced; the phosphorus content was under better control.

It was only with the availability of tonnage oxygen that steelmaking techniques reverted to the old style of blowing the carbon out. (No nitrogen here! And a better grip on phosphorus.) Bessemer had foreseen this possibility in a patent, but in his time, oxygen was not available in industrial quantities. Oxygen converters were built; soon open-hearth furnaces were retrofitted with lances by which oxygen was blown on to the liquid metal surface. By the middle of the 20th century, it seemed evident that oxygen steelmaking would be responsible for most of the world's steel tonnage.

Recycling, developments in electric furnace steelmaking, the advantage of small, integrated mills ("mini-mills"), and the efficacy of continuous casting are yet again changing the landscape of steelmaking. In the context of stainless steel, no less important are the incredible advantages offered by careful control, now common to all steelmaking practices, and the monitoring of composition by rapid, sophisticated, analytical techniques. In any event, we now have tonnage steel, clean and of predictable quality, susceptible to intentional alloying.

2.1.1 Chromium

What makes steel stainless is its chromium content. Of course, other elements, especially nickel, have their important effects. Chromium however, is crucial. It was first isolated by Louis Vauquelin in 1797 from the mineral crocoite (or crocoisite), which is lead chromate. Crocoite is not a commercially important mineral. Today chromium is produced from chromite, an iron chromate containing other odds and ends, which occurs in many parts of the world but not to any extent on the North American continent. The principal source is Africa, with important deposits in Eastern Europe, Finland, and Asia.

Pure chromium is produced by electrolytic refining, but for steelmaking purposes, ferrochromium, which contains 40 to 80% Cr, is made by electric furnace smelting. Such an alloy was used as early as the 1860s in the production of low-chromium alloy steels.

Commercial ferrochromium had, and much still has, a high carbon content. This was not troublesome to makers of alloy steels because they needed a touch of carbon, but it led to misleading initial appraisals of the corrosion resistance of stainless steel. It continued to impede the manufacture of low-carbon grades, whose importance will become apparent as we go along and whose availability is more recent.

2.1.2 Nickel

We are prepared to wager that more is known about—certainly, more has been published about—the influence of nickel in stainless steels than about any other element with the exception of carbon in iron. As we have already remarked, the use of nickel in iron preceded its isolation as an element and its purposeful application.

The metal was first identified by Cronstedt in 1751 and exemplifies the happy circumstance in which the usefulness of a material is recognized and exploited in proportion to its availability. The major world resource of nickel was, and remains, the vast deposit of complex sulfide ores in the Canadian Shield in proximity to Sudbury, Ontario. Originally, nickel lived up to the diabolic derivation of its name. It stood in the way of the production of copper—the stuff that the prospectors and their backers wanted. Then, ingenious separation processes, which are continually improved, made clean copper from the ore and, no less, extracted gold, silver, and precious metals. The process also presented steelmakers with an important alloying element, nickel, without which the manufacture of specialty steels is as unthinkable as life without sliced bread.

2.2 The Evolution of Stainless Steels

With the increasing availability and application of steel came a scientific interest in its constitution and properties. As the effects of intentional alloy additions (no less than unwanted elements) grew more important, so studies became more sophisticated. The examination of metals under the microscope, made possible by Sorby in the middle of the 19th century, became a principal tool of researchers. This study was supplemented in the 1920s by x-ray diffraction techniques for the determination of crystal structure. Better methods of chemical analysis, as well as many other means of elucidating the constitution and properties of metals, were introduced, reintroduced, and refined. The puzzling allotropy of iron became resolved, and the effects of carbon on its properties were systematized. It is not surprising that the initial and vital understanding of stainless steels happened about the turn of the century. Techniques allowed it; potential uses encouraged it.

Although earlier work on alloys of iron and chromium came close to applicable discoveries, the period from 1900 to 1915 marks a clear emergence. Among the near misses was Berthier's work of almost a century before. Around 1821, he produced ferrochromium, and he made chromium-bearing iron alloys that straddled, but unfortunately did not include the effective composition range and whose high carbon content was a further impediment.

Other investigators came close, unaware of the effects of a high carbon content, while several scientists appraised corrosion resistance in infelicitous corrodents. Collectively, their results tended to stand in the way of further investigation. Then, just before the turn of the century, Carnot and Goutal identified the pernicious influence of carbon on the corrosion resistance of iron-chromium alloys. Their work set the scene for the productive enterprises of 1900 to 1915.

Carl Zapffe, an American metallurgist from whose assiduous work we draw, suggested three classes of discoveries for this period: those having to do with constitution, corrosion resistance, and industrial usefulness. In the first of these, Leon Guillet, in France, stands out as the key researcher. He made what, on contemporary standards, are low-carbon alloys and tested them with the resources that were then available, describing their metallographic features and constitution as well as mechanical properties. His work, encompassing alloys that we now describe as ferritic, martensitic, and austenitic, was complemented by the research of Giesen and of Portevin.

The phenomenon of passivity was, however, left to others to discover. Monnartz, in Germany, under the direction of Borchers, ascribed the corrosion resistance of iron alloys containing more than 12% Cr to passivity. He backed this up with electrochemical measurements, recognized the requirement of oxidizing conditions, and identified the effects of additional alloying elements. Zapffe declares, "one is free to point to Monnartz as the discoverer of stainlessness in the stainless steels."

The possibilities of industrial usefulness apparently struck simultaneously in England, the United States, and Germany—countries that at the time were the world's industrial giants, not slow to exploit a commercial opportunity. There were earlier recognitions and, indeed, earlier protective patents, but what we now write about is when industry and commerce brought stainless steel into the marketplace.

Harry Brearley, head of research for the combined laboratories of two English firms, is often said to have been the initiator of the age of stainless. Despite the skepticism of his superiors, he was persistent and recognized the corrosion resistance of the hardenable stainless steels, for which he obtained patents in Canada and the United States (but, curiously, not in England) in 1915 and 1916. These were for alloys with 9 to 16% Cr and less than 0.7% C that were appropriately heat treated to produce what we now class as the martensitic stainless steels. They made Sheffield famous for sharp-edged cutlery, and surgeons for their neater incisions.

Meanwhile, Dantsizen in the United States came to appreciate that alloys similar to those that Brearley was investigating characterized a new class of stainless steels—stainless irons, if you like—if the carbon content were kept low. Initially these were used for the lead-in wires for electric light bulbs and (at the suggestion of Whitney in 1914) for turbine blades. These are the ferritic stainless steels, which we describe in later chapters and whose commercial importance has increased in recent years. Becket, about the same time, working with higher carbon levels, produced a corrosion resistant "chrome-iron," which necessarily called for a higher chromium content (more than 25%). No less important to the history of stainless steel, Becket introduced a process by which low-carbon ferrochromium could be made, still more expensive than the regular grade, but viable. Several other names are associated with the industrial introduction of this ferritic class of stainless steels. Probably there are more names of lawyers than of metallurgists.

In Germany, the austenitic stainless steels, (heralded by Guillet's earlier work to which we have referred) were brought into industrial prominence by Maurer and Strauss of Krupp's, during the period 1909 to 1914. The question whether credit should be equally distributed is nicely summarized by Zappfe: "...we accept here that Maurer did the discovering, that Strauss performed the tests, but that Strauss's total stature and his role in the further development of the austenitic steels earns him a prominent place on the roster."

In Monypenny's ground-breaking book, "Stainless Iron and Steel," which was published in 1926 and, presumably, was in preparation a couple of years or so earlier, the austenitic stainless steels find themselves in an omnibus chapter, "Special Stainless Steels." Their treatment shows a clear understanding of their constitution; and alloys subscribing roughly to the formula 18-8 were manufactured under company trade names. However, the state of the market is summed up by Monypenny's cautious enthusiasm: "... although they have the disadvantage that they cannot be hardened except by cold work, they are likely to prove exceedingly useful for a variety of purposes."

Among the studies that developed the constitution diagrams of iron-nickel-chromium-carbon alloys, the work of E.C. Bain and his co-workers should be recognized. His determination of what is called the gamma loop in iron-chromium alloys (the range of composition and temperature over which austenite is the stable phase) and the effects of additional alloying elements on the persistence of the phase at room temperature are especially important and are discussed in Chapter 3.

The austenitic stainless steels, in terms of tonnage, have dominated industrial application. The martensitic stainless steels have always had their specific and vital uses where high strength or a cutting edge has been required. The ferritic class suffered from a difficulty imposed by a carbon content that not only impaired fabricability but pushed required chromium levels to a value that offset possible economies. Recent increases in consumption are most spectacular in the automotive industry but, as we shall see, are significant in several other arenas. However, the austenitic stainless steels have retained the market that they captured early on, and the proportion of nickel-bearing stainless steels has represented about three-quarters of world consumption for the past half century.

Contributors to developments since 1930 are difficult to identify. Not only had the grandest discoveries been made, but metallurgical research in all quarters and for all aspects of constitution, properties, and production had become more intensive, and consequently discoveries became widely applicable. Advances in electrochemistry, for instance, were as important to the corrosion of aluminum as of steel. Constitution diagrams for binary and ternary alloys were not only a fascinating academic exercise but affected a corporation's statement of accounts. Electron microscopy has played no favorites, and improvements in steelmaking techniques have been as valid to diemakers as to architects.

While we cannot identify the appropriate recipients of honorable mention, we will point to significant developments that have built upon the integrity of the three basic classes of stainless steel (ferritic, martensitic, austenitic) that were current by 1930.

2.3 Further Developments of Stainless Steel Alloys

Manganese was an early addition to stainless in order to improve hot workability, as it does in plain-carbon and low-alloy steels. It was recognized in the 1930s as an austenitizer, but not until nickel conservation was impressed upon us by wars and threats of more wars in the early 1950s did the manganese-substituted class really go commercial. Its significance cannot be separated from the influence of nitrogen because nitrogen is a powerful austenitizer and its solubility is increased by manganese. The properties of the manganese-nitrogen austenitic stainless steels are discussed later, but it is not inappropriate in this brief history to remark that at the time of writing, the potential of this sub-class of material has yet to be fully realized.

Precipitation hardening was first exploited in aluminum and in other soft metals when it was called "age hardening." Only later did we recognize that such beneficence could be enjoyed by basically stronger materials. Despite references as early as 1928 in German literature, precipitation-hardened stainless did not come into use until the middle of the 20th century. Stainless W, with a titanium addition, was developed by U.S. Steel and patented in 1946.

More recent still are the duplex stainless steels: hybrids of ferrite and austenite, which to a useful extent present advantages of each class. Although they were first developed, somewhat by chance, in the 1930s, they do not emerge in production figures until about 1987. They must feel embarrassingly juvenile in a chapter on history; but they appear with more dignity in subsequent sections, where their characteristic properties are described.

As a bridge from these paragraphs about new alloys to the next section, we mention the development of very low-carbon stainless steels. In the ferritic class, these allow the chromium content to be reduced to attractive economic levels. In the austenitic class, they alleviate some constitutional problems, which are to be diagnosed and treated later.

2.4 Recent Processing Enhancements

The advantages of making a continuously cast billet, rather than many ingots, occurred to Henry Bessemer in the mid-19th century, but the practical difficulties could not be overcome. An important benefit of continuous casting is that large heats that would otherwise have to be accommodated in big ingots can be cast in continuous strands of comparatively small cross sections. Hence, the amount of rolling (and reheating) is substantially reduced.

Inevitably, there is segregation and shrinkage in a steel ingot. It has to be cropped top and bottom to present a piece of roughly consistent composition for soaking and subsequent forming. The problems of ingot segregation increase as the steel is more highly alloyed, and the lower yield because of cropping, and despite recycling, grows more costly. Briefly, then, both metallurgical and economic advantages to continuous casting are specially felt in the stainless steel plant where the practice has become common since the 1970s.

While continuous casting is now a customary steelmaking practice, the argon-oxygen decarburization process (AOD) was specifically developed for stainless steel production, although it now enjoys a wider application. Developed in the late 1960s by Union Carbide in collaboration with Joslyn Manufacturing and Supply Company, the process first went into commercial operation at Joslyn, Fort Wayne, Indiana.

The process is described in section 6.2.1. In the historical context of this chapter, we remind you of the old bugaboo of high carbon, the importance of clean steel, and the requirement that nitrogen be scrupulously controlled in ferritic, austenitic, and duplex grades. AOD attends to these matters and improves chromium recovery.

These virtues, combined with the economic and metallurgical benefits of continuous casting, present a formidable advance in the recent history of stainless steel manufacture.

Some Metallurgical Principles

3.1 Structure of Metals and Alloys

Metals and alloys were successfully used long before there was any knowledge of their constitution, their internal structure. Trial and error led blacksmiths along the right path, as trial and error generally do in their extravagant way. It would be brash to assert that trial and error no longer have a role today, but metallic properties can be rationalized and fair predictions made through an understanding of constitution. The magic of what was once a black art has been replaced by a different pleasure presented by elegant elements of congruence and conformity.

To learn about the internal structure of a metal or alloy, we must not only know what its atoms are—iron, chromium, nickel, and so on—but also the way in which they are arranged. In solid metals they are arranged in a regular pattern—that is, a crystalline pattern. We have to admit at once that if you were an atom, you probably wouldn't see things quite this way. At any temperature above absolute zero, you and all the atoms around you are vibrating with such ecstasy that any sense of order would be difficult to perceive. However, outside observers and their instruments see trillions of atoms, and however quick the snapshot, such a period of time to any individual atom would seem like half an eternity. The external observer thus puts the atoms in positions in which they spend most of their time and that, with such a big sample, evens out variations.

In this way, we are able to describe what is a most useful characteristic of a metal's internal structure: the particular crystal pattern to which its atoms conform. Such a pattern is defined by its structural unit, which is the smallest possible atomic assemblage that represents the crystal. Repeated extensively in three dimensions, it produces the crystal.

Although such units can be very complex, common metals generally have quite simple structures. But before we go any further, we have to remind ourselves that as we look at pictures of these structures, or try to capture them in our minds, we grossly magnify reality. The diameter of the iron atom is about 2.5×10^{-8} cm. The smallest fragment of iron that we would notice contains many times more atoms than there are people in the world. Thus, while the atom is unimaginably small, its number in any useful bit of metal is unimaginably large; so predictability and reproducibility become infinitely better (well, almost infinitely better!) than a pollster's best hopes.

Among iron's qualities, two have made it our most used metal. The first has to do with its availability: not only is it fairly easily extracted from the vast quantities of iron minerals that occur near the surface of the earth's crust, but it is recyclable. Second—the quality that concerns us here—is that iron exists in two crystal structures: this lies at the heart of its adaptability to fabrication and heat treatment and, consequently, to its usefulness.

In a single crystal of iron at temperatures below 910 °C (1670 °F), the atoms are arranged in the configuration shown in Fig. 3.1, the body-centered cubic (bcc) structure. This is known as alpha iron. It loses its magnetism at about 765 °C (1410 °F), but this loss of ferromagnetism is not accompanied by any crystallographic change. Nor, for that matter, is the loss accompanied with any change of great concern to us other than hot ingots can't be picked up with an electromagnet. Between 910 and 1400 °C (1670 and 2550 °F), the structure is face-centered cubic (fcc), called gamma iron (Fig. 3.2). At 1400 °C (2550 °F) up to the melting point (1540 °C, or 2800 °F), the iron reverts to a bcc structure, known as delta iron.

Fig. 3.1 Body-centered-cubic unit of structure

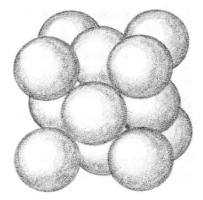

Fig. 3.2 Face-centered-cubic unit of structure

We have to be concerned with two other issues that are of immense practical significance. Neither is difficult to comprehend. First, most metals of engineering usefulness are not single crystals; they are aggregates of crystals. Second, in this book we are involved with alloys, not with pure metals.

As to crystals: That a piece of metal is composed of many crystals (or grains) can be seen by the naked eye in old-fashioned brass door latch releases, etched by the acid from many thumbs, or in those beautiful big crystals of zinc on galvanized steel. More often, however, the crystals are not so evident, but they are there nonetheless! The structure of a piece of fairly pure iron is shown in Fig. 3.3. Every crystal is, practically speaking, a crystal of iron, but each has a different orientation (suggested by Fig. 3.4) that arises during the solidification of the metal. While there may be considerable modification during subsequent treatment, the metal's polycrystalline structure persists. This leads, inevitably, to boundaries of disorientation

Fig. 3.3 Annealed structure of fairly pure iron

between the crystals. These are commonly called grain boundaries, illustrated in Fig. 3.5. In the section revealed in Fig. 3.3, the boundaries appear as lines; in a solid, three-dimensional piece of metal, they are surfaces.

Initially formed from molten metal, and subsequently processed by deformation and heat treatment, metal crystals do not have surfaces with the bold geometric shapes that characterize crystals of substances grown from aqueous solution. When those crystals that are brittle are smashed, the new facets will continue to reveal the internal symmetry. And if iron is treated so that it becomes brittle, it too will cleave in a similar way, revealing bright surfaces. This has led people to say that the iron has crystallized. In fact, solid metals are always crystallized. They just don't usually show it, because the ones that we use are not generally brittle.

The grain boundaries are most important; because while their existence contributes to a metal's strength, they are also regions of chemical reactivity. In a later chapter, we discuss an effect known as sensitization, in which chromium carbides form at grain boundaries with deleterious results.

Now a word or two about alloys. With a few important exceptions, metals of engineering importance are alloys. We already know, for example, that stainless steel is an alloy of iron with chromium, some carbon, and probably other elements. Now, an alloy of iron and, let us say, 13 wt% Cr will consist

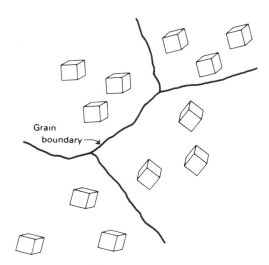

Fig. 3.4 Different orientations in adjacent grains

of a random mixture of iron and chromium atoms in an approximate ratio of six to one. Both iron and chromium atoms, which happen to be roughly the same size, are to be found in exactly equivalent sites, randomly distributed. This mixture of atoms in a crystal, in which the atoms of the second element are simply distributed in the parent crystal structure, is known as a solid solution. In the example we have just described, because the chromium atoms are to be found in exactly similar sites to the iron atoms, the solid solution is known as a substitutional solid solution.

If carbon atoms are added to the alloy of iron and chromium, these distribute themselves in the gaps between the other atoms, so long as no more than about 0.1% is added. The carbon is said to have been taken in interstitial solid solution. If larger amounts are added, the solution will not accept the carbon atoms into its structure in much the same way that, at a given temperature, water will only accept so much salt. The rejected carbon (that which exceeds the solid solubility limit in the alloy) mates with chromium to form chromium carbide. It does this at those active grain boundaries that we described.

Under the microscope, a solid solution cannot be distinguished from a pure element except in some cases by a characteristic change of color vis-

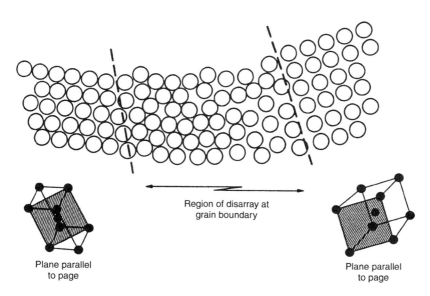

Region of disarray at
grain boundary

Plane parallel
to page

Plane parallel
to page

Fig. 3.5 Atomic disarray at grain boundary

ible even to the naked eye. (The brasses, alloys of copper and zinc, are a case in point.) Figure 3.6 is a micrograph of a solid solution of 18% Cr and 8% Ni in iron, an austenitic stainless steel. Compare this with the similarity of Fig. 3.3. Note the distinguishing presence of annealing twins, which are revealed by those parallel lines in some of the grains. These are common to cold-worked and annealed fcc structures.

We can now add some substance to the classes of stainless steel introduced in section 1.4. The ferritic class has the bcc structure of alpha iron (Fig. 3.1). With a minimum possible chromium content of 11% to ensure corrosion resistance, at least two in fifteen iron atoms must be substituted by chromium. More than that may be substituted and, indeed, must be in all but the very low-carbon grades. As higher chromium levels are reached, the difference in size of chromium and iron atoms, acceptable at lower concentrations of chromium, leads to the formation of a second phase, and with it embrittlement may occur. This is a topic considered in section 7.2.2 because it affects mechanical properties.

An fcc structure is generally more easily worked, but it is not attainable in binary alloys of iron and chromium at room temperature. Figure 3.7 shows the range of composition and temperature over which that structure persists, within what is called the "gamma loop." However, the gamma phase can be made to persist at lower temperatures by the alloying addition of one or

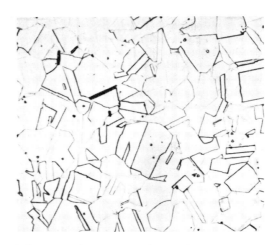

Fig. 3.6   Annealed structure of austenitic stainless steel (AISI 201). 250×

more of the family of austenitizers, of which nickel is the longest-serving member. Figure 3.8 gives the location of 18%Cr-8%Ni in the display of phases that persist in iron-chromium-nickel alloys at room temperature. The word *persist* is purposefully chosen, because transformation from austenite to ferrite at room temperature can be induced in a steel of that composition by cold work: the austenite is said to be metastable.

Nickel has specific attributes in improving corrosion resistance, but these do not have the universality of chromium. The principal purpose of nickel in the austenitic steels is, in fact, to make them austenitic—to give them an fcc structure (Fig 3.2). But, as we mention in section 1.4.4, a partial substitution of nickel by manganese and nitrogen presents a more economical austenitic grade with some advantageous mechanical properties. Manganese itself is an austenitizer; no less important, it increases iron's solubility for nitrogen—an interstitial atom—which is yet more powerful.

A more familiar interstitial element is carbon, which brings to the stainless steels the opportunity of heat treatment that roughly parallels the scope

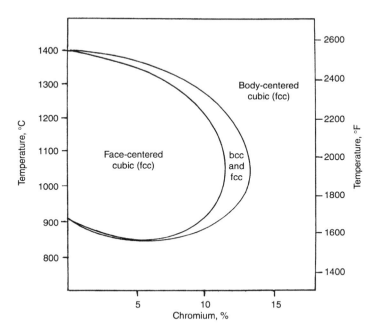

Fig. 3.7 Partial iron-chromium phase diagram: the gamma loop

in lower alloy steels. For a steel to be susceptible to that sort of heat treatment (quenching and tempering), it must be austenitic when it is heated prior to quenching (that is, cooling at more than a critical rate); and it must contain sufficient carbon to give it the required hardness and strength. Now, at very low carbon levels, a steel that contains enough chromium to make it stainless cannot be heated into the austenitic range; we have left the gamma loop behind us (recall Fig. 3.7). But the addition of carbon—imperative to

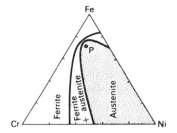

Fig. 3.8 Compositions of iron-chromium-nickel alloys for which austenite persists at room temperature. Point P indicates the position of an alloy containing 18%Cr-8%Ni.

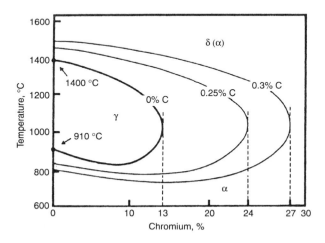

Fig. 3.9 Effect of carbon on the gamma loop. Courtesy of *Stainless Steels*, P. Lacombe, B. Baroux, and G. Bérauger, Ed., Les Editions de Physique Les Ulis, 1993

the process of hardening by quenching from austenite—extends the gamma loop into a higher chromium range (Fig. 3.9). The gods are on our side! So, at the carbon levels required for a hardening process to take place, a steel with sufficient chromium to be stainless can be heated into an austenitic condition and cooled to form martensite.

3.2 Strengthening Processes

When a metal is loaded beyond its elastic limit and deforms plastically, it does so by the process of "slip." This is a sliding movement of those crystallographic planes that contain the greatest number of atoms. Not every plane moves, however. Blocks several thousand atoms thick, with no relative motion between their planes, slide over a similar block. This behavior is elegantly explicated by dislocation theory, which describes how unidimensional (or line) irregularities that occur in some of the atomic planes permit slip to take place at a much lower stress than is required by those planes with a perfect atomic array. The aim of any strengthening mechanism is to prevent slip from taking place, while preserving so far as possible the metal's ductility and toughness.

We will review strengthening processes in general terms and suggest the mechanisms by which they are rationalized. These processes include cold working, solid solution strengthening, martensite formation, precipitation hardening, and duplex structure strengthening. Chapter 7 covers the mechanical and physical properties of each of the stainless grades in more detail.

3.2.1 Cold Working

The most ancient way of strengthening a piece of metal is by cold working. Thousands of years ago, as a copper or bronze blade was hammered to form an edge it became stronger, harder, and less ductile. The phenomenon is easily demonstrated by taking a piece of iron baling wire and bending it to and fro (a piece of copper wire has already been work-hardened, so if you experiment with it, anneal it first!). A fair picture of what goes on is that within each crystal, slip processes begin to compete with each other, preventing each other's continued movement. As we recall that the metal is polycrystalline, we can imagine, too, conflicting preferred directions of slip in adjacent crystals.

With more control than the blacksmith's hammer offers, stainless steels are strengthened by cold work as they are rolled into plate and sheet or drawn into rod and wire at (roughly) room temperature. The austenitic grades are more readily worked and their strength increases to an extent that depends upon the composition and can be associated with the formation of martensite (which we come to later). The ferritic grades are more notch-sensitive; hence, the extent to which they may be strengthened is limited.

As in any strengthening process (the shorthand generally refers to it as a hardening process), there is a sacrifice of ductility. Work hardening is no exception. As the metal gains strength through being plastically strained, it becomes less tolerant of more plastic strain. Yield point and ultimate tensile strength converge. In its last attempt to attain that final bit of deformation, the metal, as strong as it will ever be snaps.

3.2.2 Solid Solution Strengthening

Solid solution strengthening is old, too, in the accidentally produced bronzes of prehistory. In some locations where minerals containing copper and tin occurred together, the smelted metal was found to be stronger than native copper. Whatever the rationalization was then, today's explanation is that when atoms of slightly different size get together in substitutional solid solution, there is less ease of movement of atomic planes.

But while strengthening by substitutional atoms is of significance in some alloy systems, it is not very important in stainless steels. However, the interstitial atoms—carbon and nitrogen—are most influential. In solid solution, they create distortions of the cubic crystal structures so that plastic deformation is impeded, and strength is increased. This leads naturally to the next section.

3.2.3 Martensite Formation

Taking maximum advantage of cubic crystal distortion is martensite formation. Gamma iron (fcc) has a much greater solubility for carbon than has alpha iron (bcc). Consequently, if the carbon is taken into interstitial solid solution at temperatures roughly above 910 °C (1670 °F) to form austenite and then quenched at a rate to prevent the precipitation of carbides, the bcc structure we might have expected is very severely distorted. The cube has become tetragonal. What we might have called ferrite (alpha iron containing carbon in solid solution) is now martensite: a hard structure, whose strength and brittleness increase as its carbon level is raised. Except at very low carbon levels this structure has to be moderated by tempering.

Under cold working, a few paragraphs previously, the formation of martensite was mentioned. It is like this. When iron-carbon alloys containing strong austenitizing elements such as nickel, manganese, and nitrogen are quenched, martensite is not produced; the austenite is retained. However, depending upon the extent of the alloy additions, the austenite is not always stable at room temperature, and if it is cooled to sub-zero temperatures, it changes to martensite. The process of cold working has a similar effect. In more practical terms, while a piece of 18-8 steel plate is austenitic (see Fig. 3.8), it may not be entirely so after it has been cold rolled to sheet. Some of its structure will not be face-centered cubic any more, but (distorted) body-centered cubic. Both of these structures will contain whatever carbon content was in the original prescription, so the carbon-containing ferrite has become a sort of martensite. This adds to the effects of the normal process of work hardening.

3.2.4 Precipitation Hardening

The term precipitation hardening is something of a misnomer because when precipitates become visible under the microscope, softening has already begun. In the days when the phenomenon was commonly called age-hardening, the alloy was said to have become overaged.

The general principle behind what is a most complex business is that a supercooled solid solution is created from which compounds might eventually precipitate. Such a solution is metastable. A simple analogy is to be found in a liquid solution in which a maximum amount of table salt is dissolved in hot water. When the water is carefully cooled rapidly, the salt will remain in supersaturation but is eager to precipitate. In much the same way in the solid solution, there are more atoms of the alloying element than the parent metal structure can really accommodate. The unwelcome atoms are induced to move out of their ungenerous quarters (in this case by encouraging their mobility through heating them), and they begin to form clusters having a higher concentration of alloying elements. This creates irregularities in the crystal structure, thus impeding slip.

The compounds associated with precipitation hardening are complex and require additional elements (usually aluminum, molybdenum, or copper) to the basic stainless compositions.

3.2.5 Duplex Structures

Duplex structures represent the most recent strengthening process in stainless steels. Perhaps it is more accurate to say that it is the most recent consciously applied process, for it probably occurred before it was specifically identified, named, and controlled.

Duplex stainless steels are of a composition that produces roughly equal quantities of ferrite and austenite in the finished product. That composition is influenced by the heating and working program of the product during its fabrication. When these alloys solidify, they are completely ferritic. During subsequent cooling, austenite precipitates within the ferrite crystals, first growing from the grain boundaries and then within the crystals. There is, then, a very intimately mixed conglomerate of two sorts of crystal, each with its preferred planes along which slip takes place, but less readily in the ferritic than in the austenitic crystals. In its simplest exposition, we can imagine that the ductility offered by the latter impinges upon the resistance of the former. The effect is a nice combination of strength and ductility. The carbon content may be kept to low concentration, especially in what has come to be known as the second generation of duplex alloys where a carefully controlled nitrogen content assists the formation of austenite.

3.3 Principles of Heat Treatment

The purpose of heat treatment is to imbue the stainless steel with the best combination of properties—mechanical, physical, and chemical—that can possibly be attained. The right heat treatment can only be selected within the context of the alloy's composition and its entire history of shaping—casting, forging, rolling, drawing, welding, and so on. Because every sort of heat treatment (applicable not only to steels but to nonferrous alloys as well) seems to have found its way into the stainless steel lexicon, the opportunities are extensive.

This section defines and describes very briefly what those heat treatments are so that repetition is avoided when the terms are used later.

3.3.1 Stress Relieving

The simplest (and, regrettably, sometimes the most overlooked) heat treatment is that of stress relieving. When a piece is shaped, by casting, forming, welding, or machining, it unavoidably acquires residual stresses. These may be intentional and contribute to the product's required properties (e.g., in wire). But when they are unwanted and deleterious, (e.g., creating opportunities for corrosion) they are mitigated by the process of stress relieving. No general rule for the required temperature of stress relief can be given, because this varies with prior history. The process will necessarily reduce the yield strength and hardness of the metal, but that is not its intention. If softening is required, usually to make the metal more workable, the proper heat treatment is annealing.

3.3.2 Annealing

Annealing means different things to different metals. For a ferritic or an austenitic stainless steel, the annealing process heats the metal to a temperature at which it recrystallizes. This temperature (as in stress relieving) depends upon prior history. Unlike the stress relieving process, annealing austenitic and ferritic stainless steels will cause the nucleation and growth of new crystals, whose size will depend upon the temperature and time of the annealing cycle.

To a martensitic stainless steel, annealing means being heated until it is austenitic followed by slow (very slow) cooling, so that martensite doesn't form again. The steel is no longer martensitic; it comprises ferrite with dispersed carbides. This is known as a full anneal. A subcritical anneal below the austenitizing temperature will allow the martensite to decompose. This means a longer time at the lower temperature, but the cooling rate is not significant.

3.3.3 Homogenization

This occurs when stainless steels are heated into the austenite range and held there for some time in order to even out segregation.

3.3.4 Quench and Temper

When a steel is cooled from an austenitizing temperature at a rate sufficiently rapid to form martensite (which, in the case of the stainless steels, is generally accomplished by air cooling), it is said to be quenched. Subsequent heating to temperatures too low to fully decompose the martensite (as in a subcritical anneal) is tempering.

3.3.5 Solution Hardening

Precipitation-hardened stainless steels are solution treated (or solution annealed) when the elements essential to hardening are taken into solid solution. Subsequent aging contrives that pre-precipitation process at a temperature appropriate to the specific alloy.

3.3.6 Surface Hardening

This process not only enhances wear resistance but improves fatigue properties. Stainless steels may be surface hardened by the same means that are used for plain-carbon and low-alloy steels. Flame hardening and induction hardening, for instance, do not change the chemical composition of the surface, but they do rely upon the existing chemistry to produce a martensite through local heating and quenching. Other surface treatments depend upon the introduction of hardening elements to the surface. Carbon, boron, and nitrogen are the active elements in, respectively, carburizing, boriding, and nitriding.

3.3.7 Carburizing

At the outset, we should point out that in stainless steels, carburizing is more of a problem than a purposeful heat treatment. A carburizing atmosphere around a stainless steel produces chromium carbides at the metal surface, leading to localized chromium depletion and consequent corrosion. Where carburizing is intended, the purpose is to produce a high-carbon austenite, which transforms to martensite on cooling. Chromium carbides may be intentionally allowed to form (for they complement the surface wear resistance) in a high-chromium alloy.

3.3.8 Boriding

In boriding, a boron-containing gas, liquid, or solid at temperatures between 700 and 1000 °C (1290 to 1830 °F) surrounds the piece to be surface hardened. Extremely high hardness levels are attained.

3.3.9 Nitriding

Nitriding depends upon an active nitrogen source at a quite low temperature (about 550 °C, or 1020 °F), usually provided by ammonia. The nitrogen occupies both substitutional and interstitial sites in the atomic structure until the solubility limit is exceeded, when nitrides preform and eventually precipitate. More recently, nitrogen is introduced via plasma arc providing a better control of chemistry and nitrogen distribution. Of surface hardening processes for stainless steels, nitriding is probably the most commonly used.

Among the practical details surrounding any heat treatment of stainless steels, the requirement of absolute cleanliness has to be emphasized: fingerprints and crayon marks leave an indelible reminder. In furnace heating, the atmosphere is usually air: the steel is subsequently cleaned by pickling, grit-blasting, or salt bath treatment. Controlled atmospheres for bright annealing may be of dissociated ammonia, hydrogen, or inert gas.

As with alloy steels, salt baths can be used, and often are, for the heat treatment of martensitic parts. The choice of furnace or pot is an economic one. The subject is discussed in more detail in section 8.12 for fabrication.

Principles of Corrosion

4.1 Introduction

The root of the word corrode is the Latin *rodere*, as in rodent. It means to gnaw. The word *erode* has the same root. Different prefixes, such as "cor-" and "e-," do little to help us differentiate. "Cor-" (like "co-" or "com-") means "with," while "e-" (short for "ex-") means "out of." So it seems that if a thing corrodes, it is with gnawing, while if it erodes, it is a result of gnawing. This is a nice point! It is amusing in a court of law, no doubt, but not one to bring a smile to the lips of a plant manager ankle deep in cooling water late on a Friday afternoon.

Common sense tells what the dictionary hedges as it offers second definitions. Corrosion is an eating away by chemical action; erosion is a wearing away. The two sometimes act in concert, as is discussed later. By way of introduction, mechanisms of corrosion are described, and more specifically than as eaten away by chemical action. Rather, in the context of this book, corrosion is the undesirable chemical reaction of a metal or alloy with its environment.

Another word precedes the mechanisms. It is good to realize that as we combat corrosion, we oppose Mother Nature. Hard work reduces the earth's minerals to metals. Nature resents this and does its best to convert metals back to minerals. Iron oxide is mined, concentrated, fed to the furnaces, reduced and refined to steel, rolled into shape, and put into a structure, say a building or a car. Weather and time work on the steel, convert it to iron oxide, and wash it back into the earth whence it came. This (although it has been expressed more eruditely) is what entropy and nature are about.

4.2 Aqueous Corrosion

Although many undesirable chemical reactions with a metal or alloy (our definition of corrosion) take place in gases, far more occur in liquid environments, and most of those are in aqueous solutions. Fortunately, these provide the best means of introducing the principles of corrosion.

At the heart of aqueous corrosion is the formation of a galvanic cell, a battery. There are two electrodes, generally of different composition, immersed in an aqueous solution (the electrolyte) and joined externally by an electrical conductor, which is usually, but not necessarily, a metal. Figure 4.1 illustrates such a cell where the two electrodes are of different elements. To make our exposition easier, we have separated the electrolyte so that each electrode is immersed in a solution of its own salt.

Notice that the solutions are said to be composed of ions. The word *ion* is from Greek and means "going," or if we are allowed a little license, "wanderer." In the 1830s, Michael Faraday, who formulated the laws of electroly-

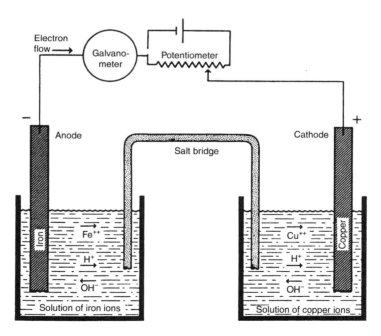

Fig. 4.1 Example of a galvanic cell

sis, realized that the flow of electricity in a galvanic cell was associated with charged particles. Not until the early 1900s was there a general acceptance that aqueous solutions are, indeed, ionized. They are ionized at all times. Ionization is not caused by the passage of electricity; rather, the ions are ready carriers of the electric charge. Figure 4.1 shows the direction of movement of the ions; and although we have separated the two electrodes, the salt bridge is necessary to complete the circuit.

An important distinction between what happens in the electrolyte and what happens in the wire that connects the electrodes must be underlined, for in both there is a movement of electrons (i.e., an electrical conductance). Only in the electrolyte however, is the movement of electrons accompanied by a transfer of matter, of stuff, of electrically charged copper and iron (and other ions) that are in motion. Without that sort of transfer, there would be no corrosion process, only an electric current.

As iron is dissolved and copper is deposited, the potential difference of the iron/copper cell will be measured at 0.785 V. In order to determine the contribution of each half cell to the total potential, a standard has to be adopted against which all electrode potentials may be measured. This is the standard hydrogen electrode—a platinized platinum electrode surrounded by hydrogen ions, all to meticulous specification. The inconvenience of such an apparatus can be imagined and while the hydrogen standard persists (electrode potentials are referred to its zero value), most measurements are actually made with another, more manageable standard. This is the calomel electrode, wherein a platinum wire dips into mercury covered by a specified chloride solution.

Both halves of the galvanic cell shown in Fig. 4.1 are responsible for the electrical potential developed and measured by the potentiometer. If each half were connected separately to a standard hydrogen electrode, the copper electrode would register 0.344 V on one side of hydrogen's zero. The iron half-cell registers 0.441 V, but on the other side of hydrogen's zero. This gives a total when the cell is put together again of 0.785 V (assuming that it operated under conditions that pertained when the standard potentials were measured).

The standard electrode potentials for common elements are listed in Table 4.1. Their order expresses what is commonly called the electromotive series. In the convention used here, the so-called noble metals show a positive value with respect to the standard, and the reactive metals show a negative potential. There is often confusion about electrical polarities and sometimes about what is called anode and what is called cathode. There should be no doubt that the less noble corroding metal generates electrons, is therefore negatively charged, and is the anode. The more noble metal does not corrode; positive ions go towards it. It is the cathode. If the ions are metallic, they plate out and adhere or drop off. The convention used for polarity in Table 4.1 is more arguable, and frequently the signage is opposite to the one adopted here. However, for the sake of consistency, the anodic metals are given a negative polarity here.

Potentials may be measured under field conditions to develop a galvanic series that can be applied to practical circumstances (Table 4.2). Notice the relative positions of stainless steel when active and passive.

We can digress for a moment from what might seem to be an overly theoretical presentation to a practical example. It is not uncommon for copper and steel pipes or fittings to be joined together in plumbing. The circumstances do not replicate exactly what we have just described, but water flowing through the plumbing is ionized. It is an electrolyte. In this case, we do not have the presentational convenience of two different electrolytes joined by a salt bridge for there is a common electrolyte. In it, iron ions move from the anode to the cathodic copper, where they combine with hydroxyl ions (which are moving away from the copper) to form iron hydroxide. To complete the picture, this hydroxide is further oxidized to form red rust, which accumulates on the copper side of the plumbing.

Table 4.1 Standard electrode potentials at 25 °C (77 °F)

Electrode	Corrosion reaction	Volts
Cathodic		
Au	$Au > Au^{3+} + 3e$	+1.498
Pt	$Pt > Pt^{2+} + 2e$	+1.200
Ag	$Ag > Ag^+ + 1e$	+0.799
Cu	$Cu > Cu^{2+} + 2e$	+0.337
H	$H > H^+ + 2e$	+0.000
Anodic		
Pb	$Pb > Pb^{2+} + 2e$	−0.126
Sn	$Sn > Sn^{2+} + 2e$	−0.136
Ni	$Ni > Ni^{2+} + 2e$	−0.250
Co	$Co > Co^{2+} + 2e$	−0.277
Fe	$Fe > Fe^{2+} + 2e$	−0.440
Cr	$Cr > Cr^{3+} + 3e$	−0.744
Zn	$Zn > Zn^{2+} + 2e$	−0.763
Al	$Al > Al^{3+} + 3e$	−1.662
Mg	$Mg > Mg^{2+} + 2e$	−2.363

This look at the plumbing lets us illustrate another vital aspect of galvanic corrosion. In the sort of cell described, the voltage tends to drop as the reaction proceeds. The reaction products (especially oxygen on the anode) impede the passage of the electric current; and what a splendid thing this is, for it has to do with the creation of the passivity that makes stainless steel stainless and about which more is said. In the piping just alluded to, the flow of water removes those corrosion products that otherwise can slow the reaction. The small amount of iron compounds that flush along with the water will not spoil the coffee, but their constant removal can cause an eventual flood.

The reactions occurring in the cell shown in Fig. 4.1 can be described:

$$Fe > Fe^{++} + 2e^- \text{ at the anode}$$

$$Cu^{++} + 2e^- > Cu \text{ at the cathode}$$

Other electron-consuming reactions will also take place at the cathode, generating hydrogen or possibly producing water. Meanwhile, depending on its composition, the alloying elements of the anode (as well as its major constituent) may move into solution, becoming ionized and generating electrons.

Table 4.2 Galvanic series in seawater at 25 °C (77 °F) and flowing at 13 ft/s

Metal	Steady potential (negative to standard calomel), V
Zinc	1.03
Aluminum 3003	0.94
Carbon steel	0.61
Gray iron	0.61
304 stainless steel (active)	0.53
Copper	0.36
Admiralty brass	0.29
70/30 copper-nickel (0.47% Fe)	0.25
Nickel 200	0.20
316 stainless steel (active)	0.18
Inconel alloy 600	0.17
Titanium	0.15
Silver	0.13
304 stainless steel (passive)	0.08
Monel alloy 400	0.08
316 stainless steel (passive)	0.05

Data from F.L. LaQue, *Proc. ASTM*, Vol 51, 1951, p 495

4.2.1 Oxidation and Reduction Reactions

When the reactions at anode and cathode present themselves for the amusement of chemists, they are respectively called oxidation and reduction reactions. Samuel Glasstone's time-honored text, *Physical Chemistry*, suggested that those words—to which we generally attach more obvious manifestations of substances becoming oxidized or reduced—are, in the electrochemical context, being used in a somewhat narrow sense.

But perhaps the converse is true, because the term oxidation gradually became applied not only to reactions in which a material was changed to an oxide, but also to similar reactions involving chlorine or sulfur. Their common feature was that they gave out energy; they were exothermic. Later, when more became known of atomic structure, such oxidation reactions were recognized in terms of electron transfer. As the substance is oxidized, it goes into solution and gains a positive charge; its electrons remain behind. For instance in the cell shown in Fig. 4.1, iron goes into solution as a positively charged ion. It leaves its negative charge behind to create the anode. Conversely, at the cathode, the copper ions in solution deposit as metallic copper as they release their positive charge and consume electrons. This constitutes a reduction process.

This is reviewed albeit briefly, because more advanced texts write of reactions in these chemical terms that, in turn, lead to the application of thermodynamic principles. The creation of a potential difference, a voltage, implies that a spontaneous reaction has occurred in which the products have a lower chemical-free energy than have the reactants. The thermodynamic treatment of electrochemical processes is captivating, but we must move on.

4.2.2 Sources of Corrosion Current

In the example considered, an iron/copper galvanic cell, the corrosion current derives from two different metals in solutions of their ions. A corrosion current would have arisen had the two metals been in a common conducting solution, but our explication of electrode potentials would have been subject to academic criticism.

A corrosion current will arise from differences in constitution within the same piece of material. For instance, in structural steels, iron and iron carbide set up their local corrosion cells. This is the reason that the structure of a piece of mild steel is revealed in a polished and etched sample under the microscope. Even where the material is compositionally homogeneous, cold-worked metal is anodic to an adjacent part that has been intentionally or inadvertently stress relieved, with results that are too frequently evident in corroded steel structures. Even when a metal appears to be homogeneous, it will present microscopic and submicroscopic anodic and cathodic sites by which its general corrosion may be explained.

Concentration cell corrosion arises when metal of uniform constitution is present in an aqueous solution whose concentration varies. A common manifestation is when local concentrations arise because of stagnant regions. Here, the metal in contact with the more dilute solution is anodic and corrodes. This may appear to be counter-intuitive. It is rationalized by recognizing that the electrolyte seeks equilibrium; hence, the metal around the more dilute solution will be called upon to donate its ions.

4.2.3 Thermodynamics and Kinetics

What we have described so far has had to do largely with the thermodynamics of corrosion, that is to say, whether something will or will not corrode. That is thermodynamics, a sort of materialistic theology that is concerned for the beginning and the end. We have said little about how quickly something will corrode other than to relate it in a qualitative way to the corrosion current. That is kinetics, the life it leads, the path by which the end is reached. The potential between anode and cathode tells what force there is to urge the reaction—the distance, if you like, between the top of the stairs and the bottom. The potential does not tell the speed of the reaction or how quickly one drops while trying to break a fall. Nor does the thermodynamic approach tell that there may be some sort of obstacle in the way of the reaction (i.e., an activation barrier, shown schematically in Fig. 4.2).

The thermodynamics of corrosion processes have been put together in a useful set of diagrams named after their originator, Pourbaix. A typical Pourbaix diagram for iron is shown in Fig. 4.3. Areas delineated within the coordinates of electrode potential and pH (a measure of acidity) show when iron may be expected to corrode, or to be immune, or to be passive. Immunity represents an arbitrary (but justifiable) concentration of ions in solution of less than 10^{-6} moles per liter. A mole is related to the atomic mass of an element: 1 mole of iron is approximately equal to 56 g. Hence, a concentration in one liter of one-millionth of this amount is extremely small. Pourbaix diagrams are available for practically all elements in equilibrium with aqueous solutions; they tell of the conditions for which a given corrosion reaction is or is not possible.

The activation barrier is the link between the thermodynamics (can it happen?) and the kinetics (how fast will it happen?), because it determines the rate at which atoms release themselves and can recombine. It arises because only those atoms that are in a sufficient frenzy of vibration can tear away from their bonds, ready to be accepted by other atomic configurations. The kinetics of processes are difficult to generalize because they are so dependant upon local circumstances whose quantification is elusive: the nature of a surface, the turbulence of a solution, the adherence of a protective film. Overall weight loss of a corrosion sample may give some idea, and that is very useful. But it does not tell whether the corrosion is general or local or whether the corrosion rate was constant over the test period, and it will only pertain to the special circumstances under which the test was made.

An appreciation of the relationship between crystal topography and reactivity has improved the understanding of corrosion kinetics. The effect of metal imperfections, especially of dislocations has been a rewarding study. Some of these one-dimensional aberrations in the otherwise regular array of atoms in the crystal structure necessarily emerge at the metal's surface. Of

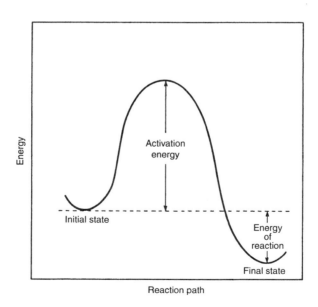

Fig. 4.2   Concept of energy barrier

these, some create a sort of kinked atomic texture from which the removal of atoms does not smooth out the surface but continues, as it were, to unravel it. Under these circumstances the corrosion rate is expected to increase. So it can, but that very sort of imperfection at the metal surface is also a preferred location for impurities, which themselves may be a cause of an increased corrosion rate.

In the early stages of anodic reactions, before an observable corrosion product is formed, a layer of atomic proportions may be created that protects the metal from further corrosion. It is invisible to the naked eye, but this is not a metallurgical version of *The Emperor's New Clothes*. This is the phenomenon of passivity, which is central to the usefulness of stainless steels and will be given a section of its own. It also allows us to emphasize the importance of electrochemical methods in understanding the corrosion resistance of stainless steels and, of more significance to the user, how electrochemistry has contributed to corrosion testing methods, which are described in the next chapter.

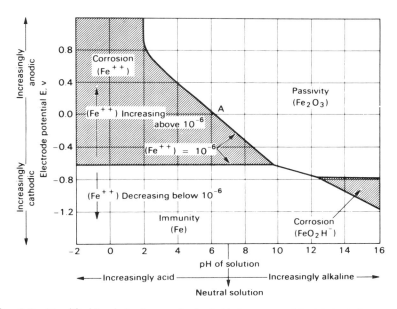

Fig. 4.3 Simplified Pourbaix diagram for the Fe-H$_2$O system at 25 °C (77 °F) showing the domains of corrosion behavior. The symbol (Fe++) represents the equilibrium concentration of Fe++ ions in units of moles per liter of solution. Source: A.G. Guy and F.N. Rhines, *Metal Treat. Drop Forging*, Vol 29, 1962, p 45

4.2.4 Passivity

The passivity created by chromium in a stainless steel is illustrated by the values of electrode potential for AISI 304 given in Table 4.2. The value –0.53 V (against an arbitrary zero of the standard calomel electrode) compares to the potential of the passivated steel of only –0.08 V. This reduction of electrode potential is due to the formation of the initial products of the corrosion process, which create an activation barrier at the surface of the stainless steel that cannot be penetrated by even the liveliest of charged atoms. So the electrode potential falls, and because so few electrons flow, the current drops to nearly zero. The corrosion reaction has virtually stopped.

The barrier is not like a paint film that can be scraped off with a knife. Not only is it much thinner (it is only a few atoms thick), it is chemically bonded to the metal surface. Its precise composition need not be a concern (this continues to be a matter of lively debate), but it is of oxide and hydroxyl bondings with chromium. The film (for that is what we have to call it) is in a dynamic state, continually being reformed as it dissolves, which is consistent with its necessary property of self-healing should it be abraded.

Its vitally important property is to present a substantial activation barrier to the flow of ions to and from the metal surface. However, because it is continually formed and reformed by anodic reactions, we can readily appreciate that the presence of ions which do not contribute to, or which prevent, the formation and maintenance of the film nullify the passivity. The chloride ion is particularly obnoxious.

An electrochemical method presents us with a quantitative view of passivity. When a piece of stainless steel is dipped into sulfuric acid, it corrodes because of electrochemical action at microscopic and submicroscopic anodic and cathodic sites on the metal surface. The current passing between these sites is a measure of corrosion rate, but of course it cannot be measured directly. It is measured indirectly by making the steel an electrode in a cell, whose other electrode is of platinum. Then, controlled by a potentiostat, a current is allowed to flow between the steel and the platinum. The potentiostat, as the name implies, allows current to be applied at a controlled potential, whose value is measured against a standard reference electrode in the circuit. Measurements of current flow at many potentials—both positive and negative with respect to the steel—can then be made to produce what is commonly called a polarization curve.

If the steel is made the cathode, a series of measurements produces the lowest part of the curve in Fig. 4.4. As the applied potential is increased, the current diminishes until, at what is called the corrosion potential, E_{corr}, the current is zero. At this potential, the sum of all the reaction rates at all the microscopic anodes equals the reaction rates at the cathodes; there is no corrosion.

By impressing a potential in the noble direction, away from E_{corr}, the steel acts anodically and the corrosion current increases, indicating a greater corrosion rate. Then, at a potential indicated by E_{pp}, the active-passive transition, the current density quickly diminishes as the applied potential increases. The metal becomes passivated. The vertical part of the curve (i.e., the passive potential range) tells that substantial increases in potential are not accompanied by any increase in corrosion rate, until at E_t the passive film breaks down and current density increases rapidly with small increases of applied potential.

If the experiment is repeated in a solution containing chlorine ions, the polarization curve resembles the solid lines in Fig. 4.5. Here, when the corrosion potential lies beyond the passive potential range, as at C, passivation does not occur; the metal is susceptible to corrosion. At the point E_p, the current density increases dramatically and the corrosion process produces localized pits, which are the subject of a later section.

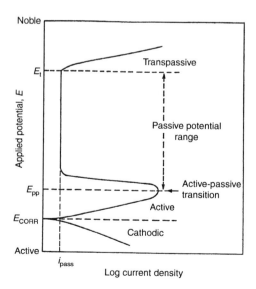

Fig. 4.4 Schematic polarization curve for a stainless steel in sulfuric acid. Reprinted with permission from A.J. Sedriks, *Corrosion of Stainless Steels*, John Wiley & Sons, Inc., 1996

4.3 Corrosion in Gases

The electrochemical theory of corrosion can be extended to reactions in the gaseous phase, such as oxidation, sulfidation, and nitriding. This may seem to be a long way round of explaining something that might be more simply expressed. For example, if a metal is heated in oxygen, metal plus oxygen produces the metal oxide, so why introduce complications? But the fact that the process can be described electrochemically adds strength to the generality of that sort of approach. Figure 4.6 depicts in electrochemical terms the oxidation of iron at elevated temperature. The cathode, at which reduction occurs, is considered to be the interface of the gas and the metal compound; the anode, at which oxidation occurs, is the interface of the metal and the metal compound.

4.4 Types of Aqueous Corrosion

Here we summarize the most common forms of metallic corrosion—keeping in mind that we are concerned with stainless steels, whose corrosion characteristics and resistance are dealt with in Chapter 10.

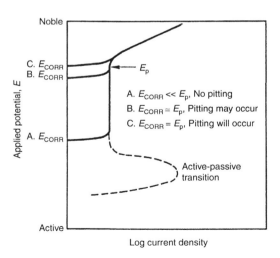

Fig. 4.5 Schematic polarization curve showing conditions for pitting. Reprinted with permission from A.J. Sedriks, *Corrosion of Stainless Steels,* John Wiley & Sons, Inc., 1996

4.4.1 General Corrosion

General corrosion is seen when, for example, a mild steel plate is covered in red rust, or a copper pipe is uniformly coated with green patina. Usually, general corrosion can be rationalized as extensive, continuous local corrosion. That is, differences in metallic constitution on a microscopic or submicroscopic scale present electrochemical opportunities. Anodic regions react to form the corrosion product across the entire surface. Were the steel plate or copper pipe to be in a completely dry atmosphere at temperatures about atmospheric, they would not develop visible corrosion.

General corrosion at high temperatures may occur in dry atmospheres. While there are many possibilities, the usual experience is with an oxidizing atmosphere (which, in most practical cases, is not entirely free from water vapor). The metal is attacked over its entire surface.

4.4.2 Pitting Corrosion

Pitting corrosion, on the other hand and as its name emphatically suggests, is highly localized. Why does the metal not corrode evenly across the entire surface? The chances are that it does to some extent, but the blatantly visible curse is pitting. This may be because there are particularly active sites at the metal surface or, more often, that a passive film breaks down locally—perhaps nothing more subtle than a speck of soot settling on the surface, preventing an ingress of oxygen.

It is not unusual for pitting corrosion to take off at an alarming speed, covering the metal surface with terrifying pockmarks that seem to signal quick local failure. The pockmarks can turn out to be superficial, and as

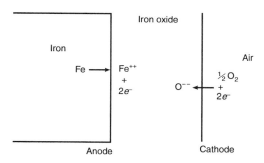

Fig. 4.6 Oxidation of iron at elevated temperatures

quickly as their formation begins, they peter out. This is common where the passive layer has been locally and temporarily impeded from forming. For example, there may be a speck of foreign matter lying on the surface. When it is flushed away, passivity will be regained. There can be a local constitutional irregularity that, when it has been removed by corrosive action, presents a surface for passivation. However, circumstances are not so fortunate when the passive film simply cannot be formed. This is the case when the corrosion potential lies above the passive potential range, as is illustrated in Fig. 4.5.

Pitting may be initiated by environmental circumstances that create a concentration cell (discussed in section 4.2.2 of this chapter), which may lead to a particularly virulent form, crevice corrosion.

4.4.3 Crevice Corrosion

This highly localized attack occurs where a surface protected by its passive layer holds a stagnant aqueous solution in a crevice. The crevice can be the tight gap between a bolt and a washer, the interstices in a wire rope, or an O-ring in its groove. In mild steels, the phenomenon is common enough where water is drawn under a discontinuity in a painted surface. An oxygen concentration cell is established in which the oxygen-lean solution within the crevice creates an anodic condition allowing rusting and blistering to occur.

In stainless steels (and in other metals whose corrosion resistance depends upon their passivity), the situation is more complicated. The initiation of crevice corrosion remains contentious, and suggested mechanisms of its propagation, while persuasive, do not seem to accommodate every variety. However, here is a working model. It begins with the formation of a local pit, created by the sorts of circumstance we have already described, or (another school of thought) by manganese sulfide inclusions at the metal surface. In either event, within the crevice, the pit propagates rapidly because of a deficiency of those oxidizing ions, which are necessary for passivity, in the confined solution. If chloride ions are present, the situation is made more vicious. As metal is ionized in the crevice, chloride ions seek to neutralize them, forming metal chloride, which, in turn, produces the metal hydroxide and hydrochloric acid. The solution within the crevice becomes highly acidic and saturated with chloride ions. Under these circumstances, passivation is out of the question and localized corrosion continues.

4.4.4 Intergranular Corrosion

Intergranular corrosion may happen at the surfaces of most metals, given the appropriate—or, should one say, inappropriate—environment. The crystal boundaries are anodic in that particular environment to the crystals themselves. This may be caused by a concentration of unwanted elements there, created initially as the alloy solidifies and not removed by subsequent thermomechanical treatment. Or it may arise because the inevitably disordered atomic distribution at grain boundaries (which makes them hyperactive) is particularly susceptible to the environment.

Naturally, the phenomenon is most keenly observed when it happens in a metal that has been specially chosen for its corrosion resistance but a particular susceptibility to intergranular attack has been overlooked.

Among those corrosion phenomena about which we generalize, there are three that are associated with mechanical conditions: stress-corrosion cracking, hydrogen embrittlement, and corrosion fatigue.

4.4.5 Stress-Corrosion Cracking (SCC)

All corrosion processes are speeded by the application of stress, but stress-corrosion cracking is in a different category. Even in metals that are normally ductile, such failure is brittle and catastrophic. It happens at low tensile stresses (applied or residual) in the presence of specific media. With the exception of ultra-high purity metals, there is for all metals and alloys (and also, by the way, for some plastics and ceramics) a combination of circumstances of stress and environment under which such failure may be anticipated.

In stainless steels, especially in austenitic grades, SCC is most common in chloride solutions. Here the cracks are transgranular (Fig. 4.7). In caustic environments, ferritic as well as austenitic grades are susceptible to intergranular attack (Fig. 4.8).

Theories—not inconsistent with each other but, nevertheless, embracing a wide spectrum of possibilities—are of two sorts, both accommodating the brittle nature of the failure. One proposes the accelerated anodic dissolution of metal; the other suggests the repeated formation of a brittle film as the crack progresses. The second of these theories recognizes the possible role of hydrogen, which is especially pertinent to the case of hydrogen sulfide SCC.

4.4.6 Hydrogen Embrittlement

Many metals and alloys fall prey to the damage and disasters caused by hydrogen. Least destructive of these is the formation in steels of hydrogen blisters. Here hydrogen penetrates as atomic (or ionic) hydrogen, is welcomed at some defect or other (probably an inclusion), and recombines as hydrogen gas to form a blister. This is unsightly but generally not disastrous.

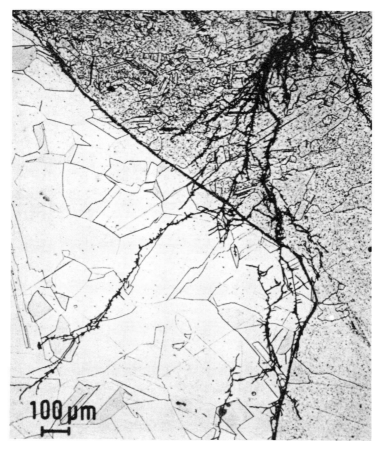

Fig. 4.7 Chloride SCC of type 304 stainless steel base metal and type 308 weld metal in an aqueous chloride environment at 95 °C (200 °F). Cracks are branching and transgranular.

The more malignant effect of hydrogen is its embrittlement of metals. This book concerns only stainless steels but offers the consolation that the misery enjoys the company of many other metals. The source of hydrogen may be simply an environment that contains hydrogen gas, or it may derive from hydrogenous compounds of which hydrogen sulfide is a frequent bad actor. No less, the source of hydrogen can be an aqueous solution. Its effects become more noxious as the tensile strength (or the residual stress) of its victim increases.

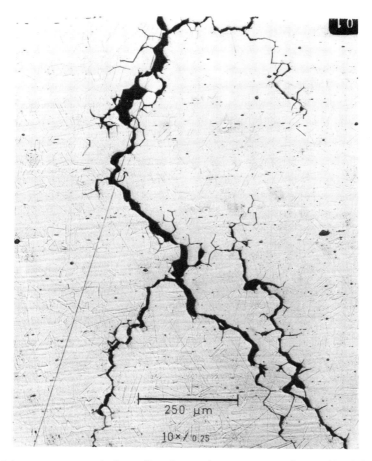

Fig. 4.8 Caustic SCC in the heat-affected zone of a type 316L stainless steel NaOH reactor vessel. Cracks are branching and intergranular.

If the hydrogen enters the metal during processing, or during some stage of the metal's application from which it may be temporarily withdrawn, then a low temperature treatment will drive out the hydrogen and recapture the metal's ductile condition. Usually things are not so simple. In an environment of hydrogen sulfide or in an acid solution, a susceptible component of process equipment cannot be temporarily hospitalized. The circumstances (environment, design, alloy) must therefore be adjusted so that the possibilities of hydrogen embrittlement are reduced.

4.4.7 Corrosion Fatigue

Even in innocuous environments, all metals will fail under repeated or cyclical tensile stress at a level far below that which they will sustain a single, steady load. This is the fatigue stress. A dangerous rule of thumb is that in innocuous environments where cyclic stresses are equally compressive and tensile, the fatigue stress is one-half the ultimate tensile stress. In specific corrosive environments, the fatigue stress is substantially reduced, and in some alloy/environmental combinations it may be near zero.

The initiation of fatigue failure is encouraged by a stress concentration, presented by a visible or a microscopic notch. The latter may be created at the tip of a corrosion crack. The mechanical propagation of the crack is then accelerated by the corrosion process.

Corrosion fatigue is by no means limited to high-strength components, but it should be cautiously anticipated in high-strength parts that are subjected to alternating stresses, such as impellers, shafts, and rolls. It is in these types of applications that the reduction of apparent strength and the susceptibility to brittle failure by fatigue is most pronounced.

4.4.8 Erosion-Corrosion

As the name implies, erosion-corrosion brings together two foes of the longevity of metals and alloys in service. Erosion-wear is a subject in itself. It has become the bailiwick of tribologists, who are concerned, among other things, with the ways in which friction between surfaces may be reduced and wear mitigated. We introduce the subject in Chapter 7.9. Corrosion can be the helpmate of wear because the abrasiveness of its products contributes to erosion. Meanwhile, wear removes a protective film and so encourages corrosion.

Erosion-corrosion is not limited to moving metallic interfaces. Common examples arise when there is a rapid relative movement between fluids (usually liquids) and metal parts, such as aqueous solutions swirling along pipes or impellers churning in vats.

As shown in Chapter 10, these forms of corrosion described so briefly cover most of the corrosion problems that arise in stainless steels.

The Measurement of Significant Properties

5.1 Introduction

It is important to know how to measure those properties to which most frequent reference is made in this book and to get some idea of their meaning and reliability. This chapter describes the measurement of mechanical properties and corrosion testing. The measurement of physical properties such as thermal and electrical conductivity or specific gravity is not dealt with. Physical properties are, of course, important, and we do refer to them. But these properties are fairly constant within each stainless steel class. Both manufacturer and user know—or accept, however unwittingly—the physical properties of the steels they make and use. They know, too, that these will not vary significantly from one shipment to the next. This consistency is shown in Table 5.1, which gives physical properties of annealed, wrought stainless steels.

Such consistency is not necessarily the case with mechanical properties. A recognition that these may vary from heat to heat and are considerably affected by subsequent processing is acknowledged by the fact that user specifications prescribe requirements of strength, ductility, and other properties whose measurements we will describe.

We shall not deal with chemical analysis. This is routine for the steelmaker, whose analytical techniques are necessarily careful and sophisticated because performance depends upon an adherence to the correct chemical composition on which the initial choice of steel has probably been based. Of course, errors can be made and sampling techniques, which are central to the validity of reliable results, can go awry. But fabricator and user rely upon the steel manufacturer to provide accurate chemical analyses of each and every heat that the shipment comprises.

Table 5.1 Typical physical properties of wrought stainless steels in the annealed condition

Type	UNS number	Density, g/cm^3 (lb/in.^{3})	Elastic modulus, GPa (10^6 psi)	Mean CTE from 0 °C to: 100 °C μm/m·°C (μin./in.·°F)	315 °C μm/m·°C (μin./in.·°F)	538 °C μm/m·°C (μin./in.·°F)	Thermal conductivity 100 °C W/m·K (Btu/ft·h·°F)	500 °C W/m·K (Btu/ft·h·°F)	Specific heat(a), J/kg·K (Btu/lb·°F)	Electrical resistivity, nΩ·m	Magnetic permeability(b)	Melting range, °C (°F)
201	S20100	7.8 (0.28)	197 (28.6)	15.7 (8.7)	17.5 (9.7)	18.4 (10.2)	16.2 (9.4)	21.5 (12.4)	500 (0.12)	690	1.02	1400–1450 (2550–2650)
202	S20200	7.8 (0.28)	...	17.5 (9.7)	18.4 (10.2)	19.2 (10.2)	16.2 (9.4)	21.6 (12.5)	500 (0.12)	690	1.02	1400–1450 (2550–2650)
205	S20500	7.8 (0.28)	197 (28.6)	...	17.9 (9.9)	19.1 (10.6)	...	...	500 (0.12)	...	...	...
301	S30100	8.0 (0.29)	193 (28.0)	17.0 (9.4)	17.2 (9.6)	18.2 (10.1)	16.2 (9.4)	21.5 (12.4)	500 (0.12)	720	1.02	1400–1420 (2550–2590)
302	S30200	8.0 (0.29)	193 (28.0)	17.2 (9.6)	17.8 (9.9)	18.4 (10.2)	16.2 (9.4)	21.5 (12.4)	500 (0.12)	720	1.02	1400–1420 (2550–2590)
302B	S30215	8.0 (0.29)	193 (28.0)	16.2 (9.0)	18.0 (10.0)	19.4 (10.8)	15.9 (9.2)	21.6 (12.5)	500 (0.12)	720	1.02	1375–1400 (2500–2550)
303	S30300	8.0 (0.29)	193 (28.0)	17.2 (9.6)	17.8 (9.9)	18.4 (10.2)	16.2 (9.4)	21.5 (12.4)	500 (0.12)	720	1.02	1400–1420 (2550–2590)
304	S30400	8.0 (0.29)	193 (28.0)	17.2 (9.6)	17.8 (9.9)	18.4 (10.2)	16.2 (9.4)	21.5 (12.4)	500 (0.12)	720	1.02	1400–1450 (2550–2650)
304L	S30403	8.0 (0.29)	...	...	...	...	...	...	...	...	1.02	1400–1450 (2550–2650)
302Cu	S30430	8.0 (0.29)	913 (28.0)	17.2 (9.6)	17.8 (9.9)	...	11.2 (6.5)	21.5 (12.4)	500 (0.12)	720	1.02	1400–1450 (2550–2650)
304N	S30451	8.0 (0.29)	196 (28.5)	...	...	...	...	...	500 (0.12)	720	1.02	1400–1450 (2550–2650)
305	S30500	8.0 (0.29)	193 (28.0)	17.2 (9.6)	17.8 (9.9)	18.4 (10.2)	16.2 (9.4)	21.5 (12.4)	500 (0.12)	720	1.02	1400–1450 (2550–2650)
308	S30800	8.0 (0.29)	193 (28.0)	17.2 (9.6)	17.8 (9.9)	18.4 (10.2)	15.2 (8.8)	21.6 (12.5)	500 (0.12)	720	1.02	1400–1420 (2550–2590)
309	S30900	8.0 (0.29)	200 (29.0)	15.0 (8.3)	16.6 (9.2)	17.2 (9.6)	15.6 (9.0)	18.7 (10.8)	500 (0.12)	780	...	1400–1450 (2550–2650)
310	S31000	8.0 (0.29)	200 (29.0)	15.9 (8.8)	16.2 (9.0)	17.0 (9.4)	14.2 (8.2)	18.7 (10.8)	500 (0.12)	780	1.02	1400–1450 (2550–2650)
314	S31400	7.8 (0.28)	200 (29.0)	...	15.1 (8.4)	...	17.5 (10.1)	20.9 (12.1)	500 (0.12)	770	1.02	1375–1400 (2500–2550)
316	S31600	8.0 (0.29)	193 (28.0)	15.9 (8.8)	16.2 (9.0)	17.5 (9.7)	16.2 (9.4)	21.5 (12.4)	500 (0.12)	740	1.02	1375–1400 (2500–2550)
316L	S31603	8.0 (0.29)	...	...	...	...	...	...	...	...	1.02	1375–1400 (2500–2550)
316N	S31651	8.0 (0.29)	196 (28.5)	...	...	...	...	...	500 (0.12)	...	1.02	1375–1400 (2500–2550)
317	S31700	8.0 (0.29)	193 (28.0)	15.9 (8.8)	16.2 (9.0)	17.5 (9.7)	16.2 (9.4)	21.5 (12.4)	500 (0.12)	740	1.02	1375–1400 (2500–2550)
317L	S31703	8.0 (0.29)	200 (29.0)	16.5 (9.2)	...	18.1 (10.1)	14.4 (8.3)	...	500 (0.12)	790	1.02	1375–1400 (2500–2550)
321	S32100	8.0 (0.29)	193 (28.0)	16.6 (9.2)	17.2 (9.6)	18.6 (10.3)	16.1 (9.3)	22.2 (12.8)	500 (0.12)	720	1.02	1400–1425 (2550–2600)
329	S32900	7.8 (0.28)	...	...	...	...	...	...	460 (0.11)	750	...	...
330	N08330	8.0 (0.29)	196 (28.5)	14.4 (8.0)	16.0 (8.9)	16.7 (9.3)	...	...	460 (0.11)	1020	1.02	1400–1425 (2550–2600)
347	S34700	8.0 (0.29)	193 (28.0)	16.6 (9.2)	17.2 (9.6)	18.6 (10.3)	16.1 (9.3)	22.2 (12.8)	500 (0.12)	730	1.02	1400–1425 (2550–2600)
384	S38400	8.0 (0.29)	193 (28.0)	17.2 (9.6)	17.8 (9.9)	18.4 (10.2)	16.2 (9.4)	21.5 (12.4)	500 (0.12)	790	1.02	1400–1450 (2550–2650)
405	S40500	7.8 (0.28)	200 (29.0)	10.8 (6.0)	11.6 (6.4)	21.1 (6.7)	27.0 (15.6)	...	460 (0.11)	600	...	1480–1530 (2700–2790)
409	S40900	7.8 (0.28)	...	11.7 (6.5)	...	...	...	...	...	...	700–1000	1480–1530 (2700–2790)
410	S41000	7.8 (0.28)	200 (29.0)	9.9 (5.5)	11.4 (6.3)	11.6 (6.4)	24.9 (14.4)	28.7 (16.6)	460 (0.11)	570	...	1480–1530 (2700–2790)
414	S41400	7.8 (0.28)	200 (29.0)	10.4 (5.8)	11.0 (6.1)	12.1 (6.7)	24.9 (14.4)	28.7 (16.6)	460 (0.11)	700	...	1425–1480 (2600–2700)

(continued)

Table 5.1 (continued)

Type	UNS number	Density, g/cm³ (lb/in.³)	Elastic modulus, GPa (10⁶ psi)	Mean CTE from 0 °C to: 100 °C, µm/m · °C (µin./in. · °F)	315 °C, µm/m · °C (µin./in. · °F)	538 °C, µm/m · °C (µin./in. · °F)	Thermal conductivity 100 °C, W/m · K (Btu/ft · h · °F)	500 °C, W/m · K (Btu/ft · h · °F)	Specific heat(a), J/kg · K (Btu/lb · °F)	Electrical resistivity, nΩ · m	Magnetic permeability(b)	Melting range, °C (°F)
416	S41600	7.8 (0.28)	200 (29.0)	9.9 (5.5)	11.0 (6.1)	11.6 (6.4)	24.9 (14.4)	28.7 (16.6)	460 (0.11)	570	700–1000	1480–1530 (2700–2790)
420	S42000	7.8 (0.28)	200 (29.0)	10.3 (5.7)	10.8 (6.0)	11.7 (6.5)	24.9 (14.4)	....	460 (0.11)	550	...	1450–1510 (2650–2750)
422	S42200	7.8 (0.28)	...	11.2 (6.2)	11.4 (6.3)	11.9 (6.6)	23.9 (13.8)	27.3 (15.8)	460 (0.11)	...	...	1470–1480 (2675–2700)
429	S42900	7.8 (0.28)	200 (29.0)	10.3 (5.7)	...	...	25.6 (14.8)	....	460 (0.11)	590	...	1450–1510 (2650–2750)
430	S43000	7.8 (0.28)	200 (29.0)	10.4 (5.8)	11.0 (6.1)	11.4 (6.3)	26.1 (15.1)	26.3 (15.2)	460 (0.11)	600	600–1100	1425–1510 (2600–2750)
430F	S43020	7.8 (0.28)	200 (29.0)	10.4 (5.8)	11.0 (6.1)	11.4 (6.3)	26.1 (15.1)	26.3 (15.2)	460 (0.11)	600	...	1425–1510 (2600–2750)
431	S43100	7.8 (0.28)	200 (29.0)	10.2 (5.7)	12.1 (6.7)	...	20.2 (11.7)	....	460 (0.11)	720	...	....
434	S43400	7.8 (0.28)	200 (29.0)	10.4 (5.8)	11.0 (6.1)	11.4 (6.3)	....	26.3 (15.2)	460 (0.11)	600	600–1100	1425–1510 (2600–2750)
436	S43600	7.8 (0.28)	200 (29.0)	9.3 (5.2)	...	...	23.9 (13.8)	26.0 (15.0)	460 (0.11)	600	600–1100	1425–1510 (2600–2750)
439	S43035	7.7 (0.28)	200 (29.0)	10.4 (5.8)	11.0 (6.1)	11.4 (6.3)	24.2 (14.0)	...	460 (0.11)	630	...	....
440A	S44002	7.8 (0.28)	200 (29.0)	10.2 (5.7)	...	...	24.2 (14.0)	...	460 (0.11)	600	...	1370–1480 (2500–2700)
440C	S44004	7.8 (0.28)	200 (29.0)	10.2 (5.7)	...	...	24.2 (14.0)	...	460 (0.11)	600	...	1370–1480 (2500–2700)
444	S44400	7.8 (0.28)	200 (29.0)	10.0 (5.6)	11.4 (6.3)	11.4 (6.3)	26.8 (15.5)	...	420 (0.10)	620	...	....
446	S44600	7.5 (0.27)	200 (29.0)	10.4 (5.8)	10.8 (6.0)	11.2 (6.2)	20.9 (12.1)	24.4 (14.1)	500 (0.12)	670	400–700	1425–1510 (2600–2750)
PH 13-8 Mo	S13800	7.8 (0.28)	203 (29.4)	10.6 (5.9)	11.2 (6.2)	11.9 (6.6)	14.0 (8.1)	22.0 (12.7)	460 (0.11)	1020	...	1400–1440 (2560–2625)
15-5 PH	S15500	7.8 (0.28)	196 (28.5)	10.8 (6.0)	11.4 (6.3)	...	17.8 (10.3)	23.0 (13.1)	420 (0.10)	770	95	1400–1440 (2560–2625)
17-4 PH	S17400	7.8 (0.28)	196 (28.5)	10.8 (6.0)	11.6 (6.4)	...	18.3 (10.6)	23.0 (13.1)	460 (0.11)	800	95	1400–1440 (2560–2625)
17-7 PH	S17700	7.8 (0.28)	204 (29.5)	11.0 (6.1)	11.6 (6.4)	...	16.4 (9.5)	21.8 (12.6)	460 (0.11)	830	...	1400–1440 (2560–2625)

CTE, coefficient of thermal expansion. (a) At 0 to 100 °C (32 to 212 °F). (b) Approximate values

In all but the hardness test, mechanical properties must be measured on a sample that, of necessity, cannot be the piece of steel that is to be used. The test destroys it. Generally, the sample is representative, but cases are known where segregation or irregularities in processing have presented misleading results.

In corrosion testing, long-term tests provide a continuously updated arsenal of invaluable information (maintained by several sources) about corrosion in a variety of atmospheric conditions and soils. If the circumstances of alloy and environment have not been explored, there is no option but to take a sample and try to reproduce the anticipated environmental conditions or, more commonly, to apply a test which is known to be indicative of performance. Here, the difficulty of getting useful results is exacerbated by the necessity of determining in a short time what can be expected in the long haul. "What is a twenty-year life expectancy?" asks the general manager, a graduate in business administration. "I need to know next week."

Laboratory corrosion tests offer important signals, especially where mechanical failure is associated with the corrosion process. As every corrosion engineer will confirm, nothing can substitute for an encyclopedic knowledge of past experiences and their interrelationship.

With these provisos in place, the methods of testing and the interpretation and meaning of the results are reviewed, and some cautions are noted.

5.2 Mechanical Testing

5.2.1 Hardness Testing

Hardness testing is the least fundamental of mechanical tests, but hardness values are so easily measured and so frequently used as a preliminary check on conformity that we deal with it first. Except in extreme circumstances, hardness testing is nondestructive, and the test can often be made in situ.

The earliest measure of hardness was on a relative scale that indicated which material could scratch another. Moh's ten-point scale is still used by mineralogists, rating diamond at the top of the list with a value of 10, while talc is the least resistant with a value of 1. This is a handy aid in mineral identification, and a metal's resistance to scratching with a pocket-knife has been known as a desperate last resort in settling an argument in the plant.

The principle upon which quantitatively reliable hardness testing depends is the measurement of a metal's resistance to indentation. In the oldest of these tests, the Brinell test (introduced by J.A. Brinell around 1900), a specified load is applied to a hardened steel ball on the metal surface. The size of the indentation is measured under a microscope, and the hardness figure is derived by dividing the load by a function of the area of indentation. Load and ball diameters are appropriately adjusted so that the indentation is neither too small to be significant nor too large to sink the ball near to its equator. Accordingly, values of the ratio of load divided by the square of the ball diameter are prescribed for specific materials. For steels, the Brinell number is derived from the indentation made by a ball of 10 mm diam with a load of 3000 kgf. If the sample is not big enough to sustain such punishment, a smaller ball with a correspondingly lighter load is used.

The Vickers hardness test, or diamond pyramid hardness test, is a variant that uses a square-based pyramid diamond as indenter. This test offers two advantages: the diamond doesn't deform and the impression made by the indenter is always of the same geometric shape. Hence, simply by changing the load, hardness values of a wide variety of materials, and over a range of thickness, can be obtained. Surface preparation is more demanding than in Brinell testing.

Both Vickers and Brinell require a measurement to be made of the indentation widths. The Rockwell hardness test avoids this. It automatically reads the depth of the impression made by the indenter and transfers this to a dial whose reading is the Rockwell hardness number. Although, as with all hardness tests, the specimen surface should be adequately prepared, the Rockwell tester reduces the effects of minor surface irregularities by seating the indenter with a smaller load before applying the standardized major load. The hardness value is based upon the difference in indentation depths.

Once again, the difficulty of accommodating a wide range of hardness values arises. Rockwell commonly uses two scales: for harder materials, the C scale with a conical diamond penetrator; for softer materials, the B scale, with a steel ball.

Brinell, Vickers, and Rockwell tests can be made with portable instruments. These are used in the field and incorporate means by which the instrument is firmly attached to the part being tested and to ensure that the axis of the indenter is normal to the surface. Another type of portable testing machine—the scleroscope—depends upon a different principle: that of measuring the rebound of a diamond-tipped weight, which is dropped down a glass tube onto the metal surface. Once very useful, such instruments have been overtaken by indentation testers, which have much greater precision, equal portability, and may be positioned at any angle.

We hope to be forgiven for not describing several other hardness testing machines, fixed and portable, because all testers depend upon the principles outlined.

Hardness values are often converted to give an idea of a material's ultimate tensile strength. For any specific class of material, the conversion is sufficiently accurate to be useful, but the specificity must be emphasized. For example, the conversion factor for plain-carbon steels is different from that for alloy steels which, again, is different for stainless steels. Within stainless steels, the conversion factors are not the same for different classes; and within a class, the conversion factor is affected by a material's thermomechanical history.

Two cautions should be observed in assessing ultimate tensile strength from a hardness value. First, the design capability of a structure is more properly related to yield strength to which the hardness value cannot be converted. Second, by its nature, the hardness value is a surface measurement, which may not be characteristic of the cross section. Surface phenomena, such as decarburization, nitriding, alloy depletion, and localized work hardening, lead to hardness values that are not typical of the whole.

5.2.2 Tensile Testing

Of the mechanical properties specified for stainless steel application, those that emerge from the tensile test are the most common and the most useful. A straight sample is gripped at its ends and pulled until it breaks. The stress applied to the sample (whose dimensions are standardized) is calculated by dividing the measured load by the original cross-sectional area of the sample. The strain is obtained by dividing the increase in length by the initial length of a specified gage length.

If measurements of load and extension are continuously made and stress and strain are computed, a curve such as Fig. 5.1 is obtained. This curve, the engineering stress-strain curve, is characteristic of all stainless steels. Point A is where the initial linearity of the graph disappears; point B is where the stress is a maximum. During the course of the test incorporated by the line OA, the sample behaves elastically. Were the load to be removed, the sample would regain its original dimensions. The slope of the line OA, measured by dividing OC by OD, gives us what is called Young's modulus of elasticity, sometimes known as the elastic modulus, even though there are other elastic moduli.

The stress at which the sample breaks corresponds to that at point G (Fig. 5.1). The drop in stress from B to G occurs because the sample thins locally;

it necks as a result of plastic yielding. Initial plastic yielding (from *A* to *B*) is accompanied by work hardening to an extent that more than compensates for the reduction in cross section. The maximum load, reached at *B*, divided by the original cross-sectional area is the ultimate tensile strength. The enquiring reader will appreciate that the value of ultimate tensile strength is not really so "ultimate," because it is based upon the original cross-sectional area, not the area when fracture occurs, and it is not the stress recorded when the sample breaks.

While the importance of the ultimate tensile strength cannot be denied, designers (not to mention their clients) have a greater concern for the load a component or structure will sustain without deforming; that is to say, without yielding. This yield stress occurs at, or very close to, the elastic limit; but in the tension test, the point *A* is difficult to locate precisely. Where a marked yield extension occurs, as in the mild steels, the yield stress is evident (Fig. 5.2). Consequently, the definition of yield stress is arbitrarily agreed upon and is usually that stress at which the sample has suffered a permanent strain of 0.2%. This value of stress is determined by drawing a

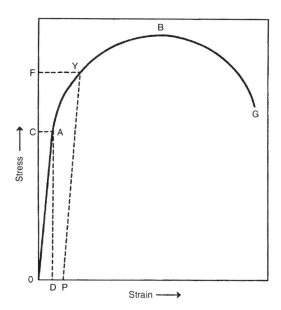

Fig. 5.1 Stress-strain curve. Point *P* represents a plastic extension of 0.2%.

line parallel to *OA*, displaced along the horizontal axis by a value of strain equal to 0.2% (line *PY* in Fig. 5.1). The yield stress is given by the value at point *F*. It should be clearly designated as the 0.2% offset yield stress because there are other, less common, definitions.

Before the test piece is put between the grips of the testing machine, a gage length is marked out according to one of several possible specifications. The cross-sectional dimensions are also carefully measured. When the test is completed, the two pieces of the broken sample are put together, and the new dimensions of length and of cross section are measured. From these, the ductility is ascribed in two ways. First, it is denoted by the elongation, which is the increase in length divided by the original gage length, expressed as a percentage. The gage length should be specified when the elongation is quoted. The second expression of ductility is by the reduction of area. This is the decrease in cross-sectional area divided by the original area, expressed as a percentage.

These values, as an indication of ductility, are of obvious importance to the fabricator who shapes stainless steel sections. Measures of ductility are no less significant in structural design, where anticipated stresses, overall, are substantially lower than the yield stress. The significance arises because

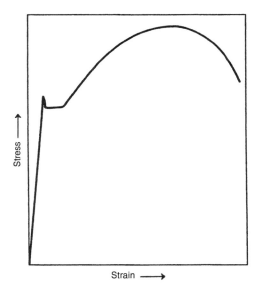

Fig. 5.2   Stress-strain curve typical of mild steel

the structure is not simply a scaled-up version of the tensile test piece. At changes of section (intentional or otherwise, macroscopic or microscopic) and under multidirectional loads, local stresses may exceed the yield point (i.e., parts of the structure will deform plastically). An indication of their ability to do this is given by the ductility measurements obtained in the tensile test. It's worth mentioning, too, that local plastic deformation is a necessity if, for example, surfaces of a mechanical joint are to make a snug fitting. Also, the mating threads of a tightened nut and bolt are, inevitably, plastically deformed.

5.2.3 Notch Brittleness and Impact Testing

If a localized section of metal does not deform plastically when it is at the focus of simple or multiaxial stress, then, at what appears to be a nominal stress as measured on the entire structure, it snaps, suffering a brittle, cleavage fracture. Unfortunately, because of the way in which brittleness is appraised, there is a misapprehension that such catastrophic failure occurs only under impact loads. The purpose of impact testing is not to evaluate the performance of a material under impact loads in service. It is to give an indication of the ability, or lack of ability, to plastically deform under multiaxial stress with a rapidly applied lead.

The subject is too complex to cover here, but if the purpose of testing for brittleness is to be appreciated—indeed, if it is not to be misunderstood—a few introductory words are necessary.

Most metals may be induced to fail in a brittle fashion by changing their internal constitution (e.g., nonductile precipitates at grain boundaries), by influencing their external environment (as in stress-corrosion cracking), or by applying multiple stresses that will impede plastic slip. In practical terms, however, body-centered cubic (bcc) structures are far more susceptible and face-centered cubic (fcc) structures far less. And while there are specific environments that cause embrittlement in almost any metal, and combinations of stress that are deleterious to all metals, bcc structures have an additional problem: their fracture behavior is temperature dependent.

The temperature at which ferritic steels exhibit brittle failure in the tension test is very low. Under more complex circumstances of stress (created by the nature of the design, accidental defects, or quirks of internal constitution), the temperature at which brittle behavior occurs is substantially raised and may reach, or exceed, normal atmospheric levels. Meanwhile, the fracture behavior of the fcc austenitic steels is independent of temperature.

This brings us to the impact test, commonly said to assess the toughness of steel. Values obtained in laboratory impact tests are not directly transferable to any service condition; they only permit a comparison of behaviors. Also, they are used to determine the temperature at which the failure mode of the steel will change from ductile to brittle.

To encourage the generation of triaxial stresses, a notched sample is prepared in accordance with scrupulous dimensional specifications, and it is held in an anvil or supported in a cradle. A hammer at the end of a swung pendulum provides a rapidly applied load. The energy absorbed by the specimen is computed from the difference in height between the starting and finishing points of the pendulum. In the Izod test, the test piece is clamped in a vertical position at the lowest point of the pendulum's arc, with the notch facing the pendulum and level with the top of the vice. The Charpy test (Fig. 5.3) supports the specimen horizontally; the pendulum strikes the sample face opposite the notch. By testing samples at different temperatures and plotting energy absorbed (or the percentage of cleavage seen in the fracture) against temperature, curves such as those shown in Fig. 5.4 are obtained; and the ductile/brittle transformation temperature can be assessed.

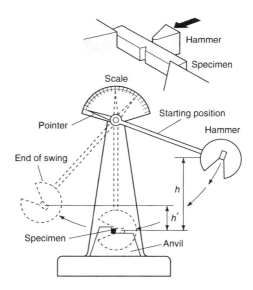

Fig. 5.3 Charpy impact test

Testing at lower than room temperature is easier in the Charpy machine; because the sample is more quickly placed, and there is less chance of heat absorption from the fixture than in the Izod machine.

5.2.4 Creep Testing

The tension test is performed in a few minutes, but one may want to evaluate the behavior of a material when it is subjected to a load for a long while. At room temperature, most engineering materials will sustain for

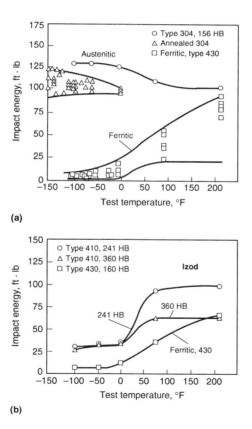

(a)

(b)

Fig. 5.4 Impact toughness comparison of stainless steels. (a) Ferritic type 430 and austenitic type 304. (b) Ferritic type 430 and martensitic type 410. Each point represents an average of five tests, Izod specimens.

long periods the loads indicated by the tension test. At elevated temperatures, the length of time a material is under load is a major factor in determining what load may be safely applied. The topic is germane, because stainless steels are often selected on account of their high-temperature strength.

There are two sorts of tests. The purpose of one, the creep test, is to determine either the stress that will produce a specified minimum rate of creep or a total specified creep strain in a given period. The purpose of the second sort of test, the creep-rupture test, is to give the time for failure under stated conditions of stress and temperature.

Testing equipment is similar in both cases. A static tensile load is applied, usually by levered weights, to a specimen held at constant temperature in a furnace that may require a controlled atmosphere. In the creep test (but not in the creep-rupture test), sensitive measurements of extension have to be made. Because measurements of creep and of creep-rupture incorporate several temperatures and stresses, many tests are usually run concurrently in a battery of furnaces.

Creep testing can be a long process. Consequently, extrapolations from higher temperatures or larger loads are often made to predict how a material will behave over a longer period of time under less severe conditions. The extrapolations are not always reliable.

5.2.5 Fatigue Testing

When a metal is subjected to repeated or cyclic stresses that include a tensile component, it fractures by fatigue at levels substantially below the ultimate tensile stress. Although we mentioned corrosion fatigue in section 4.4.7 and have commented upon the fatigue resistance of some classes of stainless, fatigue values are not included in any of the mechanical properties tables in this book. The reasons should become evident with this description of fatigue testing, which gives us an opportunity to briefly describe the phenomenon and discuss the applicability of test results.

Fatigue measurements were made as early as the 1860s, when it was discovered that the ultimate tensile strength of steels was not realized if the load were alternately applied and released. Today, fatigue probably represents the most common cause of metallurgical failure. Many components are subjected to alternating stresses of which we are immediately aware, such as rotating or reciprocating shafts, springs, or gear teeth. Less obvious are situations where the alternation is less rapid—a vessel that is pressured and depressured, or a seemingly static unit that endures sympathetic vibrations.

A fatigue crack is usually initiated at a metal surface and slowly moves in a direction perpendicular to the axis of the tensile load. During this process, although ductile slip takes place, it does so on such a microscopic scale that the component suffers no measurable dimensional change. However, visible ripples are produced on the progressing fracture surfaces, which rub together and become burnished. Eventually, the cross-sectional area bearing the load becomes so decreased that it cannot withstand the tensile load. It breaks, revealing a faceted, crystalline appearance, which has led many people to remark, "The metal has crystallized." We know better; the metal was crystalline at the outset. A typical fatigue fracture is shown in Fig. 5.5.

Because the initiation of fatigue is almost always at a surface, the avoidance of surface imperfections, sharp changes of contour, corrosion pits, and metallic inclusions is vital. The effect of surface finish on fatigue life is especially important, and test samples whose finish varies from rough turned to a high polish can show up to an order of magnitude decrease in the number of loading cycles to failure.

Fatigue testing machines are designed to create alternating flexure in a sample. If the piece to be tested is of a flat section, it is gripped at one end while the free end is attached to a crank that provides a reciprocating motion so that the sample is bent back and forth. More common, however, are the

Fig. 5.5 Fatigue fracture of AISI type 316L stainless steel wire due to cracking originating at corrosion pits. The wire was used for electrodes in an electrostatic precipitator that treated the gaseous effluent from a paper mill. Note beach marks on fracture surface.

rotating beam and rotating cantilever tests. In each, a rotating cylindrical specimen is loaded so that it suffers a bending moment, which subjects the cross section to equal and opposite tension and compression stresses at each revolution.

Fatigue test results are presented in graphs that plot the stress (S) against the number of cycles (N). Steels in a noncorrosive environment characteristically present data illustrated in Fig. 5.6. Nonferrous metals, and steels in a corrosive environment, exhibit curves characterized by Fig. 5.7. Figure 5.6 shows a leveling of the curve, which may be taken to mean that for all practical purposes the specimen (but not necessarily a structure) would have an infinite life below the value S_D, which is known as the fatigue limit. This is usually about one-half of the ultimate tensile strength. In circumstances shown in Fig. 5.7, there is no suggestion, however misleading, of immortality. Consequently, an endurance limit, S_N, is given; this is the allowable stress for a stated number of cycles.

Even the most meticulously performed fatigue tests show scatter, which increases as surface conditions become more erratic. The situation in Nevil Shute's *No Highway*, which dramatically suggests that fatigue would fell an aircraft prior to landing, is flawed, as it were, by the statistical nature of fatigue in practical circumstances.

A further impediment to the applicability of fatigue test data has to do with the speed of stress variation. This may be of marginal significance under circumstances of a benign environment; however, where failure is hastened by corrosion, a rapidly conducted test (in which contact with the corrodent is for a short period) may give overly optimistic results.

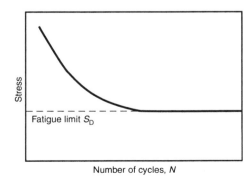

Fig. 5.6 *S-N* curve showing a fatigue limit typical of steels in a noncorrosive environment

The mechanical tests described are the subjects of several specifications of which the most comprehensive are written by the American Society for Testing and Materials (ASTM), to whose Annual Book of Standards reference should be made for a more detailed exposition.

5.3 Corrosion Testing

5.3.1 Laboratory Testing

The least devastating of corrosion processes is general corrosion, where a metal is eaten away fairly evenly across its entire surface. While this may be simulated in the laboratory, attempts to speed the process can give results that do not reduce to less severe conditions, or, worse, different corrosion processes are encouraged by the severity of the test.

Generally, laboratory corrosion tests become more reliable for evaluating extreme conditions, such as assessing susceptibility to stress-corrosion cracking, corrosion fatigue, intergranular corrosion, and pitting. This reliability is extremely valuable, because these conditions, unlike general corrosion, lead to failures that may be catastrophic and unexpected.

As we have already come to realize in this chapter, laboratory testing does not often give us numbers that can be directly applied to service conditions. Rather, the tests offer a means of comparison (hardness tests); they suggest limits (fatigue tests); and they signal danger (impact tests). Laboratory corrosion testing carries the same sorts of justification.

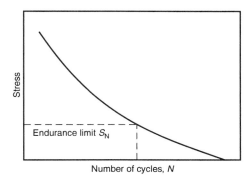

Fig. 5.7 S-N curve showing an endurance limit typical of nonferrous metals and steels in a corrosive environment

5.3.2 Stress-Corrosion Cracking (SCC)

The susceptibility of austenitic stainless steels to chloride SCC was first recognized about 1940, and the first test specifications were laid down a few years later. They have not changed very much since then and involve immersing a stressed sample in a boiling (155 °C, or 310 °F) 45% magnesium chloride solution. The shape of the sample depends upon whether the intention is to determine a threshold stress below which no cracking will occur or simply to find out if the steel is susceptible at all. In the latter case, a flat specimen is bent through at least 180°. In the former case, pieces are bent to various curvatures (each producing a calculable stress) and held in a base plate or by a bolt. Specific procedures are set out by ASTM G 36. A more recent specification for a less severe sodium chloride test (G 123) is being used, but there are fewer data available about correlations with service performance.

The wick test (ASTM C 692) was developed to simulate conditions at the surface of a hot insulated pipe exposed to rainwater. A dilute chloride solution is drawn by capillary action through glass wool onto the surface of a bent specimen, which is electrically heated to 100 °C (212 °F). A high chloride concentration develops at the surface, and cracking occurs at a lower temperature than in the magnesium chloride test.

As we mention in section 11.2.5, polythionic acid causes what may be SCC or intergranular corrosion. Whichever it is, a standard test (ASTM G 35) describes the method of producing polythionic acid, in which test specimens are immersed in order to determine their relative susceptibility.

Although caustic and other solutions may induce SCC in stainless steels, service conditions have not been sufficiently conducive to this sort of failure for the development of standard tests.

5.3.3 Intergranular Corrosion

As we mentioned in section 4.2.2, grain boundaries are sites of chemical activity where preferential corrosive attack may occur. The earliest example of intergranular attack in an austenitic stainless steel dates to 1926, and the test, which followed the detection, simulated the service conditions of a copper sulfate-sulfuric acid pickling solution. Since then, a daunting array of tests that either simulate service conditions or, in a shorter term, indicate susceptibility has been devised and standardized. Tests for the most common austenitic stainless steels are incorporated in the comprehensive specification ASTM A 262 "Standard Practices for Detecting Susceptibility to

Intergranular Attack in Austenitic Stainless Steels." This begins with a short term screening test in which a sample is electrolytically etched in oxalic acid and examined under the microscope. If there is no evidence of intergranular attack, no further testing is required. Otherwise, several tests are subsequently conducted and, by weight loss and sample appearance, permit some ascription of cause and indicate levels of susceptibility.

5.3.4 Pitting Corrosion

Weight loss measurements alone are of little use in assessing pitting corrosion. Consequently, accelerated tests involve the measurement of pit depth, the frequency of pits, and the general appearance of the sample. ASTM G 48 prescribes a ferric chloride solution at one of two temperatures (depending upon the speed with which the test is to be conducted), and a further specification (ASTM G 46) suggests methods by which pits may be characterized. Although the test is said to simulate seawater conditions, such a correlation is thwarted by differences in the effects of temperature, oxygen concentrations, and the presence of living cells in the water. As is often the case, the value of the tests lies in the comparisons they permit.

An electrochemical method offers a more sophisticated way of evaluating the possibility of pitting. This method is based upon polarization curves described in section 4.2.4, (see Fig. 4.5). In the test, a potential is applied to the sample immersed in a ferric chloride solution, and the current density is measured. Passivation does not occur, and a corrosion current is detected at potentials more noble than that represented by point A. Then, if the current density remains constant with further increases in potential, it may be surmised that pitting is not likely. If, however, the potential approaches point C (at a value, say, of E_p) before current density increases dramatically, then pitting is to be expected. Susceptibility to pitting increases as the difference between E_{corr} and E_p diminishes, and that separation is, not surprisingly, very sensitive to the compositions of the steel and its environment.

5.3.5 Crevice Corrosion

The ferric chloride immersion test (ASTM G 48) used to assess pitting corrosion is amended to evaluate crevice corrosion, by creating crevices at contact sites with plastic washers. In order to speed evaluation, multiple-crevice assemblies have been designed. Serrated washers, for instance, hold about 20 coupons at top and bottom edge. The washers are held together with the coupons firmly between them by a bolt.

The test, which is described in ASTM G 78, is easy enough. The matter of interpretation is less so! Conditions of testing (time, temperature, and environment), as well as the torque applied to the assembly, should be specified, and, generally, the number of sites and the maximum depth of attack are reported.

Electrochemical methods for assessing susceptibility to crevice corrosion, based on similar principles to those outlined under pitting corrosion, have also become standard and are captured in ASTM G 61.

5.3.6 General Corrosion

In the laboratory, either weight loss in a sample or electrochemical methods will determine whether a steel is susceptible to general corrosion in a given environment. Weight loss is generally converted to thickness loss that may be expressed as mils per year (a mil is one-thousandth of an inch) or, as the metric system becomes more familiar, in millimeters per year. When the corrosive environment is made more severe so that testing may be speeded by a greater concentration or a higher testing temperature, care must be taken to ensure that the corrosion process itself is not changed.

For an assessment by electrochemical methods, refer to the polarization curve of Fig. 4.4. If the "nose" characterizing passivity is present, then at potentials above it, current density remains constant: there is no corrosion. If passivation does not occur, then after a small increase in potential, current density increases: the metal corrodes. In practice, this means that the greater the potential that is developed by the half-cell (that is the stainless steel in the corrodent), the more rapid the corrosion rate.

While quantitative estimates of corrosion loss can only be realized by a precise replication of service conditions, weight loss or potentiometric methods permit a qualitative prediction to be made whether or not a stainless steel will resist general corrosion. If the steel is acceptable in this respect, then tests of the sort described earlier should be made regarding susceptibility to localized corrosion, which present much more frequent, and hazardous, modes of failure.

5.4 Pilot Plant Testing

New production processes are preceded by pilot plant tests, which follow the smaller scale justifications from work in the laboratory. The pilot plant offers splendid opportunities, which should not be missed, for corrosion testing under what approaches service conditions. These may not be an exact replication. For instance, fluid flow at changes of contour or section is unlikely to be the same in a scaled-up version of the pilot plant, and hence the extent of corrosion, or corrosion-erosion, will be different.

Obviously, every material failure (not only corrosion failures) in the pilot plant should be carefully examined so that corrections can be considered. And the pilot plant should be used to test coupons of materials other than those used in its construction, so that these may be evaluated for subsequent application. The design of the pilot plant also presents an opportunity that should be repeated at the time of actual plant construction; that is, to emphasize the importance of coordinating materials selection with plant design. Design is an integral part of corrosion control. Consequently, the presentation of finished design drawings to a corrosion engineer with the request "What materials shall we specify?" shows a depressing—but not altogether unknown—lack of understanding.

5.5 Field Testing

Field testing is the name given to corrosion evaluation in atmospheric or soil environments. In order of intensity, atmospheric environments are classified as rural, semi-industrial, and industrial, with the added category, marine. A marine environment may or may not be as cruel as the other categories, depending upon the attitude of the metal tested, but it is generally punishing to stainless steels. Consequently, the data collected at the LaQue Center for Corrosion Technology, Inc., on Kure Beach, NC, are especially significant. Here, tens of thousands of samples are continuously exposed to a saline atmosphere and evaluated.

Making Stainless Steels

6.1 Introduction

Steel isn't made in test tube quantities under laboratory conditions. It is produced in the millions of tons and hundreds of grades, and wherever it is made, it is expected to have the reproducible and reliable properties of a pharmaceutical product at an attractive price. That expectation has grown increasingly exacting. The foundation on which such reproducibility and reliability depends is the strict control of the chemical composition of the steel.

In the earliest days of tonnage steel, control of composition was inevitably limited and inexact. Discovering which elements were present was difficult enough, let alone measuring how much of each was there. As analytical methods improved, there was a reluctant acceptance that minimal quantities of elements known as undesirable could not be further reduced economically. Steel specifications reflected that conviction, by the minimums they prescribed or by the absence of any prescription. Steelmakers had to make their product by the techniques available to them; steel users had to use the only products available to them.

Meanwhile, vitally important aspects of the behavior of steel that depended on its chemistry were gradually being revealed. For example, the deleterious effects of phosphorus were discovered with the introduction of the Bessemer process in the middle of the 19th century, and the importance of a generous manganese to carbon ratio was realized during World War II. The dangers of nonmetallic inclusions, always appreciated, became a more acceptable topic of conversation among steelmakers when economical methods of composition control became available relatively recently.

Who was leading and who was being led? Which came first—the demand or the technical ability to produce—would make an interesting story. But not now, because it is the outcome that concerns us. Today there is a control of composition and a reduction in the amount of unwanted elements that would have been unimaginable in commercial steelmaking practice even twenty or thirty years ago.

These improvements are important to all steelmakers and to their customers because many aspects have been incorporated in the manufacture of mill products of all grades of steel. But the makers of stainless are special! Although steelmakers whose major products are plain-carbon grades may also produce low-alloy structural grades, they rarely make stainless. Traditionally there has been a separation, and today the production of stainless continues to demand procedures that are more demanding than for plain-carbon and low-alloy steels.

Figure 6.1 shows a processing route for the production of typical stainless steel mill products. Melting and refining in the electric arc furnace (EAF) has been common practice for many years. Although argon oxygen decarburization (AOD) is comparatively recent (its place in history is mentioned in section 2.4), today's production of most of the world's stainless involves this process.

Figure 6.1 not only shows a continuous casting route for slabs, but it also suggests the older, traditional ingot practice for blooms and billets—that is, for shapes with a square (or nearly square) cross section. Such shapes can, of course, be made by continuous casting, as they often are in mills making plain-carbon steels. The illustration (Fig. 6.1) probably reflects the relative tonnages of production. Currently in the United States, mill shipments and domestic consumption of flat-rolled products represent more than 80% of the market. Given the wide variety of structural shapes that represent less than 20% of overall need, ingot casting rather than continuous casting may at times be the preferred route.

Before we highlight significant aspects of stainless steel manufacture, we should emphasize one particular aspect that influences both EAF and AOD practices: the carbon/chromium struggle. In all stainless steels other than the martensitic grades, a low carbon content is sought. Meanwhile, a high chromium level must be maintained. Any oxidation process that lowers the carbon content during steelmaking and refining carries the risk of converting expensive elemental chromium to an uneconomical slag. Consequently the name of the game is to avoid chromium loss while reducing the carbon content.

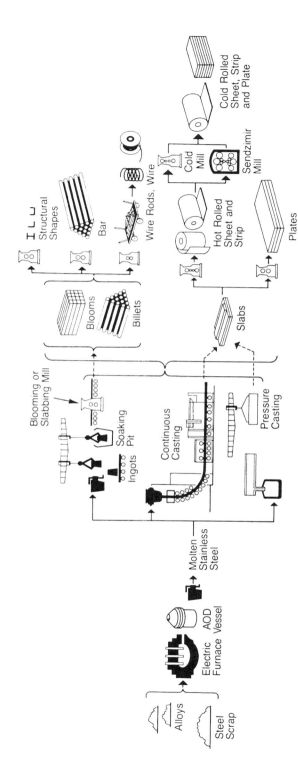

Fig. 6.1 Stainless steel manufacturing routes. Courtesy Specialty Steel Industry of North America

6.2 Electric Arc Furnace Processing

With the advent of "mini-mills," the electric arc furnace has taken over an increasing portion of production for all steels. Its charge is almost always entirely scrap steel, which is melted then refined by slag control and brought to the required chemistry in the furnace itself, in the ladle, or by subsequent refinement.

The production of stainless steel used to follow a similar pattern in the sort of electric furnace shown in Fig. 6.2. Its capacity may be over 150 tonnes, but this is unusually large; more commonly, furnace capacities lie between 10 and 50 tonnes. Decarburization was effected through the oxidizing constituents of the slag that were subsequently to be supplemented by the direct injection of oxygen, a technique that had become part of basic open-hearth steelmaking. Indeed, at one time, it was thought possible that the basic oxygen process of open-hearth steelmaking used for tonnage steel might become an important producer of stainless. However, that sort of oxygen injection leads to costly chromium loss when low carbon values are reached in the melt.

6.2.1 Argon Oxygen Decarburization

With the advent of AOD, the electric furnace has become primarily a melting vessel. Decarburization and adjustments to chemistry are made during the AOD process, and by including nitrogen gas with argon at appropriate stages, nitrogen values may be controlled to levels called for in the manganese/nitrogen austenitic grades.

A schematic of the AOD vessel is given in Fig. 6.3. Oxygen and argon (and nitrogen when it is needed) are introduced by blowing them beneath the surface of the bath. The oxygen supply is often supplemented in the early stages by a lance inserted through the top of the vessel. The importance of appropriate refractory linings must not be overlooked, nor the means by which one vessel can be quickly replaced by another, as the melt-shop cycle may require. We do not underestimate the significance of these and other practical matters, but an introductory text is not the place for their elaboration. We must, however, give some indication of the way in which AOD produces stainless steels of exquisitely controlled composition and has thereby added to the arsenal of opportunities.

Assume, for a start, that only oxygen is blown into a charge of stainless steel melted from scrap and containing both carbon and chromium. Carbon monoxide is generated and the carbon content of the molten charge is

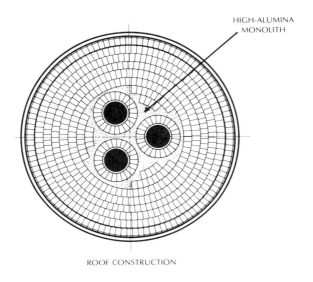

HIGH-ALUMINA MONOLITH

ROOF CONSTRUCTION

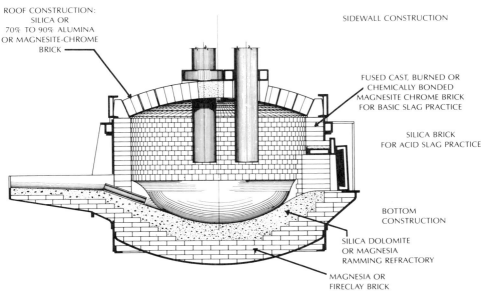

ROOF CONSTRUCTION:
SILICA OR
70% TO 90% ALUMINA
OR MAGNESITE-CHROME
BRICK

SIDEWALL CONSTRUCTION

FUSED CAST, BURNED OR
CHEMICALLY BONDED
MAGNESITE CHROME BRICK
FOR BASIC SLAG PRACTICE

SILICA BRICK
FOR ACID SLAG PRACTICE

BOTTOM
CONSTRUCTION

SILICA DOLOMITE
OR MAGNESIA
RAMMING REFRACTORY

MAGNESIA OR
FIRECLAY BRICK

Fig. 6.2 Typical electric arc furnace for stainless steel production

reduced. With reduced carbon levels in the bath, the susceptibility of chromium to oxidation increases. Figure 6.4 shows that at a given temperature the amount of chromium in the molten steel that can remain in equilibrium with carbon falls drastically as the carbon content is reduced. For example (see the intercepts in Fig. 6.4) at 1705 °C (3100 °F), a reduction of carbon from 0.2 to 0.02% reduces the equilibrium value of chromium from about 12 to 1%. The chromium is oxidized to chromic oxide, which joins the slag and is lost.

However, if the partial pressure of carbon monoxide above the bath can be reduced by mixing it with a nonoxidizing, benign gas, then, as carbon is removed, the chromium content will not be as substantially lowered. The intercepts in Fig. 6.5 illustrate this dramatically. At 1705 °C (3100 °F), a

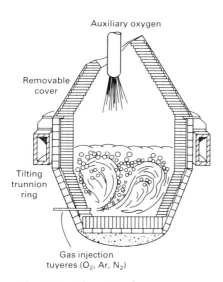

Fig. 6.3 Schematic of argon oxygen decarburization vessel

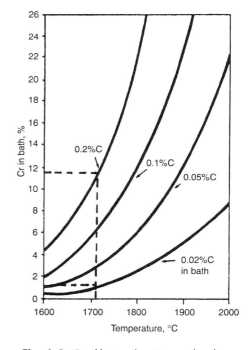

Fig. 6.4 Equilibrium chromium and carbon contents in 1 atmosphere carbon monoxide. Source: T. Gladman, *Met. Mater.*, Vol 4 (No. 6), 1988

reduction of carbon from 0.2 to 0.02% is accompanied by virtually no chromium loss when the partial pressure of carbon monoxide is reduced from one atmosphere to one-tenth of an atmosphere.

But this is a drastic reduction in the partial pressure of carbon monoxide, which would slow the rate of decarburization substantially and therefore make the steelmaking process unacceptably lengthy. Consequently, in the early stages of decarburization, when the carbon content of the bath is sufficiently high that chromium is not significantly oxidized, a correspondingly high partial pressure of carbon monoxide is permissible. During this initial part of the process, the oxygen-argon mix is rich in oxygen (typically in a ratio of 3 to 1). That is when the overhead lance may be used. Exothermic reactions increase the temperature of the bath. As blowing continues, carbon levels and bath temperatures are monitored and the gas ratio is adjusted accordingly until at the end of the blow it is typically 1 to 3.

About an hour after the charge was introduced, silicon or aluminum, with lime and fluorspar, are added to make a reducing slag that will further enhance chromium recovery and lower the sulfur content in the metal. Reactions are encouraged by an argon stir, which also degasses the melt and helps to get rid of hydrogen. The slag is poured off, the composition adjusted, and the steel tapped. Chromium recovery may be expected to be

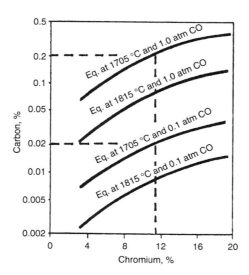

Fig. 6.5 Effect of lowering carbon monoxide partial pressure on chromium-carbon equilibrium. Source: T. Gladman, *Met. Mater.*, Vol 4 (No. 6), 1988

about 97.5%; nickel and molybdenum are practically totally retained.

The user of stainless steels will appreciate from this summary the principal advantages of AOD without our engaging in a long recapitulation. It offers a clean steel of highly controlled composition and allows very low carbon and delicately controlled nitrogen levels where these are required. Consequently, stainless steels made by this technique have mechanical properties that are generally improved (especially toughness) and that are reliable and reproducible.

Steelmakers enjoy better production efficiency, because the electric furnace is used only for melting the charge. Chromium recovery is much improved, and the cheaper, high-carbon ferrochromium can be used when chromium has to be supplemented. The technique is compatible with computerized analysis, which continuously monitors the chemistry of the bath and the atmosphere above it and calculates for the operator the necessary processing adjustments. Argon oxygen decarburization, more than the electric furnace, offers operational flexibility that can better accommodate the continuous casting machine.

6.2.2 Special Melting Techniques

Following such an accolade, one might wonder whether any special techniques remain on the books. But a few do, and we will mention a couple of

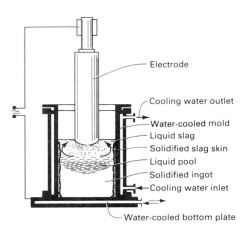

Fig. 6.6 Schematic of the electroslag remelting process

them. Both produce steel of extremely high quality essentially free from oxide and sulfide inclusions. Necessarily expensive, the products are used for very special applications, such as in the aerospace industry.

Electroslag remelting (ESR) became of commercial interest some forty years ago when Russia built tonnage units with capacities of about 40 tonnes. The process involves metal purification by letting molten drops of stainless steel fall through a refining slag of lime and alumina in fluorspar. Figure 6.6 shows schematically how this is done. An electrode of the stainless grade required is made part of an electrical circuit whose current passes through a slag pool. The arc is initially struck between the electrode and the baseplate at the bottom of the crucible on which the solid slag is placed. Both slag and electrode melt, and the drops from the electrode fall through the slag to the bottom of the crucible, forming a pool that solidifies as the electrode is raised and continuously melted.

Vacuum arc remelting (VAR) effects the refining process by maintaining a vacuum around the melted metal. Although other heating methods such as electrical induction may be used, the more common technique is of consumable electrode melting in a furnace whose capacity is typically 10 tonnes. As in ESR, the steel is cleansed; further, residual gas content and porosity are much reduced, and the rapid solidification rate mitigates segregation. Where usage demands it, double or even triple VAR melting is practiced.

6.3 Continuous Casting

Continuous casting was first developed on the North American continent for the production of stainless and other specialty products almost a half century ago. The process was slow to catch on for a number of reasons including the practical difficulties of fulfilling what appears to be theoretically simple and the economic obstacle of justifying the replacement of traditional operating processes whose capacity was not being realized.

Slowly, continuous casting has extended into the production of all steels. Some of its advantages, which are particularly germane to high-alloy steels, include improved homogeneity, enormously reduced yield loss through croppage, and minimized hot rolling (and hence of reheating).

The principle of continuous casting is to pour molten metal into an open-ended, reciprocating, cooled mold so that a sufficiently thick skin is formed to withstand the pressure of the liquid metal as the cooling ingot solidifies and is withdrawn by pinch rolls. Figure 6.7 gives a deceptively simple

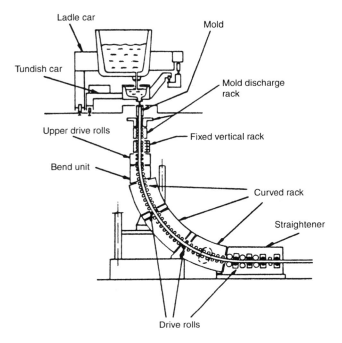

Fig. 6.7 Schematic diagram of continuous casting. Source: *The Making, Shaping, and Treating of Steel*, 10th ed., AISE Foundation, 1985

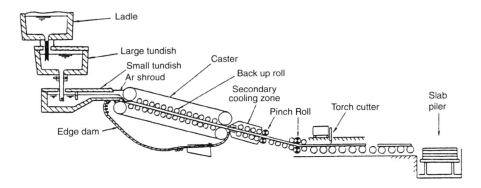

Fig. 6.8 Schematic of Hazelett continuous casting facility for the production of strip cast steel slabs. Courtesy Hazelett Strip-Casting Corporation

illustration of the process. We will not go into evolutionary developments that, among other things, turn the ingot from a vertical to horizontal posture ready for subsequent mill operations.

Today, research is directed towards reducing even further the amount of rolling required between ingot and strip or sheet. Figure 6.8, which illustrates the Hazelett belt machine, gives an idea of the continuous production of very thin slabs.

Henry Bessemer's hope (which he expressed and patented about the middle of the 19th century) of seeing a sheet product emerge from rolls into which molten steel is poured is now realized by twin-drum casters of which more than a dozen are in service. One developed by Nippon Steel and Mitsubishi casts type 304 to a strip thickness of 1.6 to 5 mm at 20 to 130 m/min from a 10 ton ladle.

In addition to the economic advantage of avoiding intermediate reheating and rolling, direct cast strip shows greater homogeneity than does the conventionally made product where a slower cooling rate in the ingot (especially if this is not continuously cast) allows nickel to segregate. The improved corrosion resistance of nickel-containing direct cast strip, as measured by pitting potential, is attributed to the homogeneity of its nickel distribution.

Metallurgy and Properties of Wrought Stainless Steels

7.1 Introduction

This chapter deals with the metallurgy and related mechanical properties of the stainless steel classes introduced in Chapter 1. Here, as a reminder of the principles we reviewed in Chapter 3, we will pin the principal classes on to the iron-chromium constitutional diagram, or phase diagram as it is often called. (The term, "equilibrium" diagram, though used, is a misnomer, because with high-alloy contents and at low temperatures, equilibrium might not occur during the reasonable career expectancy of the investigator.)

The part of the phase diagram that concerns us is shown in Fig. 3.7. To the right of the diagram, you will notice that the body-centered cubic phase, alpha, is predominant. This region, and up to much higher chromium contents, is where the ferritic stainless steels originate. We see, as we discuss this class in more detail, at temperatures below those of Fig. 3.7, other structures may occur that become a nuisance. But, for the time being, the important point is that the phase diagram shows only ferritic structures at chromium levels above about 13%.

The addition of alloying elements, particularly carbon and nitrogen, extends the bulge of the curve, known as the gamma loop, into higher chromium contents. The effect of carbon is illustrated in Fig. 3.9. Figure 7.1 gives examples of the combined effects of carbon and nitrogen. Clearly, then, in order to produce a stainless, ferritic alloy with the lowest possible chromium content, nitrogen and carbon levels must be kept low.

Within the gamma loop of austenite, steels have the potential of being strengthened by quenching and tempering. Carbon is the traditional agent (but not the only one) that does the strengthening. Consequently, alloys containing, for example, 0.15% C and 12% Cr are both stainless and heat treatable. This forms the basis of the martensitic stainless steels.

While carbon extends the gamma loop (Fig. 3.9), there is a limit beyond which such high-carbon alloys are not useful. However, other alloying elements not only extend the austenite region into higher chromium contents, they allow the austenite to persist to lower temperatures. Nickel is the best known of these austenite stabilizers and, as we have already mentioned, enhances specific corrosion-resistant properties. Figure 3.8 shows where, within Fe-Cr-Ni alloys, ferrite or austenite is expected at room temperature.

Among other austenite stabilizers, nitrogen and manganese have become especially important. Alloys based upon either of these prescriptions, where austenite is persistent at room temperature, are the class designated austenitic stainless steels. However, the manganese-nitrogen austenitic steels are considered separately.

The compositions at which we may expect ferritic, martensitic, or austenitic alloys at working temperatures are shown in the time-honored Schaeffler diagram (Fig. 7.2). The persistent phases are shown as areas within a graph whose axes are not simply chromium and nickel but are chromium equivalent and nickel equivalent. That is, the influence of other common alloying elements is included. You will notice the potency of carbon as it affects the nickel equivalent. A more complete and accurate equivalency can be expressed:

$$\%Ni \text{ equivalent} = \%Ni + \%Co + 30(\%C) + 25(\%N) + 0.5(\%Mn) + 0.3(\%Cu)$$

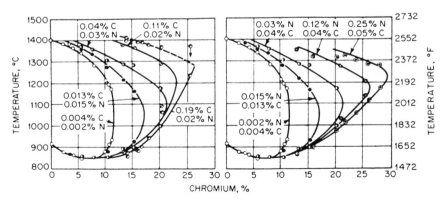

Fig. 7.1 Shifting of the boundary line ($\gamma + \alpha$)/α in Cr-Fe system through increasing additions of carbon or nitrogen

$$\%Cr\ equivalent = \%Cr + 2(\%Si) + 1.5(\%Mo) + 5(\%V) + 5.5(\%Al)$$
$$+ 1.75(\%Nb) + 1.5(\%Ti) + 0.75(\%W)$$

Recent research suggests that this formula must be subtly amended for the manganese-nitrogen austenitic alloys.

Although austenite persists at room temperature, it may not be stable. When it is cold worked, it can undergo partial transformation to ferrite or to martensite, and it is consequently strengthened to an extent that depends upon its composition.

The duplex stainless steels fall into a region that, in the iron-chromium phase diagram (Fig. 3.7), is suggested by a slender crescent, alpha plus gamma. However, that tells us only what is present at elevated temperatures in binary alloys. We are concerned with structure and properties at working temperatures where, with other alloying elements, the mixed structure has attractive properties.

Precipitation hardening might enhance the properties of any of the classes. However, its potential is greatest in the martensitic and austenitic classes. The precipitation-hardened stainless steels complete the canon that we now present.

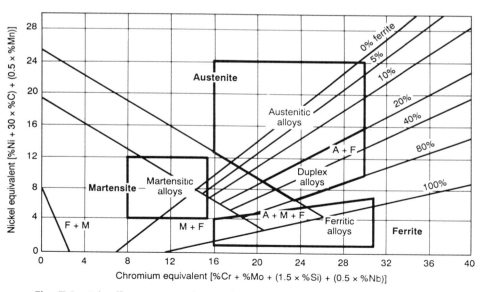

Fig. 7.2 Schaeffler constitution diagram for stainless steels

7.2 Ferritic Stainless Steels

The ferritic stainless steels have enjoyed much greater consumption since the introduction of the argon-oxygen decarburization (AOD) steel refining process, which is described in section 6.2.1. Although some important limitations still restrict the application of the ferritics, the economic attainment of low values for the interstitial elements, carbon and nitrogen, has provided the class with improved ductility and toughness.

Most of the increased consumption has been in the automotive industry, where mufflers and exhaust systems are now made of ferritic stainless steel. We deal with this specifically (may we say, exhaustively) in section 11.3.1. Although the ferritics are being used in transit vehicles where austenitics might have been applied, it would be misleading to suggest that the replacement has been to an extent that shareholders in nickel-producing enterprises need lose sleep on that account. Rather, ferritic stainless steels have found applications where stainless was previously economically unattractive (exhaust systems offer the principal example) or where, especially at high chromium levels, they have special corrosion-resistant capabilities (section 1.2 gives production figures, and section 1.3 provides price comparisons).

Even with controlled low carbon and nitrogen contents, the ferritic stainless steels, compared with the austenitic class, have poorer ductility, and they also suffer from embrittlement ailments that we will diagnose (but not cure) later in this chapter. They are not heat treatable, and some have poor weldability.

The chemical composition of what is called the "first generation" of ferritic stainless steels is shown in Table 7.1. AISI 430 was—and still is—the workhorse of this group. It is used for appliances and pots and pans, and until some years ago, it was the material of automotive trim. However, in this last application, it has been supplanted by type 434, whose molybdenum content provides better corrosion resistance on salted roads. AISI 436 has a similar composition but has niobium or tantalum as stabilizers, which preferentially form carbides, so that chromium is not depleted (see the section "Sensitization" in this chapter). Most of the first generation group, although essentially ferritic, may contain some austenite at elevated temperatures depending upon the presence of other elements, particularly carbon (Fig. 3.9 drew this to our attention). When the steel is rapidly cooled—as in the heat-affected zone of a weldment—martensite will form, creating hard spots and brittleness. This can only be ameliorated by subsequent heat treatment, which may present new difficulties. Consequently, with the exception of a couple of grades, types 439 and 446, the first generation is not considered weldable.

Type 446 has a very high chromium content and is probably better placed among the superferritics, which we describe as the "third generation." Although type 439, stabilized with titanium, might arguably be classed as a weldable grade of the first generation, it generally appears among the second (Table 7.3). Mechanical properties of these and other ferritic stainless steels are given in Table 7.2.

The composition of the second generation of ferritic stainless steels is shown in Table 7.3. Notice the very low carbon and nitrogen levels—attained by AOD refining—that, in turn, permit a minimal chromium content for adequate corrosion resistance. Type 409, the most heavily consumed of this group, contains titanium as a carbide stabilizer. This element also encourages ferrite formation; consequently, the alloy is reliably ferritic at all temperatures. It is readily formed and welded. Largely because of its consumption in the automotive industry, the United States current production of type 409 almost equals the tonnage of that most popular stainless steel, the austenitic type 304.

The third generation has the posh moniker "superferritics." These can be guaranteed to be ferritic at all temperatures on account of their very high chromium content (Table 7.4).

As we remark upon the relatively poor notch ductility of the ferritic class, we should bear in mind that the tests described in section 5.2.3, which provide the data for most compilations, involve specimens about 1 cm thick. As Fig. 7.3 shows, the ductile-brittle transition temperature (DBTT) is well above room temperature except in thin sheets, where the stress is essentially

Table 7.1   Nominal chemical composition of first-generation standard-grade 400-series ferritic stainless steels

UNS No.	Type	Composition(a), wt %			
		C	Cr	Mo	Other
S42900	429	0.12	14.0–16.0	...	...
S43000	430	0.12	16.0–18.0	...	...
S43020	430F	0.12	16.0–18.0	0.6	0.06 P; 0.15 min S
S43023	430FSe	0.12	16.0–18.0		0.15 min Se
S43400	434	0.12	16.0–18.0	0.75–1.25	...
S43600	436	0.12	16.0–18.0	0.75–1.25	Nb + Ta = 5 × %C min
S44200	442	0.20	18.0–23.0	...	...
S44600	446	0.20	23.0–27.0	...	...

(a) Single values are maximum unless otherwise indicated.

Table 7.2 Minimum mechanical properties of ferritic stainless steels

Product form(a)	Condition	Tensile strength MPa	ksi	0.2% yield strength MPa	ksi	Elongation, %	Reduction in area, %	Hardness, HRB	ASTM specification
Type 405 (UNS S40500)									
B	Annealed	415	60	170	25	20	45	...	A 479
F	Annealed	415	60	205	30	20	45	...	A 473
W	Annealed	480	70	280	40	20	45	...	A 580
P, Sh, St	Annealed	415	60	170	25	20	...	88 max	A 176, A 240
Type 409 (UNS S40900)									
P, Sh, St	Annealed	380	55	205	30	20	...	80 max	A 240
P, Sh, St	Annealed	380	55	205	30	22(c)	...	80 max	A 176
Type 429 (UNS S42900)									
B	Annealed	480	70	275	40	20	45	...	A 276
P, Sh, St	Annealed	450	65	205	30	22(c)	...	88 max	A 176, A 240
Type 430 (UNS S43000)									
B	Annealed	415	60	205	30	20	45	...	A 276
W	Annealed	480	70	275	40	20	45	...	A 580
P, Sh, St	Annealed	450	65	205	30	22(c)	...	88 max	A 176, A 240
Type 430F (UNS S43020)									
F	Annealed	485	70	275	40	20	45	...	A 473
W	Annealed	585–860	85–125	...	...	...	...	...	A 581
Type 439 (UNS S43035)									
B	Annealed	485	70	275	40	20	45	...	A 479
P, Sh, St	Annealed	450	65	205	30	22	...	88 max	A 240
Type 430Ti (UNS S43036)									
B	Annealed	515(b)	75(b)	310(b)	45(b)	30(b)	65(b)	...	...
Type 434 (UNS S43400)									
W	Annealed	545(b)	79(b)	415(b)	60(b)	33(b)	78(b)	90 max(b)	...
Sh	Annealed	530(b)	77(b)	365(b)	53(b)	23(b)	...	83 max(b)	...
Type 436 (UNS S43600)									
Sh, St	Annealed	530(b)	77(b)	365(b)	53(b)	23(b)	...	83 max(b)	...
Type 442 (UNS S44200)									
B	Annealed	550(b)	80(b)	310(b)	45(b)	20(b)	40(b)	90 max(b)	...
P, Sh, St	Annealed	515	75	275	40	20	...	95 max	A 176
Type 444 (UNS S44400)									
P, Sh, St	Annealed	415	60	275	40	20	...	95 max	A 176

(continued)

Table 7.2 (continued)

Product form(a)	Condition	Tensile strength MPa	ksi	0.2% yield strength MPa	ksi	Elongation, %	Reduction in area, %	Hardness, HRB	ASTM specification
Type 446 (UNS S44600)									
B	Annealed, hot finished	480	70	275	40	20	45	...	A 276
B	Annealed, cold finished	480	70	275	40	16	45	...	A 276
W	Annealed	480	70	275	40	20	45	...	A 580
W	Annealed, cold finished	480	70	275	40	16	45	...	A 580
P, Sh, St	Annealed	515	75	275	40	20	...	95 max	A 176
18 SR									
Sh, St	Annealed	620(b)	90(b)	450(b)	65(b)	25(b)	...	90 min(b)	...
E-Brite 26-1 (UNS S44627)									
B	Annealed, hot finished	450	65	275	40	20	45	...	A 276
B	Annealed, cold finished	450	65	275	40	16	45	...	A 276
P, Sh, St	Annealed	450	65	275	40	22(c)	...	90 max	A 176, A 240
MONIT (UNS S44635)									
P, Sh, St	Annealed	620	90	515	75	20	...	...	A 176, A 240
Sea-cure/SC-1 (UNS S44660)									
P, Sh, St	Annealed	585	85	450	65	18	...	100 max	A 176, A 240
29-4C (UNS S44735)									
P, Sh, St	Annealed	550	80	415	60	18	...	...	A 276, A 240
29-4-2 (UNS S44880)									
P, Sh, St	Annealed	550	80	415	60	20	...	98 max	A 176, A 240
B	Hot finished	480	70	380	55	20	40	...	A 276
B	Cold finished	520	75	415	60	15	30	...	A 276
B	Annealed	480	70	380	55	20	40	...	A 479

(a) B, bar; F, forgings; W, wire; P, plate; Sh, sheet; St, strip. (b) Typical values. (c) 20% reduction for 1.3 mm (0.050 in) and under in thickness

only biaxial. The superferritics, whose splendid corrosion resistance in chloride solutions makes them so attractive, are limited in their application because of their lack of toughness in thicker sections. Generally, they are used in thicknesses no more than 1.5 mm.

We recall that structural and low-alloy steels are particularly dependent upon carbon for the development of their strength. With carbon in interstitial solid solution, they are quenched to produce martensite—as, indeed, we will see happens in stainless grades. But in run-of-the-mill carbon steel

Table 7.3 Chemical compositions of second-generation ferritic stainless steels

UNS No.	Alloy designation	Composition(a), wt %				
		C	Cr	Mo	Ni	Other
S40500	405	0.08	11.5–14.5	...	...	0.10–0.30 Al
S40900	409	0.08	10.5–11.75	...	0.5	Ti = 6 × C min to 0.75 max
...	409Cb	0.02(b)	12.5(b)	...	0.2(b)	0.4 Nb(b)
S44100	441	0.02(b)	18.0(b)	...	0.3(b)	0.7 Nb(b), 0.3 Ti(b)
...	AL433	0.02(b)	19.0(b)	...	0.3(b)	0.4 Nb(b), 0.5 Si(b), 0.4 Cu(b)
...	AL446	0.01(b)	11.5(b)	...	0.2(b)	0.2 Nb(b), 0.1 Ti(b)
...	AL468	0.01(b)	18.2(b)	...	0.2(b)	0.2 Nb(b), 0.1 Ti(b)
...	YUS436S	0.01(b)	17.4(b)	1.2(b)	...	0.2 Ti(b)
S43035	439	0.07	17.00–19.00	...	0.5	Ti = 0.20 + 4 (C + N) min to 1.0 max
...	12SR	0.2	12.0	...	...	1.2 Al; 0.3 Ti
...	18SR	0.04	18.0	...	...	2.0 Al; 0.4 Ti
K41970	406	0.06	12.0–14.0	...	0.5	2.75–4.25 Al; 0.6 Ti

(a) Single values are minimum unless otherwise indicated. (b) Typical value

Table 7.4 Nominal chemical compositions of third-generation superferritic stainless steels

Alloy	Composition, %							UNS No.
	C(max)	Cr	Fe	Mo	N	Ni	Other	
Intermediate-purity grades								
26-1 Ti	0.02	26	bal	1	0.025	0.25	0.5 Ti	S44626
AISI type 444	0.02	18	bal	2	0.02	0.4	0.5 Ti	S44400
SEA-CURE	0.02	27.5	bal	3.4	0.025	1.7	0.5 Ti	S44660
Nu Monit	0.025	25	bal	4	0.025	4	0.4 Ti	S44635
AL 29-4C	0.030	29	bal	4	0.045	1.0	0.08 (Nb + Ti) max	...
Ultrahigh purity grades								
E-Brite 26-1	0.002	26	bal	1	0.01	0.1	0.1 Nb	S44726
AL 29-4-2	0.005	29	bal	4	0.01	2	...	S44800
SHOMAC 26-4	0.003	26	bal	4	0.005	...	...	...
SHOMAC 30-2	0.003	30	bal	2	0.007	0.18	...	...
YUS 190L	0.004	19	bal	2	0.0085	...	0.15 Nb	...

structurals, strength is associated with iron carbide lamellae in the constituent known as pearlite. This carbide morphology doesn't occur in the stainless steels. In the ferritic class, the formation of chromium carbide is to be avoided, and other carbides produced by stabilizing elements are not strengthening. There is some solid solution strengthening through the presence of chromium; other elements are not cost effective. The ferritic stainless steels are not precipitation hardenable; and while cold work doesn't appreciably increase strength, it substantially reduces ductility. Consequently, the strength of the ferritics rarely exceeds 600 MPa, while strengths in excess of 1000 MPa are common in austenitic and martensitic grades.

Before we continue this woeful litany and categorize the specific problems leading to embrittlement, we should remark once more upon the specific corrosion-resistant applications that make the superferritics valuable members of the arsenal of stainless steels. Type 430 (kitchenware and utensils) represents a fair tonnage; and we emphasize, too, how the second generation—the low carbon/nitrogen breed—with economically low chromium requirements finds a growing application. Such steels probably can be exploited further.

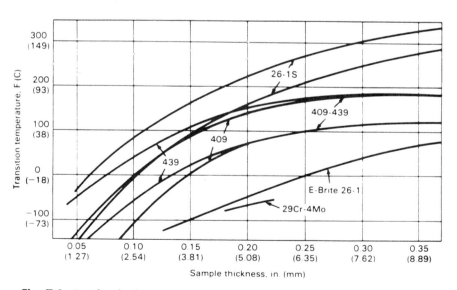

Fig. 7.3 Ductile-to-brittle transition temperatures as a function of section thickness for various ferritic stainless steels

Among the following catalog of embrittling possibilities in ferritic stainless steels, hydrogen embrittlement finds no place. Probably the resistance to chloride stress-corrosion cracking, exhibited by many of the ferritic stainless steels, and their immunity to hydrogen embrittlement are related.

7.2.1 Grain Growth

Other things being equal, the ductility and toughness of metals improve as grain size diminishes. A valuable feature of the austenite-ferrite transformation (apart from it providing a seemingly limitless opportunity for research) is that it offers a means of grain refinement. But, by their nature, the ferritic stainless steels don't enjoy this possibility; their grain size increases with temperature and with time at temperature, and is retained on cooling. Grain size can be refined by cold working and subsequent annealing, but this is rarely practicable—certainly not in the heat-affected zone of weldments where grain growth is inevitable.

7.2.2 Embrittlement at 475 °C (885 °F)

Figure 7.4 shows how the hardness of iron-chromium alloys rises dramatically when they are held at temperatures between 400 and 600 °C (750 and 1110 °F). This increase is accompanied by a corresponding drop in ductility and toughness, so severe that the higher-chromium alloys are unemployable. Figure 7.4 shows that the effect is not pronounced at the lowest of the three chromium levels, and below 13% Cr there is no embrittlement, which means that you need not worry about your car muffler on that account.

Although Fig. 7.4 relates to alloys that were held at temperature for a long while, 475 °C embrittlement can occur to some extent over much shorter periods so that even slow cooling from above 600 °C (1110 °F) may be deleterious, especially in higher-chromium alloys, which embrittle over short time spans.

The embrittling effect, which has been well researched, appears to be due to the formation of a submicroscopic chromium-rich phase that remains coherent with the iron-chromium matrix, preventing plastic deformation through slip mechanisms. The brittleness can be quickly removed by heating the alloy to 600 °C (1000 °F) or above and cooling it rapidly. This step is of little consequence if the intention is to use the alloy at or around 475 °C (885 °F).

The chromium-rich phase to which we refer is alpha prime, α', whose range of persistence is shown in the iron-chromium phase diagram, Fig. 7.5.

7.2.3 Sigma Phase Embrittlement

Before you leave the diagram (Fig. 7.5), note that sigma persists to about 820 °C (1510 °F). It forms so slowly that it is not of concern during cooling from heat treatment temperatures but arises during elevated temperature service. It is extremely hard and brittle, less elusive to the microscopist than is the 475 °C rascal, and causes its particular havoc by forming at grain boundaries. While the phase diagram suggests that sigma should not be expected at low chromium contents, its formation is encouraged at lower-

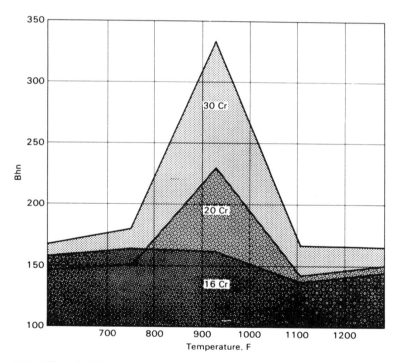

Fig. 7.4 Effect of 475 °C (885 °F) embrittlement on hardness. Alloy was held at temperature indicated for 500 h.

chromium levels by several common alloying additions including molybdenum, titanium, and niobium.

Misery loves company. Sigma-type phases, with their characteristic embrittling effect, have been detected in dozens of commercial alloys. Among these are, unfortunately, the austenitic stainless steels. We'll come to that.

It appears that sigma formation is less pronounced when carbon and nitrogen levels are low, probably because the carbide stabilizers are not so dominant (Fig. 7.6).

Before we leave sigma, we are obliged to point out that there are yet more embrittling intermetallic compounds formed in ferritic and other stainless steels. These arise, to all intents and practical purposes, in about the same way and within the same ranges of temperature and time as the sigma phase does. Figure 7.7 illustrates the substantial coincidence of the formation of these compounds in a commercial alloy, Monit, which is based upon type 446 and contains 23 to 27% Cr.

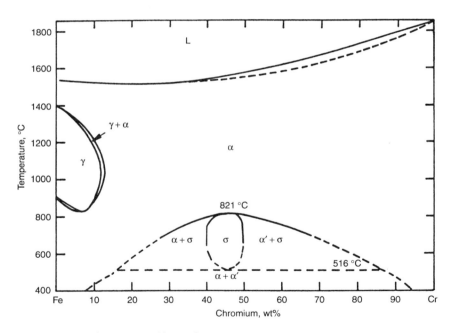

Fig. 7.5 Iron-chromium equilibrium diagram

7.2.4 Sensitization

This catastrophic phenomenon is usually associated with the austenitic stainless steels, in which it does most certainly occur (see Fig. 7.17). However, ferritic grades are also susceptible. They may have been overlooked for

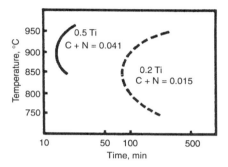

Fig. 7.6 Comparison of the kinetics of sigma phase precipitation for two superferritic stainless steels: 29% Cr-4% Mo-0.5% Ti (C + N = 0.041%) and 29% Cr-4% Mo-0.2% Ti (C + N = 0.015%). Courtesy of *Stainless Steels,* P. Lacombe, B. Baroux, and G. Béranger, Ed., Les Editions de Physique Les Ulis

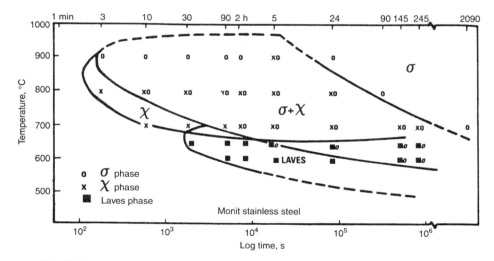

Fig. 7.7 Time-temperature-precipitation diagram for Monit superferritic stainless steel. Aged after a solution treatment at 1000 °C for 10 min and water quenching. Reprinted with permission from A.J. Sedriks, *Corrosion of Stainless Steels,* John Wiley & Sons, Inc., 1996

no other reason than that, until recently, most were considered unsuitable for welding. Welding is also where the trouble was originally diagnosed in the austenitics and where it continues to present the major source of problem in stainless steels. However, although the outcome is much the same—intergranular corrosion caused by chromium depletion at grain boundaries through the formation and precipitation of chromium carbides and nitrides—the mechanisms are very different.

The difference is illustrated by the curves of Fig. 7.8. The ferritics sensitize at lower temperatures and far more quickly than do austenitics with similar chromium contents. The probable reason is that iron-chromium ferrite has a very low solubility for carbon compared to that of austenite. At temperatures about 925 °C (1700 °F), however, the solubility is not inconsiderable; but as it becomes very much less at lower temperatures, carbides

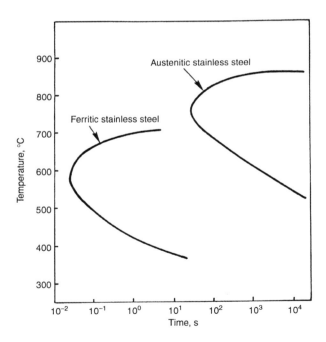

Fig. 7.8 Differences in the location of time-temperature-sensitization curves of austenitic and ferritic stainless steels of equivalent chromium content. Reprinted with permission from A.J. Sedriks, *Corrosion of Stainless Steels*, John Wiley & Sons, Inc., 1996

(and nitrides) precipitate rapidly. In contrast, austenite retains its solubility for carbon and nitrogen, and the precipitation of carbides and nitrides is more leisurely.

Why does the maximum rate of precipitation in the ferritics happen about 600 °C (1110 °F) as Fig. 7.8 indicates? True, there is a further decrease of carbon/nitrogen solubility at lower temperatures, which gives the reaction a greater drive; however, (as is generally the case with chemical reactions) the speed decreases as temperature is reduced. The optimal circumstance for precipitation is about 600 °C (1110 °F).

Air cooling or oil quenching is generally not sufficiently rapid to avoid precipitation. Consequently, one takes a quite different tack by annealing and slowly cooling through the critical range. In this way, chromium from the grain interiors can diffuse into the grain boundary region, replacing chromium consumed by carbide and nitride formation. This said, we must be aware of the evils of sigma and 475 °C embrittlement.

Intergranular corrosion caused by sensitization, when it was first revealed in the austenitic class, was called "weld decay" and occurs a little way from the weld bead. In the ferritic steels, it occurs very close to the weld metal where the cooling rate is so rapid that chromium has no opportunity to rediffuse.

Only very low carbon and nitrogen values can prevent the possibility of sensitization in ferritic stainless steels that are subjected to encouraging temperatures. And even then the additional precaution of carbide formers—titanium, niobium, and tantalum—is usually heeded. Figure 7.9 encapsulates the characteristics and uses of the ferritic stainless steels.

7.3 Martensitic Stainless Steels

The mechanical properties of this class of alloys and the manner in which they are attained follow the metallurgy of plain-carbon and low-alloy steels. The special properties of corrosion and heat resistance conferred by chromium and other alloying elements may then be superposed.

The significant underlying metallurgical principles are that hardness is principally conferred by carbon, while the capacity for hardening—the hardenability—is influenced by all alloying elements, most of them positively. Now, in any steel that is rendered corrosion resistant by chromium additions, the chromium content itself increases hardenability to such an extent that all but the very largest pieces will harden throughout their sections during air cooling. Usually, only sections more than 12 in. thick require oil quenching.

The martensitic stainless steels share with their lower-alloy cousins two genetic deficiencies: temper brittleness and hydrogen embrittlement. Temper brittleness happens following hardening when they are tempered in the range 425 to 540 °C (800 to 1000 °F). Hydrogen embrittlement may arise through any contact with hydrogen, as a gas or dissociated from gaseous or aqueous environments, during production, or application.

Temper brittleness reduces the measured notch ductility in an impact test; in fact, it raises the temperature at which the steel loses its notch toughness.

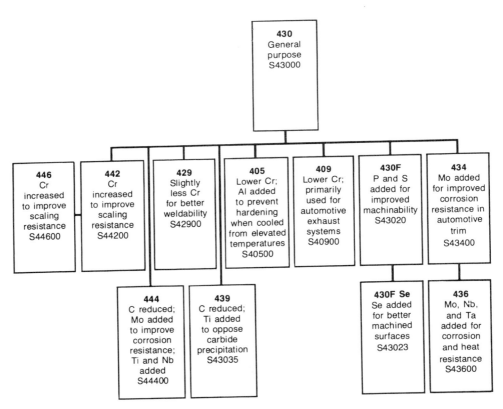

Fig. 7.9 Family relationships for standard ferritic stainless steels

Alloying elements, with the exception of molybdenum, worsen the situation. But, by and large, the best antidote is to avoid tempering in the susceptible range or, if the tempering temperature lies above it, to avoid slow cooling. If a steel has inadvertently been temper embrittled and this fact has been discovered before the component has been put into service, then the best advice is to start over. Soak, quench (in air or oil), and temper outside the temper-embrittling range.

Hydrogen embrittlement is the subject of section 4.4.6. It reduces the ductility of a steel even during slow deformation. If this cannot be tolerated in service and the environment of the steel is the cause of the problem (e.g., in hydrogen sulfide atmospheres), your alternatives are to change the environment, use a lower-strength steel, or seek another alloy. If hydrogen embrittlement occurs during manufacture (e.g., during pickling), then the process may be appropriately amended, or, if this isn't possible, ductility may be easily recovered by heating the steel to a quite low temperature that drives the hydrogen out. Even at 100 °C (212 °F), much of the hydrogen is removed. For higher-strength steels, which are more susceptible to hydrogen embrittlement, temperatures up to 370 °C (700 °F) may be required, and hydrogen removal may take several hours. (But if you are dealing with a martensitic stainless steel, don't try to hasten the process by increasing the temperature above 425 °C—for you know what will happen!)

7.3.1 The Low-Carbon Martensitic Stainless Steels

Among the low-carbon martensitic stainless steels are AISI 410, 403, 416, and 416Se. While the special applications of higher-carbon martensitic steels are important, the greatest use is for the alloys that contain about 0.15% C. Of these, the most widely used is AISI 410. "Turbine quality," the name by which AISI 403 is often known, has less silicon but is otherwise similar with better forgeability. The 416 grades offer better machinability. Type 416 itself contains sulfur, while 416Se contains selenium. Otherwise, as you will see in Table 7.5, the compositions of these four steels are identical, and their mechanical properties (other than the exceptions relating to fabrication just mentioned) are so much the same that we write only about AISI 410.

If the steel is to be shaped at room temperature by mechanical deformation, it is put in its softest condition by annealing. This involves austenitizing, followed by initial slow cooling to avoid the formation of martensite, and then more rapid cooling through the embrittling range. If the fully softened condition isn't required or if shaping involves machining, the steel may not be fully annealed in this way but rather is tempered from its initial martensitic condition. The formation of fine carbides improves machinability.

Table 7.6 summarizes mechanical properties, and Fig. 7.10 shows properties after tempering from two austenitizing temperatures for martensitic stainless steels. Temper embrittlement remains unassailable, and the choice between lower-or higher-tempering temperatures to avoid the trough in Izod values depends upon the application. At the lower end, ductility may be inadequate; at the higher end, the precipitation of carbides reduces corrosion resistance.

Temperature dependence of impact values is shown in Fig. 7.11. Note that even when the tempering temperature is adroitly chosen to avoid temper embrittlement, the ductile-brittle transition is about room temperature. We have to mention too that all impact values are worse for the free-machining grade, 416Se.

Recalling the poor thermal conductivity of stainless alloys, we are cautioned to avoid rapid heating when they are taken to temperature. It is not uncommon to preheat the martensitic stainless types prior to soaking.

The properties acquired by heat-treated alloys may be expected to persist at operating temperatures that are no higher than the tempering temperature.

Table 7.5   Compositions of the 400 series martensitic stainless steels

UNS No.	Name	Composition(a), %						
		Cr	C	Mn	Si	P	S	Other
S40300	403	11.5–13	0.15	1.0	0.5	0.040	0.030	...
S41000	410	11.5–13.5	0.15	1.0	1.0	0.040	0.030	...
S41008	410S	11.5–13.5	0.08	1.0	1.0	0.040	0.030	...
S41400	414	11.5–13.5	0.15	1.0	1.0	0.040	0.030	1.25–2.50 Ni
S41600	416	12–14	0.15	1.25	1.0	0.060	0.15(b)	0.60 Mo(c)
S41623	416Se	12–14	0.15	1.25	1.0	0.060	0.060	0.15 Se(b)
S42000	420	12–14	0.15(b)	1.0	1.0	0.040	0.030	...
S42020	420F	12–14	0.38	1.25	1.0	0.060	0.15(b)	0.60 Mo(c)
S42200	422	11–13	0.20–0.25	1.0	0.75	0.025	0.025	0.40–1.0 Ni, 0.75–1.25 Mo, 0.75–1.25 W, 0.15–0.30 V
S43100	431	15–17	0.20	1.0	1.0	0.040	0.030	1.25–2.50 Ni
S44002	440A	16–18	0.60–0.75	1.0	1.0	0.040	0.030	0.75 Mo
S44003	440B	16–18	0.75–0.95	1.0	1.0	0.040	0.030	0.75 Mo
S44004	440C	16–18	0.95–1.20	1.0	1.0	0.040	0.030	0.75 Mo
S44020	440F	16–18	0.95–1.20	1.25	1.0	0.040	0.10–0.35	0.40–0.60 Mo
S44023	440FSe	16–18	0.95–1.20	1.25	1.0	0.040	0.030	0.15 Se(b), 0.60 Mo

(a) Balance, iron. Single values are maximum values unless otherwise noted. (b) Minimum (c) Optional. Reprinted with permission from A.J. Sedriks, *Corrosion of Stainless Steels,* John Wiley & Sons, Inc., 1996

Table 7.6 Mechanical properties of martensitic stainless steels

Name	Condition	Tensile strength(a), MPa	Yield strength (0.2% offset), MPa	Elongation, %	Hardness (Rockwell B or C)
403, 410	Annealed	517	276	30	B 82
416, 416Se	Hardened by heating to 982 °C and cooled + tempered at 205 °C	1310	1000	15	C 41
	Hardened by heating to 982 °C and cooled + tempered at 316 °C	1241	965	15	C 39
	Hardened by heating to 982 °C and cooled + tempered at 538 °C	1000	793	20	C 31
414	Annealed	827	655	17	C 22
	Hardened by heating to 982 °C and cooled + tempered at 205 °C	1379	1034	15	C 43
	Hardened by heating to 982 °C and cooled + tempered at 316 °C	1310	1000	15	C 41
	Hardened by heating to 982 °C and cooled + tempered at 538 °C	1000	827	20	C 34
420, 420F	Annealed	655	345	25	B 92
	Hardened by heating to 1038 °C and cooled + tempered at 316 °C	1586	1345	8	C 50
422	Annealed	793	586	22	B 98
	Hardened by heating to 982 °C and cooled + tempered at 427 °C	1627	1282	10	...
	Hardened by heating to 982 °C and cooled + tempered at 538 °C	1476	1145	13	C 42
	Hardened by heating to 982 °C and cooled + tempered at 649 °C	1000	862	14	C 32
431	Annealed	862	655	20	C 24
	Hardened by heating to 1038 °C and cooled + tempered at 205 °C	1413	1069	15	C 43
	Hardened by heating to 1038 °C and cooled + tempered at 316 °C	1345	1034	15	C 41
	Hardened by heating to 1038 °C and cooled + tempered at 538 °C	1034	896	18	C 34
440A	Annealed	724	414	20	B 95
	Hardened by heating to 1038 °C and cooled + tempered at 316 °C	1793	1655	5	C 51
440B	Annealed	738	428	18	B 96
	Hardened by heating to 1038 °C and cooled + tempered at 316 °C	1930	1862	3	C 55
440C, 440F	Annealed	758	448	13	B 97
	Hardened by heating to 1038 °C and cooled + tempered at 316 °C	1965	1896	2	C 57

(a) 1 MPa = 145.03 psi. Reprinted with permission from A.J. Sedriks, *Corrosion of Stainless Steels*, John Wiley & Sons, Inc., 1996

But unless one is very unfortunate, operating temperatures should persist for much longer than the tempering process! Consequently, a tempered martensitic stainless steel generally sees service about 150 °C (300 °F) below its tempering temperature.

We would expect the fatigue resistance of these steels to be reduced as their operating temperatures are increased. And so it is, as Fig. 7.12 shows.

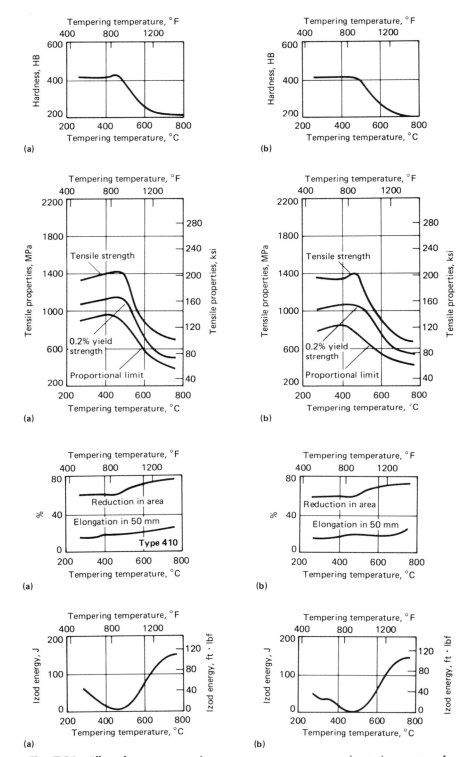

Fig. 7.10 Effect of austenizing and tempering temperatures on mechanical properties of type 410 martensitic stainless steel. Austenitized 30 min; oil quenched to 65 to 95 °C (150 to 200 °F); double stress relieved at 175 °C (350 °F) for 15 min and water quenched; tempered 2 h. (a) Quenched from 925 °C (1700 °F). (b) Quenched from 1010 °C (1850 °F)

However, this represents data for polished samples in air. In a potentially corrosive environment (where stainless steels are generally used) and with the likely possibility of a macroscopic or microscopic notch, permissible stress is far lower.

7.3.2 Nickel-Containing Low-Carbon Martensitic Stainless Steels

These include AISI 414, 422, and 431. Compositions and mechanical properties are given in Tables 7.5 and 7.6. Nickel serves three purposes. It generally improves toughness. It offsets the ferritizing effect of the molybdenum, tungsten, and vanadium in AISI 422 and of the higher-chromium content in AISI 431. At the higher-nickel levels (in 414 and 431), corrosion resistance is improved in some media—specifically, in neutral chlorides and weakly oxidizing acids.

The purpose of alloying additions to AISI 422 is to improve high-temperature properties through some solid solution strengthening by molybdenum and by the precipitation of very fine carbides. Figure 7.13 shows elevated temperature mechanical properties of AISI 422 following tempering at various temperatures. Several nonstandard grades based on 422 and bearing stylish trade names have become popular; their mechanical properties are slightly enhanced by a variety of alloying additions.

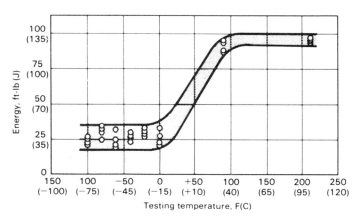

Fig. 7.11 Izod data for 410 after quenching from 980 °C (1800 °F) and tempering at 620 °C (1150 °F) (HB 228)

7.3.3 High-Carbon Martensitic Stainless Steels

These include AISI 440. As Table 7.5 shows, this grade has three carbon levels and contains molybdenum. Mechanical properties are given in Table 7.6. These are not easy steels to handle. Their greatest application is where abrasion resistance is required; and at the necessarily high hardness levels, the steels are very brittle. A complication in heat treatment arises. Because of the high chromium levels, austenite is retained after quenching and may transform isothermally to martensite. The accompanying volume change can cause cracking. Consequently, the piece is either quenched to subzero temperatures (about –75 °C, or –100 °F) to transform all austenite, or it is made the victim of a second tempering treatment after being cooled to room temperature following the first tempering treatment.

Recognizing that these hard, brittle steels have particular applications where abrasion is to be resisted, it should be realized that if they are tempered at temperatures that bring back modest ductility, an initial choice of type 410 might have been more judicious.

We have left to last the martensitic steels whose carbon content tries to find the best compromise between low- and high-carbon grades.

7.3.4 Cutlery Stainless Steels

AISI 420 and 420F are examples of cutlery stainless steels. Compositions are shown in Table 7.5, and mechanical properties are presented in Table 7.6.

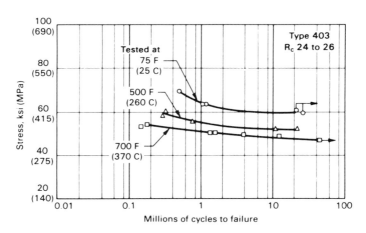

Fig. 7.12   Fatigue data for quenched-and-tempered 403 (24 to 26 HRC)

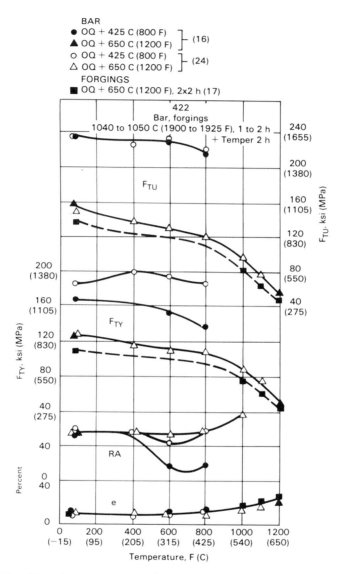

Fig. 7.13 Effect of temperature on tensile properties of 422 bar and forgings with various tempering temperatures

The 'F' grade contains sulfur to improve machinability and, other than a reduced notch toughness, is similar to type 420. Although the higher-carbon steels of the previous types (e.g., type 440) are used in cutlery and surgical instruments, type 420 appears to have gained prominence to the extent that the grade bears the distinctive name. You will notice that the carbon content is specified to be "minimum"; consequently, within the grade, various carbon levels may be requested. Generally, the carbon content is at least 0.2%, but it will not exceed 0.4%.

The effect on mechanical properties of tempering after quenching from two austenitizing temperatures is shown in Fig. 7.14. While the 410 grade shows a distinct trough in Izod impact values between 300 and 550 °C (570 and 1020 °F), AISI 420 has consistently poor values until a temperature above 600 °C (1110 °F) is reached.

AISI 420 is not generally used at high temperatures, and compromises are made to find the best composition that permits heat treatment to give knife-edge hardness with serviceable toughness and adequate corrosion resistance.

A useful overview of the general relationship between the mechanical properties of martensitic stainless steels and their heat treatment is given in Fig. 7.15, in which hardness is indicative of tensile strength. Family relationships, remarking upon the particular strengths of the grades but not mentioning their shortcomings (for that is the way of family relationships), are shown in Fig. 7.16.

7.4 Austenitic Stainless Steels

Although stainless steels were introduced to the world through the class that we now know as "martensitic"—for these were a boon to surgeons and other carvers who needed a sharp edge and a rust-free blade—it was the austenitic class that led to tonnage manufacture. Following a cautious initial acceptance, it soon dominated the market and has continued to lead.

Current figures (see Table 1.1) show a world stainless production of about 15.6 million metric tonnes. The U.S. contribution is approximately 2 million tons, which includes more than two-thirds in austenitic, nickel-bearing grades. Dangerously extrapolating this into world figures as we duck behind the barricades, we suggest that the world makes about 10 million tons of austenitic stainless steel annually.

But this (however inaccurate its quantitative estimate) isn't the whole story, because the austenitic stainless steels not only represent the greatest

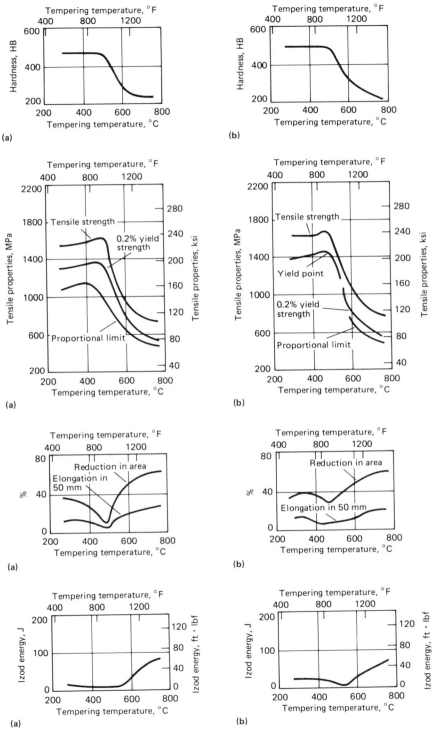

Fig. 7.14 Effect of austenitizing and tempering temperatures on typical mechanical properties of type 420 martensitic stainless steel. Austenitized 30 min; oil quenched to 65 to 95 °C (150 to 200 °F); double stress relieved at 175 °C (350 °F) for 15 min and water quenched; tempered 2 h. (a) Quenched from 925 °C (1700 °F). (b) Quenched from 1025 °C (1875 °F)

tonnage, they cover by far the widest spectrum of use. In contrast, the biggest production of nickel-free stainless steels—that is, in the ferritic class—has more restricted applications principally in vehicle manufacture. That situation may change as confidence grows in the ferritic steels and more applications prove out. Meanwhile, however, the austenitics enjoy an unmatched ubiquity among stainless steels.

Nor can we leave it there. The austenitic class, once exclusively relying upon nickel as the austenitizer, is complemented by manganese-bearing alloys, whose special metallurgical appeal lies in the way in which manganese, itself an austenitizer, increases the steel's solubility for that much more powerful agent, nitrogen. We will deal with this class separately, but

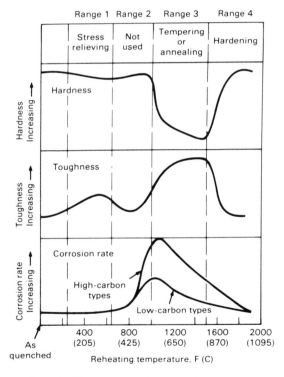

Fig. 7.15 General trend of hardness, toughness, and corrosion rate in relation to heat treating temperature

here we note that even though the manganese-bearing alloys were optimistically reviewed in earlier introductory texts as having a great potential, that potential seems slow to be realized.

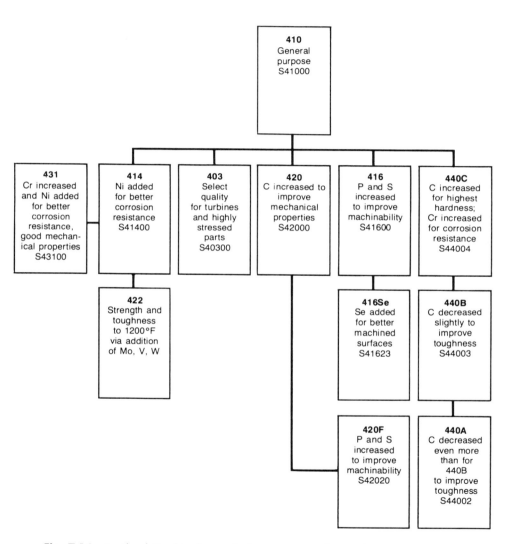

Fig. 7.16 Family relationships for standard martensitic stainless steels

In the following section, we deal with the classic chromium-nickel austenitics, which are based upon that worthy progenitor, "18-8." We hope, as we describe them, that you will become as captivated as we are by their metallurgy and related properties. Even their vulnerabilities are fascinating!

7.4.1 Chromium-Nickel Austenitic Stainless Steels

If you refer to the Schaeffler diagram (Fig. 7.2), you will see that with 18% Cr, 8% Ni, 2% Mn, and a little less than 0.1% C, these steels are fully austenitic at room temperature. They retain the nonmagnetic face-centered cubic structure, are not heat treatable, but do not suffer that notch sensitivity that is a failing of ferritic alloys.

But you will also notice that this composition is only just in the austenitic field; austenite persists, but is not stable, at room temperature. If it is cooled to subzero temperatures, ferrite is formed. More important from a practical point of view is that it can be induced to partially transform to the ferritic phase if it is mechanically deformed. Consequently, any increase in strength that would normally be anticipated as a result of cold work (as you might expect to occur in a piece of annealed copper, for example) is enhanced by the transformation to a ferrite that contains carbon—we have already called this martensite. The transformation may be qualitatively recognized by a simple magnetic test. However, we don't suggest that you try this out by stamping on coffee pots or bending spoons. Even though these will probably be austenitic (and nonmagnetic) when you first test them, they may persist in that quality as a result of other alloying elements that stabilize the austenite; more of that later.

7.4.2 Sensitization

Described in section 7.2.4 on ferritic stainless steels, the problem of sensitization has been commonly associated with austenitic steels. This is probably because, historically, these have been more widely used and more frequently welded. The phenomenon was first observed adjacent to welds and was called "weld-decay," where a region adjacent to the weld becomes susceptible to corrosion (Fig. 7.17).

In both classes of steel, the root of the cause is chromium depletion. Within a critical temperature range, chromium combines with carbon at grain boundaries. Carbon, a small interstitial atom, moves rapidly, while the substitutional chromium atoms, with which carbon seeks to combine, move much more slowly. Hence, the formation of chromium carbide at active grain boundary sites draws upon carbon from most of the grains while the chromium is pulled away from local regions close to the grain boundaries.

However, the different solubilities of carbon in ferrite and austenite lead to substantial disparities in the circumstances under which chromium depletion is most rapid. Consequently—and we must emphasize this—the heat treatments for avoidance are dissimilar.

The austenitic steels are sensitized when they are heated within the range of 480 to 815 °C (900 to 1500 °F) or are slowly cooled through it. If you will turn back to Fig. 7.8, you will see that the maximum rate occurs at about 750 °C (1380 °F). Lower temperatures around 650 °C (1200 °F) have often been quoted. The discrepancies may well arise from the effects of composition and prior mechanical history.

In contrast to the heat treatment recommended for ferritic steels (which is described in 7.2.4), the austenitic class should be rapidly cooled through the critical range following an annealing period during which the carbides redissolve and chromium is homogeneously distributed. There are other means of avoiding sensitization that are more attractive.

Steels of very low carbon content ensure that the amount of chromium depletion is minimal. In the AISI classification, these are the steels whose number is followed by L, such as 304L or 316L. In UNS, the last digit is 3: 30403, 31603. The argon oxygen decarburization (AOD) process has made low-carbon grades economically accessible because carbon levels between 0.01 and 0.02% can be attained in the steelmaking process without a serious loss of chromium.

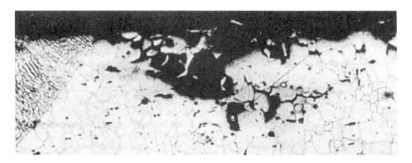

Fig. 7.17 Intergranular corrosion cracking in heat-affected zone of welded austenitic stainless steel at 100×

Before such low carbon levels could be reliably and economically attained, elements that preferentially formed carbides were a common alloying addition. They still are because even at lowest carbon levels, some chromium depletion may occur. The usual carbide formers are titanium, niobium, or niobium with tantalum (the two elements are very similar).

This may seem to be cheating, but austenitic steels that contain ferrite are very much less susceptible to sensitization than either of their constituents may suffer separately. We will deal with this happy circumstance when we come to the duplex steels.

Compositions of the standard austenitic stainless steels are given in Table 7.7 (which also includes the manganese-containing series), and mechanical properties are given in Table 7.8. We refrain from adding a daunting list of nonstandard austenitics (some of which are named in Appendix 3), but we prefer to offer working categories of all these steels, with their principal members as examples:

- The basic 18-8s: types 302 and 304
- Type 301, whose lower-alloy content gives a high rate of work hardening
- Type 305, whose higher-nickel content suppresses work hardening
- The more corrosion-resistant, molybdenum-bearing grades: types 316 and 317
- The stabilized grades: types 321 and 347
- The extra-low-carbon grades, signified by L in the AISI nomenclature
- The highly alloyed, oxidation-resistant grades: types 309 and 310
- The free-machining alloys: types 303 and 303Se

7.4.3 AISI 302 and 304: The Basic Grades of 18-8

More than one-half of U.S. stainless steel production comprises these two grades, and type 304 (with a required lower-carbon content) is dominant. In fact, the AOD process reduces the carbon level of type 304 to much lower levels than the specified 0.08% maximum, so that thin gages may be welded without fear of sensitization and require no subsequent heat treatment. The combination of good formability and weldability with corrosion resistance in the atmosphere and other common environments accounts for their widespread application.

The strength of these basic 18-8 grades is much the same as that of mild steel. However, cold working, which produces some martensite, increases strength with a corresponding lowering of ductility. Although a greater rate

Table 7.7 Compositions of standard austenitic stainless steels

Type	UNS No.	C	Mn	Si	Cr	Ni	P	S	Other
						Composition(a), %			
201	S20100	0.15	5.5–7.5	1.00	16.0–18.0	3.5–5.5	0.06	0.03	0.25 N
202	S20200	0.15	7.5–10.0	1.00	17.0–19.0	4.0–6.0	0.06	0.03	0.25 N
205	S20500	0.12–0.25	14.0–15.5	1.00	16.5–18.0	1.0–1.75	0.06	0.03	0.32–0.40 N
301	S30100	0.15	2.0	1.00	16.0–18.0	6.0–8.0	0.045	0.03	…
302	S30200	0.15	2.0	1.00	17.0–19.0	8.0–10.0	0.045	0.03	…
302B	S30215	0.15	2.0	2.0–3.0	17.0–19.0	8.0–10.0	0.045	0.03	…
303	S30300	0.15	2.0	1.00	17.0–19.0	8.0–10.0	0.20	0.15 min	0.6 Mo(b)
303Se	S30323	0.15	2.0	1.00	17.0–19.0	8.0–10.0	0.20	0.06	0.15 min Se
304	S30400	0.08	2.0	1.00	18.0–10.0	8.0–10.5	0.045	0.03	…
304H	S30409	0.04–0.10	2.0	1.00	18.0–20.0	8.0–10.5	0.045	0.03	…
304L	S30403	0.03	2.0	1.00	18.0–20.0	8.0–12.0	0.045	0.03	…
304LN	S30453	0.03	2.0	1.00	18.0–20.0	8.0–12.0	0.045	0.03	0.10–0.16 N
302Cu	S30430	0.08	2.0	1.00	17.0–19.0	8.0–10.0	0.045	0.03	3.0–4.0 Cu
304N	S30451	0.08	2.0	1.00	18.0–20.0	8.0–10.5	0.045	0.03	0.10–0.16 N
305	S30500	0.12	2.0	1.00	17.0–19.0	10.5–13.0	0.045	0.03	…
308	S30800	0.08	2.0	1.00	19.0–21.0	10.0–12.0	0.045	0.03	…
309	S30900	0.20	2.0	1.00	22.0–24.0	12.0–15.0	0.045	0.03	…
309S	S30908	0.08	2.0	1.00	22.0–24.0	12.0–15.0	0.045	0.03	…
310	S31000	0.25	2.0	1.50	24.0–26.0	19.0–22.0	0.045	0.03	…
310S	S31008	0.08	2.0	1.50	24.0–26.0	19.0–22.0	0.045	0.03	…
314	S31400	0.25	2.0	1.5–3.0	23.0–26.0	19.0–22.0	0.045	0.03	…
316	S31600	0.08	2.0	1.00	16.0–18.0	10.0–14.0	0.045	0.03	2.0–3.0 Mo
316F	S31620	0.08	2.0	1.00	16.0–18.0	10.0–14.0	0.20	0.10 min	1.75–2.5 Mo
316H	S31609	0.04–0.10	2.0	1.00	16.0–18.0	10.0–14.0	0.045	0.03	2.0–3.0 Mo
316L	S31603	0.03	2.0	1.00	16.0–18.0	10.0–14.0	0.045	0.03	2.0–3.0 Mo
316LN	S31653	0.03	2.0	1.00	16.0–18.0	10.0–14.0	0.045	0.03	2.0–3.0 Mo; 0.10–0.16 N
316N	S31651	0.08	2.0	1.00	16.0–18.0	10.0–14.0	0.045	0.03	2.0–3.0 Mo; 0.10–0.16 N
317	S31700	0.08	2.0	1.00	18.0–20.0	11.0–15.0	0.045	0.03	3.0–4.0 Mo
317L	S31703	0.03	2.0	1.00	18.0–20.0	11.0–15.0	0.045	0.03	3.0–4.0 Mo
321	S32100	0.08	2.0	1.00	17.0–19.0	9.0–12.0	0.045	0.03	5 × %C min Ti
321H	S32109	0.04–0.10	2.0	1.00	17.0–19.0	9.0–12.0	0.045	0.03	5 × %C min Ti
330	N08330	0.08	2.0	0.75–1.5	17.0–20.0	34.0–37.0	0.04	0.03	…
347	S34700	0.08	2.0	1.00	17.0–19.0	9.0–13.0	0.045	0.03	10 × %C min Nb
347H	S34709	0.04–0.10	2.0	1.00	17.0–19.0	9.0–13.0	0.045	0.03	8 × %C min– 1.0 max Nb
348	S34800	0.08	2.0	1.00	17.0–19.0	9.0–13.0	0.045	0.03	0.2 Co; 10 × %C min Nb; 0.10 Ta
348H	S34809	0.04–0.10	2.0	1.00	17.0–19.0	9.0–13.0	0.045	0.03	0.2 Co; 10 × %C min–1.0 max Nb; 0.10 Ta
384	S38400	0.08	2.0	1.00	15.0–17.0	17.0–19.0	0.045	0.03	…

(a) Single values are maximum values unless otherwise indicated. (b) Optional

Table 7.8 Minimum room-temperature mechanical properties of austenitic stainless steels

Product form(a)	Condition	Tensile strength MPa	Tensile strength ksi	0.2% yield strength MPa	0.2% yield strength ksi	Elonga-tion, %	Reduction in area, %	Hardness, HRB	ASTM specification
Type 301 (UNS S30100)									
B	Annealed	620	90	205	30	40	...	95 max	A 666
B, P, Sh, St	Annealed	515	75	205	30	40	...	92 max	A 167
B, P, Sh, St	¼ hard	860	125	515	75	25	...	...	A 666
B, P, Sh, St	½ hard	1030	150	760	110	18	...	...	A 666
B, P, Sh, St	¾ hard	1210	175	930	135	12	...	...	A 666
B, P, Sh, St	Full hard	1280	185	965	140	9	...	...	A 666
Type 302 (UNS S30200)									
B, F	Hot finished and annealed	515	75	205	30	40	50	...	A 276, A 473
B	Cold finished(b) and annealed	620	90	310	45	30	40	...	A 276
B	Cold finished(c) and annealed	515	75	205	30	30	40	...	A 276
W	Annealed	515	75	205	30	35(d)	50(d)	...	A 580
W	Cold finished	620	90	310	45	30(d)	40	...	A 580
P, Sh, St	Annealed	515	75	205	30	40	...	92 max	A 167, A 240, A 666
B, P, Sh, St	High tensile, ¼ hard	860	125	515	75	10	...	...	A 666
B, P, Sh, St	High tensile, ½ hard	1030	150	760	110	10	...	...	A 666
B, P, Sh, St	High tensile, ¾ hard	1205	175	930	135	6	...	...	A 666
B, P, Sh, St	Full hard	1275	185	965	140	4	...	...	A 666
Type 302B (UNS S30215)									
B, F	Hot finished and annealed	515	75	205	30	40	50	...	A 276, A 473
B	Cold finished(b) and annealed	620	90	310	45	30	40	...	A 276
B	Cold finished(c) and annealed	515	75	205	30	30	40	...	A 276
W	Annealed	515	75	205	30	35(d)	50(d)	...	A 580
W	Cold finished	620	90	310	45	30(d)	40	...	A 580
P, Sh, St	Annealed	515	75	205	30	40	...	95 max	A 167
Type 302Cu (UNS S30430)									
W(e)	Annealed	550	80	...	...	...	...	...	A 493
W(e)	Lightly drafted	585	85	...	...	...	...	...	A 493
Types 303 (UNS S30300) and 303Se (UNS S30323)									
F	Annealed	515	75	205	30	40	50	...	A 473
W	Annealed	585–860	85–125	...	...	...	...	...	A 581

(continued)

Table 7.8 (continued)

Product form(a)	Condition	Tensile strength MPa	ksi	0.2% yield strength MPa	ksi	Elonga- tion, %	Reduction in area, %	Hardness, HRB	ASTM specification
W	Cold worked	790–1000	115–145	...	...	...	...	...	A 581
Type 304 (UNS S30400)									
B, F(f)	Hot finished and annealed	515	75	205	30	40	50	...	A 276, A 473
B	Cold finished(b) and annealed	620	90	310	45	30	40	...	A 276
B	Cold finished(c) and annealed	515	75	205	30	30	40	...	A 276
W	Annealed	515	75	205	30	35(d)	50(d)	...	A 580
W	Cold finished	620	90	310	45	30(d)	40	...	A 580
P, Sh, St	Annealed	515	75	205	30	40	...	92 max	A 167
B, P, Sh, St ⅛ hard		690	100	380	55	35	...	...	A 666
B, P, Sh, St ¼ hard		860	125	515	75	10	...	...	A 666
B, P, Sh, St ½ hard		1035	150	760	110	7	...	...	A 666
Type 304L (UNS S30403)									
F	Annealed	450	65	170	25	40	50	...	A 473
B	Hot finished and annealed	480	70	170	25	40	50	...	A 276
B	Cold finished(b) and annealed	620	90	310	45	30	40	...	A 276
B	Cold finished(c) and annealed	480	70	170	25	30	40	...	A 276
W	Annealed	480	70	170	25	35(d)	50(d)	...	A 580
W	Cold finished	620	90	310	45	30(d)	40	...	A 580
P, Sh, St	Annealed	480	70	170	25	40	...	88 max	A 167, A 240
Type 304B4 (UNS S30424)									
P, Sh, St grade A	Annealed	515	75	205	30	27	...	95 max	A 887
P, Sh, St grade B	Annealed	515	75	205	30	16	...	95 max	A 887
Type 305 (UNS S30500)									
B, F	Hot finished and annealed	515	75	205	30	40	50	...	A 276, A 473
B	Cold finished(b) and annealed	260	90	310	45	30	40	...	A 276
B	Cold finished(c) and annealed	515	75	205	30	30	40	...	A 276
W	Annealed	515	75	205	30	35(d)	50(d)	...	A 580
W	Cold finished	620	90	310	45	30(d)	40	...	A 580
P, Sh, St	Annealed	480	70	170	25	40	...	88 max	A 167
B, W	High tensile(d)	1690	245	...	...	...	...	...	...
Cronifer 18-15 LCSi (UNS S30600)									
P, Sh, St	Annealed	540	78	240	35	40	...	...	A 167, A 240

(continued)

Table 7.8 (continued)

Product form(a)	Condition	Tensile strength MPa	ksi	0.2% yield strength MPa	ksi	Elonga- tion, %	Reduction in area, %	Hardness, HRB	ASTM specification
Type 308 (UNS S30800)									
B, F	Hot finished and annealed	515	75	205	30	40	50	...	A 276, A 473
B	Cold finished(b) and annealed	620	90	310	45	30	40	...	A 276
B	Cold finished(c) and annealed	515	75	205	30	30	40	...	A 276
W	Annealed	515	75	205	30	35(d)	50(d)	...	A 580
W	Cold finished	620	90	310	45	30(d)	40	...	A 580
P, Sh, St	Annealed	515	75	205	30	40	...	88 max	A 167
Types 309 (UNS S30900), 309S (UNS S30908), 310 (UNS S31000) and 310S (UNS S31008)									
B, F	Hot finished and annealed	515	75	205	30	40	50	...	A 276, A 473
B	Cold finished(b) and annealed	620	90	310	45	30	40	...	A 276
B	Cold finished(c) and annealed	515	75	205	30	30	40	...	A 276
W	Annealed	515	75	205	30	35(d)	50(d)	...	A 580
W	Cold finished	620	90	310	45	30(d)	40	...	A 580
P, Sh, St	Annealed	515	75	205	30	40	...	95 max	A 167
310Cb (UNS S31040)									
P, Sh, St	Annealed	515	75	205	30	40	...	95	A 167, A 240
B, Shapes	Hot finished and annealed	515	75	205	30	40	50	...	A 276
B, Shapes	Cold finished(b) and annealed	620	90	310	45	30	40	...	A 276
B, Shapes	Cold finished(c) and annealed	515	75	205	30	30	40	...	A 276
W	Annealed	515	75	205	30	35(d)	50(d)	...	A 580
W	Cold finished	620	90	310	45	30(d)	40	...	A 580
Type 314 (UNS S31400)									
B, F	Hot finished and annealed	515	75	205	30	40	50	...	A 276, A 473
B	Cold finished(b) and annealed	620	90	310	45	30	40	...	A 276
B	Cold finished(c) and annealed	515	75	205	30	30	40	...	A 276
W	Annealed	515	75	205	30	35(d)	50(d)	...	A 580
W	Cold finished	620	90	310	45	30(d)	40	...	A 580
Type 316 (UNS S31600)									
B, F(f)	Hot finished and annealed	515	75	205	30	40	50	...	A 276, A 473

(continued)

Table 7.8 (continued)

Product form(a)	Condition	Tensile strength MPa	Tensile strength ksi	0.2% yield strength MPa	0.2% yield strength ksi	Elonga- tion, %	Reduction in area, %	Hardness, HRB	ASTM specification
Type 316 (UNS S31600) (continued)									
B	Cold finished(b) and annealed	620	90	310	45	30	40	...	A 276
B	Cold finished(c) and annealed	515	75	205	30	30	40	...	A 276
W	Annealed	515	75	205	30	35(d)	50(d)	...	...
W	Cold finished	620	90	310	45	40(d)	40	...	A 580
P, Sh, St	Annealed	515	75	205	30	40	...	95 max	A 167, A 240
Type 316L (UNS S31603)									
F	Annealed	450	65	170	25	40	50	...	A 473
B	Hot finished and annealed	480	70	170	25	40	50	...	A 276
B	Cold finished(b) and annealed	620	90	310	45	30	40	...	A 276
B	Cold finished(c) and annealed	480	70	170	25	30	40	...	A 276
W	Annealed	480	70	170	25	35(d)	50(d)	...	A 580
W	Cold finished	620	90	310	45	30(d)	40	...	A 580
P, Sh, St	Annealed	485	70	170	25	40	...	95 max	A 167, A 240
Type 316Cb (UNS S31640)									
P, Sh, St	Annealed	515	75	205	30	30	...	95	A 167, A 240
B, Shapes	Hot finished and annealed	515	75	205	30	40	50	...	A 276
B, Shapes	Cold finished(b) and annealed	620	90	310	45	30	40	...	A 276
B, Shapes	Cold finished(c) and annealed	515	75	205	30	30	40	...	A 276
W	Annealed	515	75	205	30	35(d)	50(d)	...	A 580
W	Cold finished	620	90	310	45	30(d)	40	...	A 580
Type 317 (UNS S31700)									
B, F	Hot finished and annealed	515	75	205	30	40	50	...	A 276, A 473
B	Cold finished(b) and annealed	620	90	310	45	30	40	...	A 276
B	Cold finished(c) and annealed	515	75	205	30	30	40	...	A 276
W	Annealed	515	75	205	30	35(d)	50(d)	...	A 580
W	Cold finished	620	90	310	45	30(d)	40	...	A 580
P, Sh, St	Annealed	515	75	205	30	35	...	95 max	A 167, A 240
Type 317L (UNS S31703)									
B	Annealed	585(g)	85(g)	240(g)	35(g)	55(g)	65(g)	85 max (g)	...
P, Sh, St	Annealed	515	75	205	30	40	...	95 max	A 167

(continued)

Table 7.8 (continued)

Product form(a)	Condition	Tensile strength		0.2% yield strength		Elonga- tion, %	Reduction in area, %	Hardness, HRB	ASTM specification
		MPa	ksi	MPa	ksi				
Type 317LM (UNS S31725)									
B, P	Annealed	515	75	205	30	40	...	...	A 276
P, Sh, St	Annealed	515	75	205	30	40	...	96 max	A 167
Types 321 (UNS S32100) and 321H (UNS S32109)									
B, F	Hot finished and annealed	515	75	205	30	40	50	...	A 276, A 473
B	Cold finished(b) and annealed	620	90	310	45	30	40	...	A 276
B	Cold finished(c) and annealed	515	75	205	30	30	40	...	A 276
W	Annealed	515	75	205	30	35(d)	50(d)	...	A 580
W	Cold finished	620	90	310	45	30(d)	40	...	A 580
P, Sh, St	Annealed	515	75	205	30	40	...	95 max	A 167, A 240
Types 347 (UNS S34700) and 348 (UNS S34800)									
B, F	Hot finished and annealed	515	75	205	30	40	50	...	A 276, A 473
B	Cold finished(b) and annealed	620	90	310	45	30	40	...	A 276
B	Cold finished(c) and annealed	515	75	205	30	30	40	...	A 276
W	Annealed	515	75	205	30	35(d)	50(d)	...	A 580
W	Cold finished	620	90	310	45	30(d)	40	...	A 580
P, Sh, St	Annealed	515	75	205	30	40	...	92 max	A 167, A 240
18-18-2 (UNS S38100)									
P, Sh, St	Annealed	515	75	205	30	40	...	95 max	A 167, A 240
Type 384 (UNS S38400)									
W(e)	Annealed	550	80	...	...	...	...	...	A 493
W(e)	Lightly drafted	585	85	...	...	...	...	...	A 493
20Cb-3 (UNS N08020), 20Mo-4 (UNS N08024), and 20Mo-6 (UNS N08026)									
B, W	Annealed	550	80	240	35	30	50	...	B 473
Shapes	Annealed	550	80	240	35	15	50	...	B 473
B, W	Annealed and strain hardened	620	90	415	60	15	40	...	B 473
W	Annealed and cold finished	620-830	90-120	...	...	...	...	...	B 473
P, Sh, St	Annealed	550	80	240	35	30	...	95 max	B 463
Pi, T	Annealed	550	80	240	35	30	...	...	B 464, B 468, B 474, B 729
Sanicro 28 (UNS N08028)									
P, Sh, St	Annealed	500	73	215	31	40	...	70–90(g)	B 709

(continued)

Table 7.8 (continued)

Product form(a)	Condition	Tensile strength MPa	Tensile strength ksi	0.2% yield strength MPa	0.2% yield strength ksi	Elonga- tion, %	Reduction in area, %	Hardness, HRB	ASTM specification
Sanicro 28 (UNS N08028) (continued)									
Seamless tube	Annealed	500	73	215	31	40	...	...	B 668
Type 330 (UNS N08330)									
B	Annealed	485	70	210	30	30	...	...	B 511
P, Sh, St	Annealed	485	70	210	30	30	...	70–90(g)	B 536
Pi	Annealed	485	70	210	30	30	...	70–90(g)	B 535, B 546
AL-6X (UNS N08366)									
B, W	Annealed	515	75	210	30	30	...	...	B 691
P, Sh, St	Annealed	515	75	240	35	30	...	95 max	B 688
Pi, T	Annealed	515	75	210	30	30	...	...	B 675, B 676, B 690
Welded T	Cold worked	515	75	210	30	10	...	...	B 676
JS-700 (UNS N08700)									
B, W	Annealed	550	80	240	35	30	50	...	B 672
P, Sh, St	Annealed	550	80	240	35	30	...	75–90(g)	B 599
Type 332 (UNS N08800)									
Pi, T	Annealed	515	75	210	30	30	...	...	B 163, B 407, B 514, B 515
Seamless Pi, T	Hot finished	450	65	170	25	30	...	...	B 407
B	Hot worked	550	80	240	35	25	...	...	B 408
B	Annealed	515	75	210	30	30	...	...	B 408
P	Hot rolled	550	80	240	35	25	...	...	B 409
P, Sh, St	Annealed	515	75	210	30	30	...	...	B 409
Type 904L (UNS N08904)									
B	Annealed	490	71	220	31	35	...	...	B 649
W	Cold finished	620–830	90–120	...	...	...	...	...	B 649
Pi, T	Annealed	490	71	220	31	35	...	...	B 673, B 674, B 677
P, Sh, St	Annealed	490	71	220	31	35	...	70–90(g)	B 625

(a) B, bar; F, forgings; P, plate; Pi, pipe; Sh, sheet; St, strip; T, tube; W, wire. (b) Up to 13 mm (0.5 in.) thick. (c) Over 13 mm (0.5 in.) thick. (d) For wire 3.96 mm ($\frac{5}{32}$ in.) and under, elongation and reduction in area shall be 25 and 40%, respectively. (e) 4 mm (0.156 in.) in diameter and over. (f) For forged sections 127 mm (5 in.) and over, the tensile strength shall be 485 MPa (70 ksi). (g) For information only, not a basis for acceptance or rejection

of work-hardening may be required in flat-rolled products, where AISI 301 is commonly used, types 302 and 304 develop spring-quality properties when drawn into wire.

7.4.4 AISI 301: Greater Work Hardenability

In the annealed condition, this grade shows greater ductility than types 302 and 304. Yet on working (due to the lower nickel content and the consequent encouragement of martensite formation), it develops greater yield and ultimate tensile strengths (see Fig. 7.18). For this reason, it is a favorite alloy for panels in railroad cars and other transit vehicles. Although specially developed austenitic steels containing manganese and cobalt have more pronounced resistance to erosion and particularly to cavitation erosion, type 301 is the outstanding performer among the regular 18-8s (Fig. 7.19). Its diverse structural applications place it third in U.S. tonnage production of austenitic stainless steels, slightly behind the 316 grades.

7.4.5 AISI 305: Resist Work Hardening

While improved strength through cold forming is often attractive, there are circumstances in which the loss of ductility will not accommodate the severity of the forming operation. This is particularly the case in deep drawing, where shapes like sinks or pans are made, or when bolts are cold headed. Here, the work-hardening rate is diminished by stabilizing the austenite, so that martensite formation is avoided. This is usually effected by increasing the nickel content. However, we should remember that drawability is very much influenced by carbon; hence, the extra-low-carbon grades of other austenitic alloys may be just as satisfactory.

7.4.6 AISI 316 and 317: Contain Molybdenum for Improved Corrosion Resistance

Molybdenum, in amounts between 2 and 4%, improves the corrosion resistance of the 18-8 species, notably in reducing media and chloride solutions, and increases high-temperature strength. However, because it is a strong ferritizer, an offsetting addition of nickel adjusts the composition so that austenite persists. It used to be thought that molybdenum worsened the likelihood of sensitization. Although the jury still appears to be out on that one, current evidence suggests that the nature of the test, rather than the characteristics of the alloy, led to such an accusation.

7.4.7 AISI 321 and 347: The Stabilized Grades

Additions of strong carbide formers reduce susceptibility to sensitization in the form of intergranular corrosion through chromium depletion. In type 321, the carbide former is titanium, which is added in an amount about five times the carbon content of the composition of type 304. In type 347,

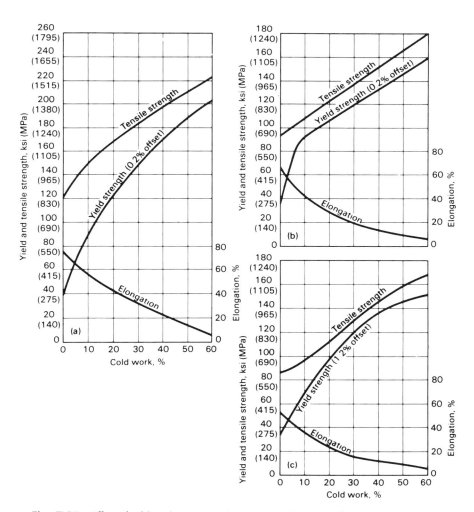

Fig. 7.18 Effect of cold working on tensile properties of (a) 301, (b) 302, (c) 304

niobium and tantalum are the effective agents. Room temperature mechanical properties are not significantly altered by the stabilizers that, however, through the formation of their particular carbides, improve creep resistance.

7.4.8 AISI 304L and 316L: The Extra-Low-Carbon Grades

Low-carbon grades—more easily attained now than they used to be—have reduced the use of (but by no means have replaced) the stabilized grades. As you would expect, lower carbon levels lower the yield and ultimate strength of the alloys; but, as you will see from the tables of composition and mechanical properties, this is compensated by the addition of nitrogen, now a controllable alloying element, in the designations LN. However, nitrogen affects sensitization. It would be easy to say that the presence of (interstitial) nitrogen impedes the diffusion of carbon (also interstitial) and hence makes the steel less sensitive. But there have been conflicting opinions, and experimental data suggest that at certain levels nitrogen is deleterious. However, from a practical point of view, so long as carbon is held below 0.02%, nitrogen additions up to 0.14% are not harmful. In the presence of molybdenum (316LN), nitrogen appears to be beneficial.

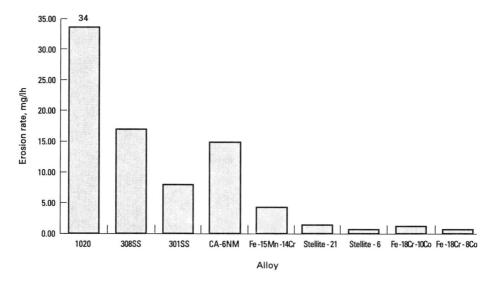

Fig. 7.19 Comparison of cavitation erosion rate of various materials

7.4.9 AISI 309, 310:
Highly Alloyed, Oxidation-Resistant Grades

These represent the alloys whose composition is such that an austenitic structure persists. They still qualify as steels (containing more than 50% Fe), and they are designed for resistance to oxidation at high temperatures. While oxides of chromium are the effective suppressor of continued attack, the formation of nickel-containing complexes retards the spalling of the film, whose adherence is important when service involves cyclic temperatures. As is generally the case, improved high-temperature oxidation resistance goes along with better creep properties. (Indeed, it is a general—but not universal—rule that if an alloy has acceptable creep properties at temperature, it will be adequately oxidation resistant.)

Some alloys (types 302B and 314), as you will note from the tables, contain more than the usual whack of silicon. The performance of type 302B in oxidizing atmospheres compared to its silicon-free sibling and to the much more highly alloyed type 310 is shown in Fig. 7.20.

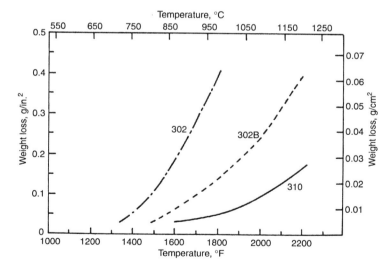

Fig. 7.20 Scaling losses developed in 12 intermittent heating and cooling cycles by various stainless steels. Reprinted with permission from A.J. Sedriks, *Corrosion of Stainless Steels*, John Wiley & Sons, Inc., 1996

7.4.10 AISI 303, 303Se: Free-Machining Grades

The trick in making free-machining grades is to present to the cutting tool a surface that (among other things) isn't gummy, doesn't cause the assembly to shudder, make unruly long turnings, or form a buildup on the tool edge. Every consideration of the metal's constitution to satisfy these requirements must be tempered by that ultimate acceptance of the alloy's function (notably corrosion resistance) and all the other fabrication and heat-treatment processes that it suffers en route to useful application.

There's a book in itself! And although we devote more attention to the subject in section 8.6, we hope you will let us make a shortcut here. Additions that produce sulfides, selenides, or some oxides present the best compromise, although corrosion resistance is often impaired. Specific tests are the only guide. The free-machining grades are generally available only in those mill shapes that are used in machine cutting bar and rod.

7.5 The Cr-Mn-Ni Austenitic Stainless Steels

Although these steels were developed in the early 1930s, only later did they come into service when, during the Korean War (1950–1953), nickel was in short supply. Even then, with the substitution of manganese for one-half to two-thirds of the nickel content in the basic 18-8s, the necessary addition of nitrogen could not be so well controlled as it now is.

Nor, perhaps, was the combined role of manganese and nitrogen so clear as it is today. Manganese, and more potently, nitrogen, are austenite stabilizers; and while manganese substantially increases austenitic solubility for nitrogen, it does not encourage the formation of nitrides.

Spiedel and Uggowitzer recently asserted that the Schaeffler diagram (Fig. 7.2) does not properly reflect the role of manganese and that the factor for nitrogen is understated. Using their amended formula, Fig. 7.21 is obtained, demarcating the composition limits for austenite persistence. Note the ingenious way in which manganese is factored to reflect evidence that at levels above 10%, it is no longer an austenite stabilizer but changes sides and becomes a ferritizer.

The mechanisms contributing to the strength of appropriately formulated alloys are solid-solution strengthening, especially by nitrogen; maintenance of fine grain size; cold work; and a form of precipitation-hardening involving nitride-rich clusters. The steels, developing very high strengths with good fracture toughness, remain austenitic.

Although the number of trade-name nickel-manganese-austenite alloys exceeds those with an AISI designation, most have been given a UNS Number. Their compositions are given in Table 7.9, and typical mechanical properties are outlined in Table 7.10. Compared with their opposite numbers in the 300 series, these alloys have, in general, substantially increased yield strength and slightly increased ultimate tensile strength with no appreciable loss in ductility. They are more susceptible to work hardening.

At high nitrogen levels (about 1%), the ductile-brittle transition temperature (DBTT) is about room temperature. However, such high nitrogen levels are not normal; and, as Fig. 7.22 shows, at more customary levels, the DBTT is about –120 °C (–190 °F). As well as the possibilities of sigma embrittlement, a further embrittling mechanism associated with chromium nitride precipitates may occur in highly alloyed steels at operating temperatures between 400 and 800 °C (750 and 1470 °F).

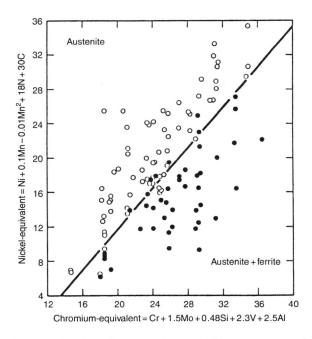

Fig. 7.21 Austenite phase boundary in stainless steels rich in manganese, chromium, molybdenum, and nitrogen

Table 7.9 Compositions of the nickel-manganese-nitrogen austenitic stainless steels

UNS No.	Name	Composition(a), %									
		Cr	Ni	C	Mn	Si	P	S	N	Mo	Other
S20100	201	16–18	2.5–5.5	0.15	5.5–7.5	1.0	0.060	0.030	0.25	...	...
S20103	201L	16.4–17.1	4.0–4.6	0.03	6.4–7.0	0.7	0.045	0.025	0.165	...	Cu 0.6
S20200	202	17–19	4–6	0.15	7.5–10	1.0	0.060	0.030	0.25	...	...
S20300	203EZ	16–18	5.0–6.5	0.08	5.0–6.5	1.0	0.040	0.35	...	0.5	Cu 1.75–2.25
S20500	205	16.5–18	1–1.75	0.25	14–15.5	1.0	0.060	0.030	0.40	...	...
S20910	22-13-5	20.5–23.5	11.5–13.5	0.06	4–6	1.0	0.040	0.030	0.2–0.4	1.5–3	Nb 0.1–0.3
S20980	22-10-5	20.5–24.0	9.5–12.0	0.05	4–7	0.9	0.030	0.1–0.3	1.5–3	...	Cu 0.75
S21400	Tenelon	17–18.5	0.75	0.12	14.5–16	1.0	0.045	0.030	0.35	...	...
S21460	Cry. Ten.	17–19	5–6	0.12	14–16	1.0	0.060	0.030	0.50	...	...
S21600	216	17.5–22	5–7	0.08	7.5–9	1.0	0.045	0.030	0.25–0.50	2–3	...
S21603	216L	17.5–22	5–7	0.03	7.5–9	1.0	0.045	0.030	0.25–0.50	2–3	...
S28200	18-18Plus	17–19	...	0.15	17–19	1.0	0.045	0.030	0.4–0.6	0.5–1.5	Cu 0.5–1.5
	REX 734(b)	22	9	0.05	4	0.25	0.015	0.005	0.4	2.6	Nb 0.3
S34565	4565S	23–25	16–18	0.03	5–7	1.0	0.030	0.015	0.4–0.6	4–5	Nb 0.1
	24	21–25	15–18	0.03	4.5–6.5	1.0	0.020	0.005	0.3–0.5	3–4.5	Nb 0.3
S21000	Sea-Fast(b)	22.75	17.75	0.02	4.25	0.45	...	...	0.4	5.5	...
	654SMO	24–25	21–23	0.02	2–4	0.29	0.021	0.001	0.45–0.55	7–8	Cu 0.3–0.6

(a) Balance, iron. Single values are maximum values unless otherwise noted. (b) Typical composition. Source: A.J. Sedriks, *Corrosion of Stainless Steels*, John Wiley & Sons, Inc., 1996

Table 7.10 Typical mechanical properties of the nickel-manganese-nitrogen austenitic stainless steels

Name	Tensile strength(a), MPa	Yield strength (0.2% offset), MPa	Elongation, %	Hardness (Rockwell B)
201	758	379	55	90
201L	744	310	57	...
202	689	379	55	90
203EZ	551	276	58	90
205	862	482	45	98
22-13-5	827	414	50	98
Tenelon	827	448	40	95
216	689	379	45	92
216L	689	379	45	92
18-18 Plus	827	476	65	95
REX 734	920	550	45	98
4565S	900	420	35	...
24	800	420	35	98
Sea-Fast	827	434	52	...
654SMO	750	430	35	...

Annealed sheet and strip. (a) MPa = 145.03 psi. Source: A.J. Sedriks, *Corrosion of Stainless Steels*, John Wiley & Sons, Inc., 1996

When this occurrence is avoided, nitrogen holds back the precipitation of chromium- and molybdenum-rich phases; hence, the steel can carry more of these passivating elements. Furthermore, nitrogen is believed to be beneficial in dilute acid media through the formation of ammonia at the metal surface, which buffers acid attack.

Before we describe some of the principal manganese-nitrogen steels, we offer Fig. 7.23, which graphically shows the superior level of combined toughness and strength of one of the steels in this class: X5CrMnN18 18—that is, 18% Cr, 18% Mn, 0.5% C, nitrogen.

7.5.1 AISI 202: The Basic Grade

This parallels type 301 of the 18-8s, with the substitution of manganese and nitrogen for one-half or more of the nickel, and may find similar applications. A free-machining grade, with approximately the same chemistry as type 202 but with additions of sulfur and copper, is descriptively named EZ (so long as one says "zee" and not "zed").

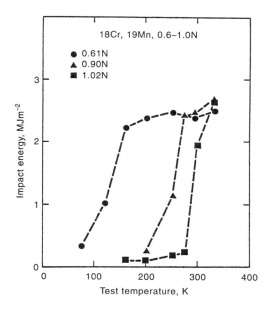

Fig. 7.22 Ductile to brittle transition temperatures of austenitic stainless steels increase with the nitrogen concentrations.

7.5.2 AISI 201: Greater Work Hardenability

As with its counterpart, type 301, the lower-nickel equivalent content encourages martensite formation during cold work. It is commonly used as cold-rolled sheet. Its low-carbon grade (L in the AISI system) is frequently used in cryogenic applications. With approximately the same chemistry but an addition of 3 to 4% Si, a grade with the trade name "Gall Tough" is formulated for abrasion resistance. We discuss galling at the end of this chapter.

7.5.3 AISI 205: Resist Work Hardening

Again, we have to make a parallel. This, perhaps, has been the bane of the manganese-nitrogen series because they are often regarded not only as poor cousins, but even more unfairly, as slightly inferior ones. Like type 305,

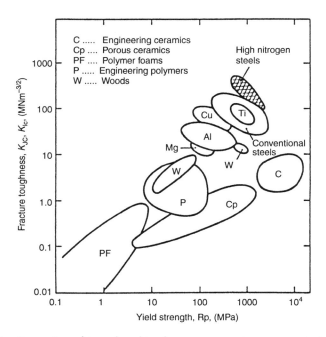

Fig. 7.23 Comparison of strength and toughness among contemporary materials

AISI 205 has a lower rate of work-hardening, but in this steel, through an increase in manganese, not nickel. The respective nickel levels are (about) 12% in type 305 and 1.5% in 205.

7.5.4 AISI 216: Contains Molybdenum for Improved Corrosion Resistance

Nitrogen levels in alloys of this type provide enhanced resistance to pitting and crevice corrosion. Several alloys, which contain substantial amounts of nickel (in addition to the manganese-nitrogen formulation), have particularly good resistance (see alloy 22-13-5 in Table 7.9). Other similar commercial products and low-carbon grades are available, and very low sulfur levels in some of the grades further reduce susceptibility to pitting. 18-18Plus and similar alloys are notable for their galling resistance.

7.5.5 Cobalt-Containing Manganese-Nitrogen Austenitic Stainless Steels

These are a recent addition to the arsenal. A typical composition, specifically designed by Hydro-Québec to resist cavitation erosion, is 17% Cr, 9.5% Mn, 9% Co, 2.5% Si, 0.2% C, and 0.2% N. The metastable austenitic structure transforms to a martensite under the influence of the shock waves generated by bursting bubbles. This alloy is reported to be ten times more resistant to cavitation erosion than the standard 300 grades, which puts it in a category with the highly alloyed (and more expensive) cobalt-rich Stellites (Fig. 7.19). General corrosion resistance is lowered because of the carbon content of the alloy.

Family relationships of the most common austenitic stainless steels are shown in Fig. 7.24.

7.6 Precipitation-Strengthened Stainless Steels

In section 3.2.4 we introduced precipitation hardening. It offers the opportunity of further strengthening the martensitic and austenitic constituents in stainless steels. The required heat treatment involves solution treating followed by aging (at a substantially lower temperature) to induce the forma-

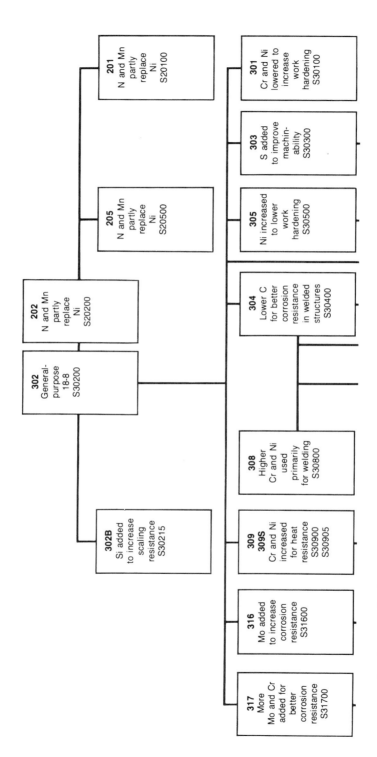

Fig. 7.24 Family relationships for standard austenitic stainless steels

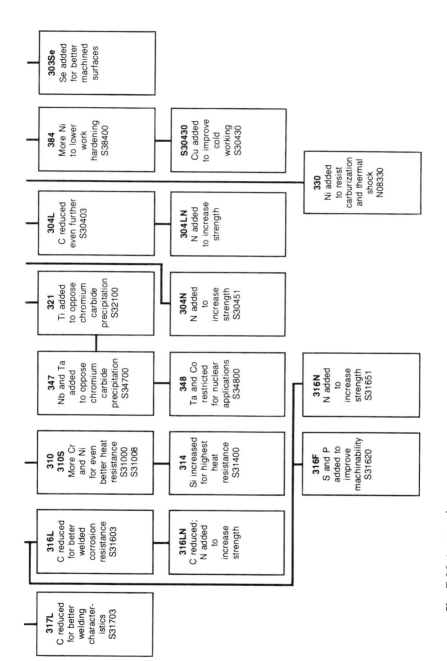

Fig. 7.24 (continued)

tion of pre-precipitates—noncoherent clusters— that impede plastic slip. In the martensitic class, such a heat treatment can be designed to complement the quenching and tempering process.

Recall that austenitic stainless steels, which are not susceptible to quenching and tempering, are strengthened by cold working. Inevitably, subsequent heating will reduce or eradicate that gain. Consequently, any age-strengthening process has to be one that is more advantageous than strengthening by cold working. Precipitation hardening offers a route. There are two elements to this method. The first is to determine which of the two strengthening processes, cold working or precipitation hardening, presents the better and more economical combination of desired properties; the second—and very important element—is to recognize the opportunity provided by age hardening to strengthen a shape that is already fabricated.

Of course, strengthening by work hardening may be part of the fabrication process; no less, it may impede fabrication. But once formed, the shape whose strength depends upon work hardening will be a potential victim of elevated temperature. Imagine for instance, an austenitic stainless steel sheet, whose strength has been acquired by cold rolling. It is then welded. The heat-affected zone of the weld will inevitably have a lower strength; and, in every likelihood, the component cannot be subsequently cold worked to regain its earlier properties.

In contrast, a precipitation-strengthened component may be formed into shape and then heat treated to develop desirable properties by aging after solution annealing. Its strength will suffer only if it is used at a temperature above the aging temperature.

Table 7.11 gives the compositions of precipitation-hardening stainless steels: martensitic, austenitic, and semiaustenitic. Many of the precipitation-hardening steels do not have AISI designations. They were introduced with proprietary names that have stuck to them; most have a UNS number.

7.6.1 Martensitic Precipitation-Hardening Stainless Steels

In the conventional heat treatments of quenching and tempering, the carbon is at first retained in austenitic solid solution during soaking. Martensite, which forms on quenching, is tempered to form coherent clusters of iron carbide and eventually, at higher temperatures, precipitates. In short, the ferrite has become strengthened as a result of its carbon content, which—of course!—gives us the martensitic series of stainless steels. How-

Table 7.11 Compositions of precipitation hardenable stainless steels

| UNS number | AISI | Name | Composition, % | | | | | | | | | |
			C	Cr	Ni	Mn	Si	Ti	Al	Mo	N	Others
Martensitic grades												
S17600	635	Stainless W	0.08	15.0–17.5	6.0–7.5	1.0	1.0	0.4–1.2	0.40	...	...	...
S17400	630	17-4 PH	0.07	15.5–17.5	3.0–5.0	1.0	1.0	...	...	...	...	0.15–0.45 Nb, 3.0–5.0 Cu
S15500	...	15-5PH	0.07	14.0–15.5	3.5–5.5	1.0	1.0	...	...	...	...	0.15–0.45 Nb, 2.5–4.5 Cu
S16600	...	Croloy 16-6PH	0.045	15.0–16.0	7.0–8.0	0.70–0.90	0.5	0.3–0.5	0.25–0.40	...	...	...
S45000	...	Custom 450	0.05	14.0–16.0	5.0–7.0	1.0	1.0	...	...	0.5–1.0	...	1.25–1.75 Cu, Nb = 8 × C min
S45500	...	Custom 455	0.05	11.0–12.5	7.5–9.5	0.50	0.50	...	...	0.50	...	0.10–0.50 Nb, 1.5–2.5 Cu
S13800	...	PH 13-8 Mo	0.05	12.25–13.25	7.5–8.5	0.20	0.10	...	0.90–1.35Al	2.0–2.5	...	...
S36200	...	Almar 362	0.05	14.0–14.5	6.25–7.0	0.50	0.30	0.55–0.9	...	...	0.01	...
Semiaustenitic grades												
S17700	631	PH17-7	0.09	16.0–18.0	6.5–7.75	1.0	1.0	...	0.75–1.5	...	...	...
S15700	632	PH15-7 Mo	0.09	14.0–16.0	6.5–7.25	1.0	1.0	...	0.75–1.5	2.0–3.0	...	...
S35000	633	AM-350	0.07–0.11	16.0–17.0	4.0–5.0	0.50–1.25	0.50	...	...	2.5–3.25	0.07–0.13	...
S35500	634	AM-355	0.10–0.15	15.0–16.0	4.0–5.0	0.50–1.25	0.50	...	...	2.5–3.25	0.07–0.13	...
Austenitic grades												
S66286	...	A-286	0.08	13.5–16.0	24.0–27.0	2.0	1.0	1.9–2.35	0.35	1.0–1.5	...	0.10–0.50 V, 0.001–0.01 B

Maximum allowable given except where compositional range provided. All data from ASM Specialty Handbook: Stainless Steels, except S45000 and S66286 data from International Metallic Materials Cross Reference, and S16600 data from UNS Data Book

ever, you'll notice that the martensitic precipitation-hardening grades contain far less carbon than the regular martensitic grades do, and often less than the ferritic grades do. But, unlike the ferritic grades, their compositions make them heat treatable by quenching and tempering; they undergo the magic of the austenite to martensite transformation. These first precipitation-strengthened steels hit the market in 1946. Their mechanical properties are summarized in Table 7.12. Following quenching (by air cooling) from their austenitizing temperatures, the low-carbon martensite is weaker but more ductile than the martensites of the 400 series. Their strength is then developed by aging.

Table 7.12 Mechanical properties of precipitation hardenable stainless steels

UNS No.	AISI	Name	Conditions(a)	Tensile strength, MPa	0.2 % yield strength, MPa	Elongation, %	Hardness (Rockwell C)
Martensitic grades							
S17600	635	Stainless W	A	827	517	7	30
			PH	1344	1241	7	46
S17400	630	17-4 PH	A	1034	758	10	33
			PH	1379	1227	12	44
S15500	...	15-5PH	A	862	586	10	27
			PH	1379	1275	14	44
S16600	...	Croloy 16-6PH	A	924	758	16	28
			PH	1303	1275	16	40
S45000	...	Custom 450	A	972	814	13	28
			PH	1344	1282	14	43
S45500	...	Custom 455	A	1000	739	14	31
			PH	1724	1689	10	49
S13800	...	PH 13-8 Mo	A	896	586	12	28
			PH	1551	1379	13	48
S36200	...	Almar 362	A	827	724	13	25
			PH	1296	1276	15	41
Semiaustenitic grades							
S17700	631	PH 17-7	A	896	276	35	85 B(b)
			SZC + PH 510 °C	1620	1517	6	48
S15700	632	7PH 15-7 Mo	A	896	379	35	88 B
			SZC + PH 510 °C	1655	1551	6	48
S35000	633	AM-350	A	1103	379	40	95 B
			SZC + PH 455 °C	1379	1172	15	43
S35500	634	AM-355	A	1206	448	30	95 B
			SZC + PH 455°C	1517	1310	13	43
Austenitic grades							
S66286	...	A-286	A	620	241	45	81 B
			PH 718 °C	1006	689	25	34

(a) A, solution annealed; PH, precipitation hardened at temperature indicated or to give maximum strength; SZC, cooled to −73 °C. (b) B indicates Rockwell B hardness instead of Rockwell C.

The earliest martensitic steels (Stainless W and 17-4PH) have compositions such that they are partially ferritic after quenching. This lowers their notch ductility. More recent alloys (and adjustments to the chemistry of the older ones) mitigate this deficiency. Alternatively, at the sacrifice of strength, a higher aging temperature will give improved impact values, but some reverse transformation of martensite to austenite may take place. That austenite is, generally, retained on cooling, with a consequent improvement in impact properties at the cost of yield strength. The effect however isn't great.

The resistance of the precipitation-hardened martensitic stainless steels to general corrosion, pitting, and crevice corrosion appears to be better than that of their standard martensitic brethren. After all, the precipitation-hardened stainless steels contain more chromium. But so much depends upon particular circumstances, that any comment is hazardous. However, because the possibilities of chloride stress-corrosion cracking and hydrogen embrittlement are central to any discussion about the applications of any of the stainless steels, we would be wimps to dodge that issue. Our opinion is this: in whatever way yield strength is improved, so the sensitivity to either of these phenomena appears to increase.

You might surmise from the variety of minor additions to the martensitic precipitation-hardening steels that the exact nature of the strengthening processes is complex. You would be right! But their precise mechanisms are matters of academic amusement and proprietorial profit, and they need not concern us as we summarize the attractive features of the martensitic precipitation-hardening stainless steels:

- Compared with regular martensitic stainless grades, the tradeoff of strength versus ductility and toughness is much more favorable in the precipitation-hardening alloys.
- At reasonable levels of ductility, the precipitation-hardening grades present higher strengths.
- At a given strength level, the chances are that corrosion resistance will be superior.
- The nature of the strengthening process gives more opportunities for easy fabrication.

So why aren't these steels more often used? Well, they cost more to make, and every degree of heat treatment costs another buck. They are, therefore, used where they can be afforded and where their special properties are needed, particularly in the aircraft and aerospace industries.

7.6.2 Precipitation-Hardening Austenitic Stainless Steels

These are the least used of the precipitation-strengthened stainless steels, because the advantages of the process are not so outstanding as in the other two categories. Specifically, strength is not markedly increased.

After solution treating and quenching, the alloys are fully austenitic. In the most frequently used of the series, alloy A-286, the austenite remains stable even after substantial cold working, due to its very high nickel content. Alloys of this sort led to the development of the nickel-base superalloys, of which the Inconel and Nimonic (Inco Alloys International, Inc.) series are commonly known.

Following solution-treating, alloy A-286 is aged at about 700 °C (1290 °F) to give the properties summarized in Table 7.12. Its combination of mechanical properties and oxidation resistance makes it a valuable material for turbines and compressors. The fact that it retains its toughness at very low temperatures has led to its application in cryogenic equipment.

7.6.3 Semiaustenitic Precipitation-Hardened Stainless Steels

These steels have a largely austenitic structure after quenching from the soaking temperature, which may be substantially transformed to martensite by subzero cooling or by cold working. Alternatively, martensite may be formed by a subtle heat treatment. After quenching, the steel is reheated to about 750 °C (1380 °F). At this temperature, often called the conditioning temperature, chromium carbides form at austenite grain boundaries, depleting the grains themselves of their dissolved carbon and chromium. At the lower composition, the temperature at which martensite will form on subsequent cooling is substantially raised (Fig. 7.25). Consequently, on cooling from the conditioning temperature, the austenite transforms to martensite. Subsequent aging (about 520 °C, or 970 °F) gives the steel its optimal properties. Characteristic mechanical properties are given in Table 7.12.

7.7 Duplex Stainless Steels

Taken literally, *duplex* defines any stainless steel that contains two phases. Most of them do; many are multiplex. But the term "duplex stainless steels" means those stainless steels that comprise ferrite and austenite, each in a substantial amount, at room temperature. Steels that may have been heat treated or cold worked to have the dual phases of martensite and austenite are not included in the duplex category. The austenite-ferrite mix in a duplex grade is clearly delineated under the microscope (Fig. 7.26).

Because both ferrite and austenite in the duplex structure must be stainless, each constituent must contain at least 12% Cr; most contain considerably more, as Table 7.13 implies.

The virtues of the duplex grades can be stated in the following bold generalizations, for which there may be exceptions:

- Better resistance to stress-corrosion cracking, pitting, and crevice corrosion than either of their constituents
- Yield strengths may be as much as twice that of the common austenitics, while retaining ductility.
- Lower nickel content has economic advantages.

Although the alloys of the first generation are strong and provide good localized corrosion resistance (their high chromium and molybdenum contents see to that), they lose the ferrite-austenite balance when they are welded. An increased ferrite content in the heat-affected zone (HAZ) leads to a loss of toughness; also, corrosion problems arise.

The advent of AOD (and the lesser used vacuum-oxygen decarburization, VOD) permits a control of carbon and nitrogen that leads to the precisely

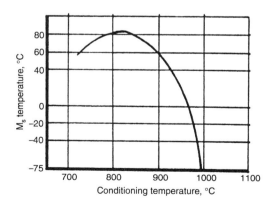

Fig. 7.25 Effect of conditioning temperature on the M_s temperature in a semi-austenitic steel. Courtesy of Les Editions de Physique Les Ulis, 1993

balanced compositions of the second generation of duplex alloys. Carbon (detrimental to all aspects of corrosion resistance) can be kept low, while nitrogen (strengthener, austenitizer, and corrosion mitigator) can be controlled for its best effect, especially in maintaining the ferrite-austenite balance. This is particularly important in weldments, where the following circumstances have to be considered.

A duplex steel solidifies as ferrite, part of which transforms to austenite during subsequent cooling, to give the anticipated and prescribed mix of the two phases at room temperature. If such a steel is welded, the HAZ of the weld reaches a temperature at which ferrite may form. This high-temperature ferrite is frequently designated delta ferrite to distinguish it from alpha ferrite, which is formed by the decomposition of austenite on cooling. During the rapid cooling experienced by the HAZ, the ferrite may not fully retransform to austenite, hence, parts of the structure may be overly rich in ferrite. Not only that, as the proportion of ferrite increases, its overall chromium content will be reduced. However, nitrogen raises the temperature at which the austenite in the HAZ transforms, and no more than the initial amount of ferrite (at the correct composition) is retained. Further, nitrogen inhibits the formation of undesirable intermetallic compounds (we discuss this in a subsequent paragraph).

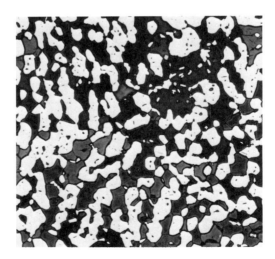

Fig. 7.26 S31200(44LN) duplex stainless steel, annealed and aged. Tint etched: ferrite dark. 200×

Table 7.13 Composition and tensile properties of common duplex stainless steels

| UNS number | Alloy name | Composition, % | | | | | | | | | | 0.2% yield strength, MPa | Ultimate tensile strength, MPa | Elongation, % |
		C	Mn	S	P	Si	Cr	Ni	Mo	N_2	Other			
First generation														
S32900	Type 329	0.06	1.0	0.03	0.04	0.75	23.0–28.0	2.5–5.0	1.0–2.0	...	...	485	620	20
J93370	CD-4MCu	0.05	2.0	...	...	1.5	25.0–27.0	4.5–6.0	1.5–2.5	...	2.5–3.5 Cu	...	...	...
Second generation														
S32304	SAF 2304	0.03	2.5	0.04	0.04	1.0	21.5–24.5	3.0–5.5	0.05–0.60	0.05–0.20	0.05–0.60 Cu	400	600	25
S31500	3RE60	0.03	1.2–2.0	0.03	0.03	1.4–2.0	18.0–19.0	4.25–5.25	2.5–3.0	0.05–0.10	...	440	630	30
S31803	2205	0.03	2.0	0.02	0.03	1.0	21.0–23.0	4.5–6.5	2.5–3.5	0.08–0.20	...	450	620	25
S31200	44LN	0.03	2.0	0.03	0.045	1.0	24.0–26.0	1.2–2.0	1.2–2.0	0.14–0.20	...	450	690	25
S32950	7-Mo PLUS	0.03	2.0	0.01	0.035	0.60	26.0–29.0	3.5–5.2	1.0–2.5	0.15–0.35	...	480	690	20
S32550	Ferralium 255	0.03	1.5	0.03	0.04	1.0	24.0–27.0	4.5–6.5	2.9–3.9	0.10–0.25	...	550	760	15
S31260	DP-3	0.03	1.0	0.03	0.030	0.75	24.0–26.0	2.5–3.5	0.10–0.30	0.10–0.30	0.10–0.50 W, 0.20–0.80Cu	450	690	25
S32750	SAF 2507	0.03	1.2	0.02	0.035	1.0	24.0–26.0	6.0–8.0	3.0–5.0	0.24–0.32	0.5 Cu	550	800	15

Tensile properties are minimums acceptable. All data from *ASM Specialty Handbook: Stainless Steels*, except tensile properties of S31260, which are from "Practical Guide to Using Duplex Stainless Steels," NiDI Tech. Series No. 10044

Consequently, the second generation of duplex alloys (with lower carbon and controlled nitrogen) can be used in the as-welded condition. To maintain the required nitrogen content during welding, the inert shielding gas is often supplemented with nitrogen to the extent of 5% by volume.

Although tonnages of duplex steels are not great, they increased twenty-fold from 1987 to 1994 (which is the most recent year for which data are available). They have become more popular as castings than as forgings or mill products.

At forming (or annealing) temperatures between 1000 and 1200 °C (1830 and 2190 °F), the steels are mixed ferritic and austenitic phases and contain more ferrite than is anticipated at room temperature. Because of the different properties of each of the constituents, forming must be carefully controlled. This is by no means daunting, but its challenge is one reason for the slow acceptance of duplex alloys in plate and strip mills.

During annealing, hot forming, or welding processes, care has to be taken to avoid a multiplicity of embrittling phenomena. The principal ones are those we have already attached to the ferritic steels: 475 °C (885 °F) embrittlement and sigma phase embrittlement. Sigma in austenitic steels can be a problem in long-term service, but heat-treatment times are not sufficiently long for its formation. Among the other embrittling constituents, complex carbides, which are rich in chromium and precipitate at grain boundaries, are particularly virulent. The intermetallic phases (compounds formed between metallic elements), whose compositions need not concern us are, like sigma, slow to form. Figure 7.27 presents an explanatory picture.

Clearly, the best way of preventing this onslaught of embrittling phenomena is to deftly sidestep it by avoiding the critical temperature ranges, or by cooling the structure rapidly through them. In welding, excessive heat input is to be avoided. In fact, these are the usual tactics. However, such optimistic simplicity has to be moderated by the realization that certain elements speed the formation of the embrittling constituents and/or increase their extensiveness. We particularly note the influence of silicon and molybdenum. Because these, especially molybdenum, may be necessary components of the alloy's chemistry, notably for corrosion resistance, compromises have to be made.

Sensitization—the depletion of chromium near to grain boundaries through the formation of chromium carbides—is, as we have already remarked, common to both ferritic and austenitic alloys. Its comparative havoc in austenitic alloys is because chromium diffusion is slow to adjust the deficiency. However, chromium diffuses much more rapidly in ferrite. Consequently, in duplex alloys, grain boundary chromium carbides deplete chromium over a substantial part of the ferrite grains, while only a very narrow, less depleted zone develops in the adjacent austenite grains. This, being small in extent and less marked in its chromium deficiency, is quickly 'healed.' In short, those problems that are named "weld-decay" are far less critical in the duplex alloys than in the austenitic steels.

Regrettably, it is not possible to present such a neat formula to rationalize the resistance of duplex steels to stress-corrosion cracking. While they are usually superior to austenitic stainless steels, in some instances they are not. As is not infrequently the case, industrial experience does not always replicate laboratory tests. When the duplex alloys are stressed within their elastic range, their superiority is clearly evident; however, beyond their yield point, their advantage is lost. The susceptibility of all steels to stress-corrosion cracking (and to hydrogen embrittlement) increases with yield strength. However, nitrogen additions to the duplex alloys are highly advantageous, because nitrogen not only raises the yield strength considerably, it also has the attribute of raising the ratio between threshold stress for stress-corrosion cracking and yield strength.

This very notable advantage in the second generation of duplex alloys has led to their increasing use in situations in the oil and gas industry where

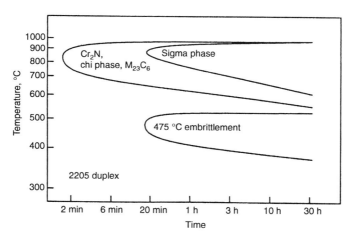

Fig. 7.27 Time-temperature-precipitation diagram for 2205 duplex stainless steel. Reprinted with permission from A.J. Sedriks, *Corrosion of Stainless Steels,* John Wiley & Sons, Inc., 1996

hydrogen sulfide is active, and in chloride and thiosulfate environments in the pulp and paper industry.

Ideally, the microstructure of duplex grades should be substantially free of intermetallic phases (complete freedom is unattainable) and contain about half of each constituent, ferrite and austenite. The importance of maintaining no less austenite in order to preserve low-temperature toughness is shown in Fig. 7.28. As one would expect, the presence of any ferrite at all diminishes the superlative cryogenic appeal held by the austenitic stainless steels; but in view of other splendid qualities of the duplex alloys, the sacrifice at an even split (as indicated by Fig. 7.28) isn't great. A note of caution: because of the lamellar structure of the rolled duplex alloys, impact tests will give results that are dependant upon the orientation of the sample with respect to the rolling direction of the plate or sheet.

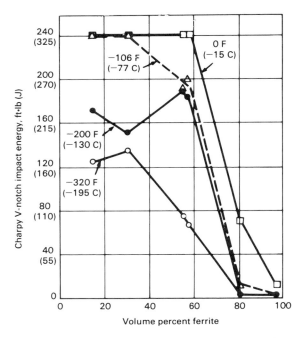

Fig. 7.28 Ferrite dependence of the impact energy of duplex stainless steels. From S. Floreen and H.W. Hayden, *Trans. ASM*, Vol 61, 1968, p 489–499. Reprinted with permission from A.J. Sedriks, *Corrosion of Stainless Steels*, John Wiley & Sons, Inc., 1996

In addition to the other qualities that we have touched upon, thermal conductivity of the duplex alloys is about 15% better than that of austenitic stainless steels; this, in turn, improves their resistance to thermal shock when hot materials are loaded into cold containers.

You will notice that the composition requirements (Table 7.13) allow an understandable deviation about a nominal value for most elements. However, the permitted range of nitrogen content in some of the alloys inevitably leads to substantial variations in mechanical and corrosion properties. A case in point is UNS 31803, which is produced by several manufacturers. Perhaps competitive pressures tend to keep nitrogen at the low end of its permissible range, 0.08 to 0.2%, to make fabrication easier. But toughness and stress-corrosion cracking resistance suffer. ASTM specifications, which are concerned for mechanical properties, are not always a sufficient safeguard.

Despite their undeniably attractive properties, the duplex steels are not so versatile as the austenitic grades. Fabrication and welding processes are fussier, and their initial manufacture requires meticulous control of the chemistry. Solomon and Devine subtitled their paper about duplex stainless steels, "A Tale of Two Phases." Indeed, depending upon your needs and your point of view, they may be the best of alloys or the worst of alloys!

7.8 Stainless-Clad Steels

There are economic opportunities to using a plain-carbon or low-alloy steel that is clad with stainless. The strength of the body of the component is more cheaply attained; the surface is corrosion resistant. The possibility should be taken into account in any life cycle costing program, which we reviewed in section 1.6. In general terms, stainless-clad steels become economical where sections are heavy, where a component is large, or where there are many similar components to be made. Conversely, in circumstances where only a small portion of the final price is due to the cost of the material itself, solid stainless is probably more economical.

Mostly, stainless is clad on to other steels. But there are many other substrates whose purposes may be to improve mechanical properties, or thermal conductivity, or to provide cathodic protection to a surrounding metal. We won't deal with these, but as an introductory teaser we have to mention one. It is the application of a ferritic stainless steel to an aluminum alloy for automobile trim and rocker panels. The aluminum isn't seen, but, in contact with the steel body of the car, it corrodes sacrificially. Meanwhile, the stainless cladding provides a corrosion-resistant surface and a saleable appearance (Fig. 7.29).

Stainlesses that are most used in cladding are of the 18-8 family, and the most common products are plate and strip, although pipe, tube, rod, and wire are also clad. Hot rolling accounts for about 90% of production of clad plate, and weld deposition accounts for much of the remainder. However, cold rolling, brazing, explosive bonding, and centrifugal casting have their specific applications.

Any of these processes provides a metallurgical bond between the two materials. Adhesive bonding, which is sometimes used, may make a tight and strong joint but does not enjoy the extent of electron sharing that celebrates metallurgical union. But in either case, problems may arise when the clad component is heated or cooled because of the different coefficients of thermal expansion that each suffers. At first blush, this might appear to be the sort of problem that any final year engineering student might solve. But it is more complex; there are residual stresses in cladding and substrate, whose extent is probably not known and whose changes during fabrication defy computation. One has to try it out.

An apparently topsy-turvy application of cladding is found in what is called the corrosion barrier system. Here, plain-carbon, corrodible steel covers the noble stainless! In chloride environments, stainless is susceptible

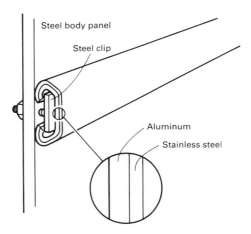

Fig. 7.29 Stainless-steel clad aluminum automotive trim provides sacrificial corrosion protection to the auto body while maintaining a bright corrosion-resistant exterior surface.

to pitting and perforation. If it is clad with mild steel, the mild steel is sacrificially corroded, so diverting the attack on the stainless. This means that, where pitting corrosion may be anticipated, a thin section of stainless may be protected by a cheaper superstrate of mild steel. Figure 7.30 illustrates this dramatically. You may imagine, without stretching too far, that the joining of clad material throws down a challenging gauntlet to welders. So it does; turn to section 8.3.5.

7.9 Abrasive Wear, Fretting, and Galling

There are two circumstances to bear in mind. First, where a stainless steel is the material of choice on account of a corrosive environment but is subjected to

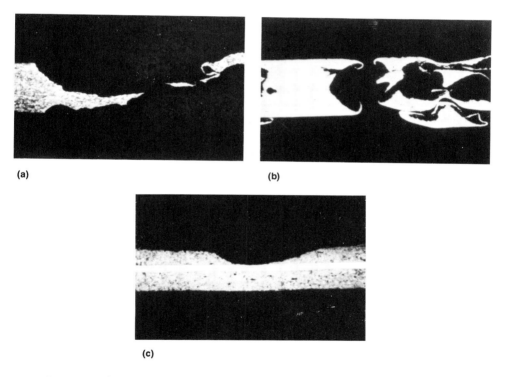

(a) (b)

(c)

Fig. 7.30 Photomicrographs of cross sections of materials after 18 months of immersion in seawater at Duxbury, MA. (a) Low-carbon steel. (b) Type 304 stainless steel. (c) Carbon-steel-clad type 304 stainless steel

surface attack by one or the other of several processes of wear. Second, where by the nature of its own wear-resistant properties, a stainless steel is the selected material. Because most stainless steels are not considered to have especially good wear resistance, the second of these possibilities can be quickly discussed.

The most normal circumstance that leads to the selection of a stainless steel due to its wear resistance is where the abrasion is comparatively light. Here, the surface is not damaged by gouging, and its good slidability (the word is accepted in tribological circles, so it's good enough for us) encourages the easy discharge of material from hoppers and chutes and conveyors. This improvement in efficiency—faster discharge, with no lodged material to make the return trip—has led to the substitution of stainless for plain-carbon or low-alloy steel, whose rust impedes flow. Both ferritic and austenitic steels are used.

When the transported material is carried as a slurry, the advantages of stainless become more apparent (Fig. 7.31). The "Hub test" on which the results are based, is a procedure by which samples—spokes on a hub—rotate through the slurry.

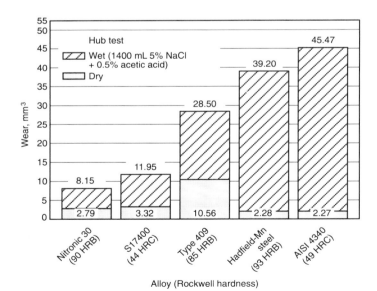

Fig. 7.31 Abrasive wear of alloy and stainless steels under dry and wet corrosive conditions

Table 7.14   Threshold galling stress results for selected self-mated stainless steels

Stainless steel	Condition	Rockwell hardness	Threshold galling stress	
			MPa	ksi
Austenitic				
S20161	Annealed	95 HRB	104(a)	15(a)
S21800	Annealed	92 HRB	104(a)	15(a)
S28200	Annealed	96 HRB	166	24
S28200	Cold drawn	35 HRC	62	9
S20910	Annealed	97 HRB	35	5
S20900	Annealed	96 HRB	48	7
S24100	Annealed	23 HRC	97	14
S30430	Annealed	74 HRB	35	5
Type 304	Annealed	86 HRB	55	8
Type 304	Cold drawn	27 HRC	17	2.5
Type 316	Annealed	82 HRB	48	7
Type 316	Cold drawn	27 HRC	35	5
Type 303	Annealed	85 HRB	138	20
Type 201	Annealed	95 HRB	104	15
N08020	Annealed	87 HRB	14	2
Martensitic				
S42010	Tempered at 204 °C (400 °F)	50 HRC	104(a)	15(a)
S42010	Tempered at 260 °C (500 °F)	47 HRC	62	9
Type 410	Annealed	87 HRB	7	1
Type 410	Tempered at 260 °C (500 °F)	43 HRC	21	3
Type 416	Annealed	95 HRB	21	3
Type 416	Tempered at 316 °C (600 °F)	37 HRC	62	9
Type 416	Tempered at 538 °C (1000 °F)	32 HRC	42	6
Type 420	Tempered at 204 °C (400 °F)	51 HRC	25	18
Type 420	Tempered at 260 °C (500 °F)	49 HRC	55	8
Type 440C	Tempered at 260 °C (500 °F)	55 HRC	125	18
Precipitation hardenable				
S45500	Aged at 510 °C (950 °F)	48 HRC	90	13
S45500	Aged at 566 °C (1050 °F)	43 HRC	59	8.5
S45500	Aged at 621 °C (1150 °F)	36 HRC	28	4
S45000	Annealed	29 HRC	69	10
S45000	Aged at 480 °C (895 °F)	43 HRC	55	8
S45000	Aged at 566 °C (1050 °F)	38 HRC	17	2.5
S45000	Aged at 621 °C (1150 °F)	33 HRC	14	2
S17400	Aged at 480 °C (895 °F)	45 HRC	69	10
S17400	Aged at 621 °C (1150 °F)	34 HRC	35	5
S13800	Aged at 538 °C (1000 °F)	46 HRC	21	3
S66286	Aged at 718 °C (1325 °F)	30 HRC	14	2
Ferritic and duplex				
S18200	Cold drawn	98 HRB	35	5
Type 430F	Annealed	92 HRB	14	2
Type 430	Cold drawn	98 HRB	10	1.5
Type 329	Annealed	25 HRC	7	1

Note: Based on button-on-block test, ASTM G 98, unlubricated ground finish. (a) Did not gall

Abrasion so severe that hard particles cut through the surface is best resisted by a yet harder material, (martensitic or surface-hardened grades). Although the austenitic grades work harden, that is insufficient to resist the gouging of sharp, heavily loaded particles.

The cases of wear that we have just touched upon have to do with external particles impinging on or rubbing against the metal. We now turn to situations in which the wear is self-imposed.

7.9.1 Fretting

Leading to wear, fretting involves the oscillation at small amplitudes between two contacting surfaces. Examples are when riveted joints vibrate or when strands of wire cable move against each other. Very small bits of detached metal or oxide continually abrade the metal surface. We will mention qualitatively (quantifying them is just too complex) some of the influential factors: load, amplitude, frequency, and the corrosivity and temperature of the environment.

While fretting leads to a reduction of the load-carrying section, it is more devastating when it leads to such high surface stresses that a fatigue crack may be initiated—usually where it can't be seen. Corrosive environments are inducive. Where lubrication is possible, it should be applied. This is not always allowable, and where allowable, is frequently inadequate because the fretting surfaces are not reached by the lubricant.

7.9.2 Galling

Especially aggravating is galling—as, indeed, the name itself suggests. It arises when two metal surfaces in tight contact resist sliding against each other. It is an extreme case of what is called "adhesive wear." After all, if two metallic surfaces are tightly clamped against each other, each will diffuse into the other. Something of the sort happens even in a short time frame, in very localized contact points. As relative movement is demanded of the surfaces, bits of metal are pulled out, the one from the other. The assembly probably seizes up.

Resistance to galling is greater in work-hardenable materials, which favors the austenitic stainless steels. Less ductile materials do not gall as much, because bits of metal break away to cause some scoring (but no deep damage) or possible seizure. Much more important is careful design: the correct tolerances, load distribution, and access of lubricants (where allowed).

Both very highly polished surfaces and comparatively rough surfaces have been found to encourage galling. The former encourages galling because there are no troughs between the ridges in which the debris may innocuously collect; the latter because hills and hollows interlock. Or so it is surmised.

The "threshold galling stress" is a measure of galling resistance between two metals. The greater the threshold is, the better the galling resistance. Table 7.14 gives values for many stainless steels in unashamed contact with themselves.

Fabrication of Stainless Steels

8.1 Introduction

Here we describe the common methods of fabrication. In an arguable order of their most frequent applications, these are cutting, joining, cold forming, machining, finishing, hot forming, and powder processing. We assume that the fabricator is supplied with a mill product—for example, plate or sheet or rod—or a casting from the foundry. This must be shaped into a structure (a building, a pipe, a valve) or a retail article (a kitchen sink or cutlery). The person we are addressing here is not the steel-mill operator or foundryman whose function is to provide the starting material that the fabricator shapes.

The fabricator is also responsible for heat treatment. We discussed the development of properties in the principal classes of stainless steels in Chapter 7, following a description of the general principles and definitions of heat treatment in Chapter 3. The special requirements of surface treatments are touched on in this chapter. Although much more can be written about heat treatment, we content ourselves in this chapter by very briefly describing heat treatment facilities required by the fabricator.

8.2 Cutting

8.2.1 Mechanical Cutting

Section 8.6 deals with the surface cutting that occurs during shaping by turning and milling. In this section we are concerned with making cuts that sever plate and sheet. Bandsaws, with high-speed blades, or abrasive cutting wheels are used for small custom jobs. Production lines generally prefer shearing, where a straight cut is made—as by a guillotine—and blanking, where a punch and die assembly makes a hole in the metal. In both cases, the metal is cut by the shearing action of a moving edge.

Ferritic stainless steels shear in a similar way to plain-carbon steels; that is, after the blade has penetrated about half the thickness, the rest of the metal shears of its own accord. Austenitic steels work harden to a greater extent, and so the moving edge must be taken substantially through the metal thickness. Further, due to work hardening, between 50 and 100% more force is required for a given cut. This can be minimized by the appropriate adjustment of clearance and shear angle (we recommend you refer to a specialized text) and by warming the steel to approximately 175 °C (345 °F). This modest heating also will reduce chipping in the more brittle ferritic steels.

8.2.2 Thermal Cutting

Thermal cutting by conventional oxyacetylene torch is not suitable for stainless steels. The exothermic reaction induced by the oxygen produces chromic oxide, which has a high melting temperature, lengthens the cutting time and consequently creates problems in the heat-affected zone (HAZ). (These are the sorts of difficulties that we describe in Chapter 7 and that we discuss more specifically as we describe welding processes.) However, the injection of fine iron powder into the oxyacetylene stream substantially reduces the cutting time. The edge produced in this way is not as clean as a sheared edge and is generally ground back; this also removes the regions where carbides might have precipitated or where hardening has occurred.

8.2.3 Air Carbon-Arc Cutting

The air carbon-arc cutting process, where a high-velocity stream of air removes the melted metal behind the arc, also requires subsequent dressing. The method is more often used for gouging the backside of welds and for cutting irregular shapes.

8.2.4 Plasma-Arc Cutting

Plasma-arc cutting directs gas through an electric arc formed between a tungsten electrode and the work surface. The gas becomes ionized (that is, it forms "plasma") and generates a high temperature (as high as 30,000 °C, or 54,000 °F) as the positively charged ions combine with electrons at the metal surface. Of the possible plasma gases, helium is probably best, but it is the most expensive. Argon is easily ionized but has a low thermal conductivity and is generally mixed with 5 to 15% hydrogen. Cutting is rapid and gives a regular edge that can be wire-brush cleaned. (A noncontaminating wire brush, please!)

8.2.5 Electron Beam and Laser Beam Cutting

These procedures are generally restricted to thin sections, where dimensional precision is important. Laser beam techniques, for instance, are used to drill very fine holes.

8.3 Joining

Fusion arc welding is the most frequently used method of joining stainless steels, and it is therefore treated more comprehensively than other methods. However, alternative methods of welding and, indeed, other methods of fastening have their important applications.

8.3.1 Metal Fasteners

Metal fasteners—studs, rivets, nuts, and bolts of many forms and styles—are available in a range of stainless steels. Assuming that mechanical requirements are fulfilled, the matter of corrosion tolerance must be considered. Assuming that the best choice of stainless has been made, clean, tight joints are essential if pitting, crevice corrosion, and fretting are to be minimized.

8.3.2 Adhesive Bonding

Adhesive bonding has become much more common since the publication of earlier versions of this book. Compared to metal fasteners, an adhesive joint transmits load more uniformly and completely between the two members. Compared to a fusion weld, metal-adhesive bonding forces are comparatively weak, and the adhesive itself does not possess the strength of the base metal. Integrating these characteristics, one can appreciate that if, for example, two sheets of stainless were to be joined across their entire area, an adhesively bonded laminate could offer more resistance to their being pulled apart than would a spot-welded or riveted assembly. On the other hand, for a simple, nonflanged butt-joint subjected to tensile loading, adhesive bonding is not a prime candidate.

Where adhesives are used in place of metal fasteners, there are additional advantages because corrodents cannot seep between the mating surfaces, and exterior surfaces are not marred by the protrusions of rivet or bolt heads or by the dimples of spot welds. Because stress concentrations are avoided, fatigue life is superior, and damping capacity is reported to be enhanced.

Thermosetting resins are used as adhesives (these do not revert to liquid when they are heated), and they are resistant to many solvents and acids although they may deteriorate in the long term. The use of any adhesive requires careful surface preparation; when anaerobic adhesives are used, as is sometimes the case, a primer is needed.

8.3.3 Brazing

Brazing shares an advantage with adhesive bonding in its ability to join stainless to a dissimilar metal which would not produce a satisfactory weldment. With carbon steels, for example, alloy diffusion across a weld produces a spectrum of compositions that is difficult to accommodate by any heat treatment. Welding to copper alloys creates compositions that are prone to corrode and crack.

By definition (an arbitrary one, as so many are), brazing is a process that uses a filler metal that is completely molten above 450 °C (840 °F) but, one need hardly say, melts below the melting temperature of the materials to be joined.

In brazing stainless steels, temperatures are reached at which austenitic grades may become sensitized. Martensitic grades may become hardened near to the join and softened, through tempering, further away.

Difficulties in making a good join arise because of that important protective oxide film, which is even more anxious to form at elevated temperatures. It prevents the brazing alloy from "wetting" and bonding with the steel. In furnace brazing, a preliminary cleaning of the stainless is of little help unless subsequent oxidation is prevented when the work is heated to brazing temperature. Consequently, the furnace atmosphere should be inert. Alternatively, if the steel is not cleaned initially, heating to brazing temperature in a reducing atmosphere—usually rich in hydrogen—will get rid of the oxide. When brazing is done by torch, neither of these procedures is appropriate; commercially available fluxes are used. After brazing, fluxes should be meticulously cleaned from the assembly.

The range of filler metals is extensive, and a choice depends in the first instance upon whether brazing is to be done in the furnace or by torch, which calls for lower temperature alloys. The most common filler metals are silver-copper-zinc alloys, with other possible additions; other fillers are nickel or copper base. A selection has to take into account not only the melting characteristics of the filler, but its wettability and the extent to which it will affect the properties of the stainless.

8.3.4 Soldering

The dividing line between silver soldering and brazing is indistinct. Soldering, while similar to brazing, requires a lower temperature and produces a weaker joint. Fluxes ensure that the solder can flow and penetrate. While silver solders encroach the range of brazing filler metal compositions, the soft solders, which have a lower melting temperature, are tin rich and generally alloyed with lead.

8.3.5 Welding: A Distinction and Its Categories

Brazing and soldering involve the diffusion of atoms of a nonferrous filler metal into the pieces surrounding it at a temperature significantly below the melting temperature of the steel. Tensile and shear strengths at a middle location in the cross section of the join are not much better than those of the comparatively weak filler. In welding, if a filler is added, it has comparable properties to the base materials and almost always has a similar composition to the base. While welding does not require the base metal to reach melting temperature, such a temperature is either attained or approached in practical welding operations.

The principal welding methods used for joining stainless steels may be divided into three classes that depend upon the way in which heat is transferred to, or generated in, the workpiece: (a) electric resistance, (b) radiation transfer—electron beam or laser, and (c) electric arc.

Of these, the electric arc is the most common. We deal with its major variants last, followed by a section on weldability, which has to do with the facility with which stainless weldments can be made in the different classes of stainless (including clad steel) and their performance. Although this is directed to electric arc weldments, it is applicable to the other welding categories.

8.3.6 Electric Resistance Welding

Electric resistance welding is used on production items, for it is not economical in the short run. The principal is simple enough: two pieces of heated metal are forged together, as a blacksmith might have done years ago. However, the heat is not supplied in the smithy forge but by the resistance of the two mating surfaces to an electric current passed through them.

In seam welding, the mating edges or their overlap runs continuously beneath an electrode in the form of a rotating wheel that supplies the power and possibly the forging pressure. Alternatively, an adjacent induction coil may generate eddy-current heat in the assembly while pressure is applied. In spot welding, the mating pieces are pressed between electrodes that simultaneously provide the necessary electric current.

Advantages of electric resistance welding accrue because stainless has good forgeability, high electrical resistance, and low thermal conductivity. There is no filler metal; hence, associated problems with galvanic corrosion are avoided.

8.3.7 Radiation Transfer—Electron Beam Welding

Here, the kinetic energy of an intense electron stream bombarded onto the workpiece is converted into heat in a highly focused region. Because the electrons penetrate deeply, melting is not restricted by conduction from the surface; consequently, a deep, narrow weld with minimal HAZ results. The effectiveness of the electron beam requires that it be transmitted through a vacuum. However, at the expense of less penetration and a wider weld bead (but with a saving in the cost of producing and maintaining high vacuums), electron beam welding is increasingly used in less rigorous conditions. The electron beam may, in fact, be directed for short distances through a gas atmosphere outside the vacuum chamber.

The process makes welds of very high quality, and the intensity of its heat not only minimizes the width of the fusion zone and the associated HAZ but also lessens distortion. The other side of the coin tells of vacuum chambers (and the restrictions they impose) or of some compromise of quality if they are not fully implemented.

8.3.8 Radiation Transfer—Laser Welding

The light from a laser beam is so intense that it melts any opaque substance, although it will pass through optically transparent materials. The object that the light beam is meant to weld can be inaccessible to us and to our conventional welding equipment, but as long as the beam can "see" it, a weld can be made.

The beam is focused through an argon shielded nozzle, but no vacuum chamber is required for the workpiece. Heating is so intense that there is virtually no HAZ, and the steel can be contained by glass or plastic.

Because penetration is limited, laser welding techniques have been most successful in, for instance, joining wire and spot welding foil and thin sheet.

8.3.9 Electric Arc Welding

The common feature of the five arc processes that we briefly describe is an arc struck between an electrode and the job, generating heat that will fuse together the pieces of parent metal, usually with the addition of filler metal. This forms a small casting—the weld bead—that joins the components. Inevitably, the metallurgical structure of the region adjacent to the weld, the HAZ, is influenced by its temperature gradient.

A common prejudice might suggest that the properties of the weld bead, because it is cast, are inferior to those of the parent metal. This is not necessarily so! For a given grain size and constitution, the properties of a casting and a forging are equivalent. If the weld bead is dirty or cracked, its properties will be correspondingly unsatisfactory. The same goes for a forging.

Because many welds are made with multiple passes, the structure of prior deposits is likely to be affected by the heat generated by subsequent ones. This is the case in plain carbon steels, low alloy steels, and martensitic stainless steels, where grain refinement occurs as a result of transformation during cooling. Such refinement resulting from successive passes is shown in Fig. 8.1. But this is not the case in ferritic and austenitic steels; here, the cast structure of the weld bead as laid down persists. It is important, therefore, to avoid excessive grain growth because this cannot be corrected except by cold work, which is generally out of the question.

The five arc-welding processes we review are (a) shielded metal-arc welding (SMAW), (b) submerged-arc welding (SAW), (c) gas tungsten-arc welding (GTAW) or tungsten-inert gas welding (TIG), (d) gas-metal arc welding (GMAW) or metal inert-gas welding (MIG), and (e) plasma-arc welding (PAW).

8.3.10 Shielded Metal-Arc Welding (SMAW)

This welding process is generally used in the field or when continuous processes are not practicable. The arc is struck between the workpiece and a clamped electrode held by the welder. The heat of the arc melts the edges of the parent metal to form an integral casting with the filler metal supplied by the electrode.

The electrode is coated with flux, which has several functions. Flux reacts with impurities from the molten metal to form a protective slag. Because it burns off more slowly than the metal of the electrode, it creates a cup, which shields the arc from the atmosphere. Protective gases are generated around the weld pool. These functions are illustrated in Fig. 8.2. If necessary, the coating can be the source of alloying elements.

8.3.11 Submerged-Arc Welding (SAW)

Submerged-arc welding is for continuous operation. The electrode is bare wire supplying the welding current. Granulated flux is separately fed into the region of the joint, beneath which the arc is struck (Fig. 8.3). Although restricted to flat and horizontal positions, this method allows a very high heat input and rapid welding speeds. A careful balance between the composition of the wire and the flux with respect to the stainless steels being welded is critically important but too complex for us to analyze here.

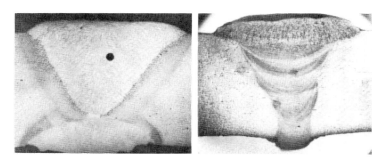

Fig. 8.1 Structure of weld bead in mild steel. Left, as cast structure. (Round black mark is a hardness indentation.) Right, refinement in structure with successive passes in multipass welding. 2.5×. Source: A. Hanson and J. Gordon Parr, *The Engineer's Guide to Steel*, Addison-Wesley, 1965

8.3.12 Gas Tungsten-Arc Welding (GTAW) or (TIG)

There are no fluxes here! In GTAW, the arc is struck between a nonconsumable tungsten electrode. A filler may be introduced manually (Fig. 8.4), and all is surrounded by inert gas, usually argon. Higher deposition rates can be attained if the filler is introduced as heated wire (Fig. 8.5).

8.3.13 Gas-Metal Arc Welding (GMAW)

Gas-metal arc welding or metal inert-gas welding is the most frequently used method, especially in production runs. The tungsten electrode of the previous system (GTAW) is replaced by a consumable electrode of the filler metal (see Fig. 8.6). It is faster than GTAW and is suited to production runs. Among variants of the process, one, with wire of very small diameter, is used for welding thin stainless sheet.

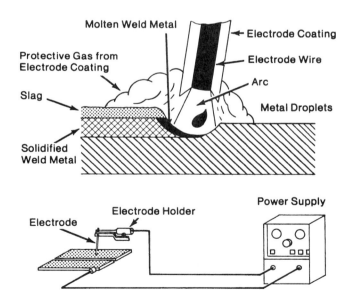

Fig. 8.2 Arc zone in shielded metal-arc welding. Courtesy of American Iron and Steel Institute and Nickel Development Institute

8.3.14 Plasma-Arc Welding (PAW)

Figure 8.7 illustrates the setup. With a tungsten electrode and no filler metal, square butt joints (up to almost 1 cm thick) can be welded with no shaping and no filler. Penetration is uniform, and as long as the underside is protected with inert gas, backing bar requirements are minimal. The process is often used for longitudinal welding of formed stainless tubing.

The usual gas for both shielding and orifice is argon, whose conductivity may be increased by additions of up to 15% hydrogen for some categories of stainless.

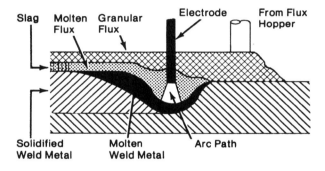

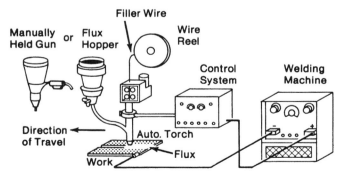

Fig. 8.3 Principle of submerged-arc welding. Courtesy of American Iron and Steel Institute and Nickel Development Institute

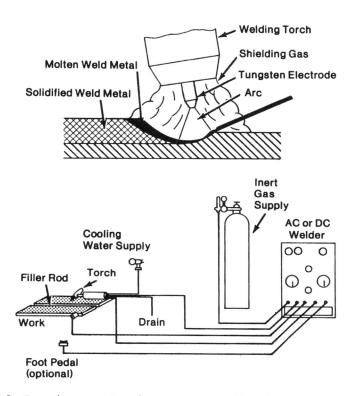

Fig. 8.4 General representation of gas tungsten-arc welding. Courtesy of American Iron and Steel Institute and Nickel Development Institute

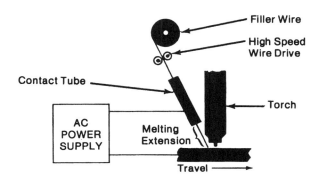

Fig. 8.5 Schematic diagram of gas tungsten-arc welding hot-wire welding system. Courtesy of American Iron and Steel Institute and Nickel Development Institute

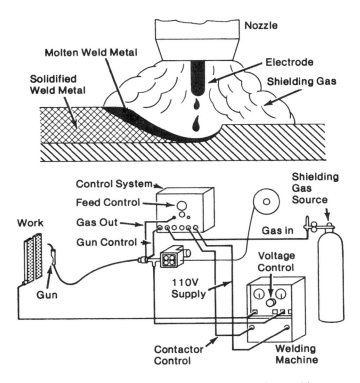

Fig. 8.6 Schematic diagram of basic components of gas-metal arc welding process. Courtesy of American Iron and Steel Institute and Nickel Development Institute

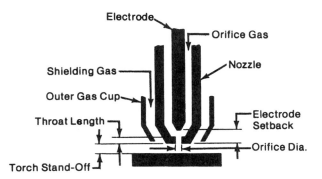

Fig. 8.7 Terms used with the plasma-arc welding torch. Courtesy of American Iron and Steel Institute and Nickel Development Institute

8.4 Weldability

All stainless steels can be welded by one or more of the methods just reviewed. Questions arise about the best way in which each of the principal classes of stainless steel should be handled, the major difficulties that may occur, and the anticipated performance in service.

Because the thermal conductivity of stainless steels is about one-half that of plain carbon and low-alloy steels, heat is dissipated more slowly from the weld region. This has to be accommodated by welding techniques involving welding current, chill bars, fixtures, and joint design. Important in any weld, but particularly so in stainless, is the cleanliness of the joint. Oil, grease, and fragments of steel from carbon steel files and brushes will lead to carbon pickup in the weldment. Following welding, the work must be thoroughly cleaned of fluxes and spatter, and irregular surfaces should be ground and buffed.

The constitution of the weldment from parent metal through HAZ, and from fusion zone to weld bead, can be derived from the Schaeffler diagram (see Fig. 7.2). The diagram has its shortcomings, and as mentioned in section 7.5, a variation is required for the manganese-nitrogen austenitic class. Although other diagrams are prescribed for particular purposes, the Schaeffler diagram offers a good guide.

8.4.1 Ferritic Stainless Steels

Ferritic stainless steels can be welded by any of the processes described. As noted in section 7.2 where the ferritic stainless steels are categorized in three groups, one of the drawbacks of the first generation of alloys was poor weldability. The second generation of ferritic steels (made available through steelmaking practices that can limit carbon and nitrogen to low levels) overcame that problem to a considerable extent. Sensitization is mitigated, and grain growth is restrained. Ferrite stabilizers ensure that martensite will not be formed during cooling. This grade, with a composition based upon 12% chromium and a very low carbon content, is readily resistance welded to form parts of automotive exhaust systems, which are described in section 11.3.1.

If fusion welding calls for filler metal, a choice has to be made between using an electrode of similar composition or an austenitic filler. The latter method gives welds that are more ductile and tough, but intermediate compositions are formed in the fusion zone and the HAZ, which may create constitutions that are hardened or less corrosion resistant. Differing coefficients of expansion may create problems, too.

The heat treatments that minimize embrittlement in ferritic stainless steels are described in section 7.2. These may be applied as postheat treatments to weldments.

8.4.2 Martensitic Stainless Steels

Although martensitic stainless may be welded in any heat treated condition—annealed or hardened—it will become martensitic in the HAZ, with the attendant possibility of cracking. This may be offset by preheating because the subsequent cooling rate is reduced, but some martensite probably will be produced. In that case, postheating is required. This may be either a tempering process or a very slow cool from a higher, austenitizing temperature. Depending on the shape, size, and location of the job, it is possible that neither of these methods can be of value beyond the pages of a textbook.

Filler metal for martensitic welds may be of identical composition to the parent metal, but austenitic beads are commonly laid down. They are not as strong but are more ductile than the surrounding metal.

8.4.3 Austenitic Stainless Steels

One of the reasons for the popularity of the austenitic steels is their weldability, against which the first generation of ferritics could not compete. (The second generation of ferritics, whose weldability is so much improved, must contend with that earlier reputation.)

While weldments are made readily by all processes, precautions must be taken to avoid those problems to which we alluded in section 7.4. Of these, the most significant is sensitization (see section 7.4.2). The problem is mitigated by the use of extra-low carbon grades, by compositions that contain stabilizers, and by avoidance of the critical range, whose limits depend upon the carbon content. Figure 8.8 illustrates this point and shows that at very low carbon contents sensitization will not occur during the time associated with welding.

If carbide formation is suspected, then heating above the sensitizing range will take carbides into solution, and rapid cooling will avoid their reformation. This heat treatment also effects a stress relief, which is to be recommended if the part is to be used in an environment where stress-corrosion cracking is possible. (When clad stainless, which is generally austenitic, is used in pressure vessels, such a stress relief is often mandatory.)

A phenomenon known as knife-line attack can occur in corrosive environments in the parent metal very close to the weld bead in stabilized austenitic grades. It is another version of chromium depletion, which goes something like the following. The stabilizing carbides of titanium and niobium (perhaps with tantalum) are redissolved in a region close to the weld bead that reaches temperatures above 1150 °C (2100 °F). During cooling through their formation temperature range of 1150 to 870 °C (2100 to 1600 °F), these carbides do not have the opportunity to be completely reestablished. Consequently, some carbon remains in solid solution to join up with chromium as the region subsequently passes through that critical range of chromium carbide formation, 815 to 480 °C (1500 to 900 °F). Furthermore, if there are subsequent welding passes, these will create that temperature at which chromium carbides form. In either event, there is a narrow band in which chromium depletion permits corrosive attack.

Although intergranular, the corrosive attack is so confined to a small region that the resulting crack is called knife-line. Not a frequent occur-

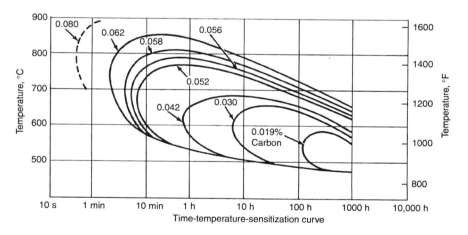

Fig. 8.8 Time required for formation of carbide precipitation in stainless steels with various carbon contents. Carbide precipitation forms in the areas to the right of the various carbon-content curves. Within time-periods applicable to welding, chromium-nickel stainless steels with 0.05% carbon would be quite free from grain boundary precipitation. Courtesy of American Iron and Steel Institute and Nickel Development Institute

rence, this can be avoided by reheating the weldment to redissolve the carbides and allowing titanium, niobium, and tantalum carbides to form during subsequent cooling, which is slower than that which the weldment originally experienced. It is not observed in the nonstabilized low-carbon grades. Almost certainly its mechanism is more complex than the simple rationalization offered.

Austenitic weldments have occasionally been troubled by cracks that can occur immediately after welding in the bead itself or in the HAZ of earlier passes. This may be avoided by choosing a filler in which small amounts of ferrite are formed. Such a solution may not please corrosion engineers, and if the ferrite is too dominant, sigma phase may form with consequent embrittlement.

8.4.4 Precipitation-Hardening Stainless Steels

During fusion welding, the most easily oxidizable elements, aluminum and titanium, must be protected by using inert gas methods, and unnecessarily high welding temperatures should be avoided.

If the steel is martensitic and in a hardened condition, the HAZ will inevitably include softened (overaged) regions. Consequently postweld treatments to reharden the structure are necessary if the original properties are to be restored.

8.4.5 Duplex Stainless Steels

Duplex stainless steels can present excellent weldments, but they are not (as the saying goes) as "forgiving" as are austenitic stainless steels. Obviously they cannot be! Their constitution and properties depend on a delicate balance of chemistry and heat treatment that is easily upset by any welding process.

Duplex stainless steels may be used in the as-welded condition as long as the carbon content is low and the nitrogen level is maintained at the balanced amounts, which are indicated in Table 7.13. Welds where filler metal is not used may become overrich in ferrite because of their rapid cooling. This may be offset by nitrogen additions to the shielding gas. Where filler metal is used, the electrodes are appropriately enriched in nickel and nitrogen. In either case, however, the ferrite content of the HAZ may increase as a result of its rapid cooling cycle. If this occurs, then postwelding heat treatment may be required. (If postweld heat treatment is required, then the filler metal might just as well be of the same composition as the parent metal.)

This all sounds dauntingly complex. In fact, excellent welds in duplex stainless steels can be made by all welding processes as long as the underlying principle is respected: by heat treatment and/or the selection of filler metal, the constitution balance of ferrite/austenite is maintained in both the fusion zone and the HAZ.

8.4.6 Stainless-Clad Plain Carbon Steels

The trick here is to avoid producing an alloy on the stainless side of the composite that is less than stainless. Two methods are generally used. The first method, which is more economical, is illustrated in Fig. 8.9. The groove in the carbon steel does not reach the stainless cladding. Alternatively, the filler may be entirely of stainless steel (see Fig. 8.10).

In both methods (and there are others), precautions should be taken to minimize the extent of diffusion that might create highly hardenable alloy

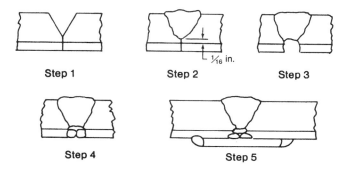

Fig. 8.9 Joint design for stainless-clad steel plate employing stainless steel weld metal only in portion where stainless steel cladding is removed for fabrication. Step 1: Tight fit-up is desirable. Point of groove should be 1/16 in. (min) above the stainless steel cladding. Step 2: Deposit carbon steel weld from carbon steel side. First pass should be deposited with a low-hydrogen type electrode to minimize possibility of cracking in the event that penetration accidentally reaches cladding. Penetration should not extend beyond 1/16 in. from cladding. Step 3: Gouge from stainless steel side until sound carbon-steel weld metal has been reached. Do not gouge deeper than necessary. Step 4: Deposit stainless steel weld metal to fill groove resulting from gouging operation. Step 5: Some plants require for severely corrosive services that a strip of stainless steel of the same composition as the cladding be fillet welded to cladding to cover the weld. Courtesy of American Iron and Steel Institute and Nickel Development Institute

compositions that would crack during cooling. Penetration should be held to a minimum. Generally, a first stringer bead of high alloy content (25% chromium, 20% nickel) is laid down with as little heat input as possible.

8.5 Cold Forming

Although in an age of space travel there are more spectacular examples of metal forming, the kitchen provides a wonderful example of metallurgical skill—the double sink. Here the appropriate alloy and sophisticated press and die design combine to mass-produce from a flat sheet of stainless a deep-drawn shape of remarkable dimensional ratios, immaculate surface, and lasting quality. Think about this when you do the dishes; it is more stimulating than grumbling that the dishwasher has broken down.

Deep drawing is but one method of cold forming, albeit a dominant one. It is an extreme form of press forming. To the extent that a differentiation may be made, in press forming the sheet is firmly clamped while a punch pushes the metal into the contours of the die. In deep drawing, the unanchored sheet is allowed to flow. Figures 8.11(a) and (b) give an impression of the distinction.

There are other cold-forming operations. Sheet is bent by press brake or by rolls commonly used in the manufacture of tube and pipe. It may be spun where a rotating sheet of metal is drawn over a die by a free-rolling tool. In all cases, highly polished tools and dies are used to avoid galling and metal pickup. Lubricants are carefully selected, and especially if the shape is to be annealed between forming operations, it must be thoroughly cleaned. The grain size for optimum formability is medium to fine.

Bar, rod, and wire are cold formed, too. Bar may be swaged and extruded, rod may be drawn to wire, and wire may be cold headed to make nails and rivets.

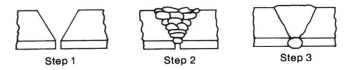

Step 1	Step 2	Step 3

Fig. 8.10 Common method of joining stainless clad steel plate employing weld consisting entirely of stainless steel. Step 1: Bevel and fit up as shown. Step 2: Deposit stainless steel weld from carbon steel side. Step 3: Clean root of weld to remove slag or oxide. Gouge if necessary. Deposit weld with electrode type normally used to weld cladding composition. Courtesy of American Iron and Steel Institute and Nickel Development Institute

In all cold forming operations, the phenomenon of springback must be accommodated in meeting dimensional tolerances. This is always important, especially in materials that work harden significantly as austenitic stainless steels do because of their transformation to martensite.

Springback arises because a plastically bent shape suffers tension stresses on one side of its neutral axis and compression stresses on the other. When the deforming force of the press or rolls is removed, the remaining elastic stresses in the workpiece reveal themselves, pulling the metal on the tension side and pushing it back on the compression side. Consequently, the piece partially returns to its original shape; this is springback. Try it with a paperclip. You might like to see what happens when you vary the amount of bending and the radius around which you bend the clip. Precise calculations of springback are difficult and depend on the method of bending, for instance, whether the material is stretched as it is bent. Compositional and dimensional irregularities add to the fun.

8.5.1 Ferritic Stainless Steel Sheet

Because they have a higher yield strength than mild steel does, the ferritic stainless steels require more power in the forming process. More important, during cold working the yield strength converges rapidly upon the ultimate tensile strength, which of course represents the point at which the steel will rupture. This lack of ductility compared to the that of the austenitic class can call for more intermediate annealing, a requirement that becomes more important as the chromium content of the steels increases.

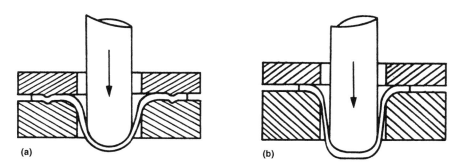

(a)   (b)

Fig. 8.11 (a) Press forming and (b) deep drawing. Courtesy of *Stainless Steels*, P. Lacombe, B. Baroux, and G. Béranger, Ed., Les Editions de Physique Les Ulis

With this precaution, the ferritics are readily formed even by deep-drawing to almost the same extent as the austenitics, especially if they and the punch and die assembly are warmed to approximately 150 °C (300 °F). This modest amount of heat reduces the chances of brittle failure, whose occurrence can also be minimized by reducing the speed at which the punch load is applied.

8.5.2 Austenitic Stainless Steel Sheet

Compared to the ferritics, these are tougher and work harden more, characteristics that increase as the nickel level decreases. Therefore, for the greatest advantage of work hardening and consequent strengthening, a grade such as 301 is used; for a lower rate of work hardening, type 304 is a more likely choice; and (as shown in section 7.4.5) the higher nickel content of 305 is beneficial in deep-drawing operations.

Because both yield strength and ultimate tensile strength increase appreciably with cold work, a more substantial single forming operation can be tolerated by austenitic stainless steels than by the ferritics. And among the austenitics, the most rapidly work-hardening grades (lowest nickel) are best in this respect.

The higher strength of the 200 series austenitic stainless steels calls for more power and leads to greater springback. However, the formabilities of the 300 and 200 series are much the same.

8.5.3 Duplex Stainless Steel Sheet

Bear in mind that the yield strength of duplex stainless steel sheet is almost twice that of the austenitic steels, while other mechanical properties—toughness, ductility, and work hardening—fall between the two constituents on which the duplex steels are based. We appreciate at once the greater power required in forming and the intermediacy of those properties that determine formability.

8.5.4 Precipitation-Hardening Stainless Steel Sheet

Best cold forming is realized if the sheet is in its softest, solution-annealed condition. Following shaping, it should be solution treated, quenched, and aged.

8.5.5 Lubricants

The importance of lubricants in cold forming is self-evident. But any review that differentiates between their relative merits would presuppose a much more detailed account than that given the forming processes themselves. However, Table 8.1 provides some notion of which lubricants are used for particular forming processes.

8.5.6 Formability Ratings

A summary of the formability ratings for the most commonly used stainless steel grades is given in Table 8.2 to conclude this section on cold forming.

Table 8.1   Suitability of various lubricants for use in the forming of stainless steel

Ratings consider effectiveness, cleanliness, ease of removal, and other suitability factors. A, excellent; B, good; C, acceptable; NR, not recommended

Lubricant	Blanking and piercing	Press- brake forming	Press forming	Multiple- slide forming	Deep drawing	Spinning	Drop- hammer forming	Contour roll forming	Embossing
Fatty oils and blends(a)	C	B	C	A	C	A	C	B	B
Soap-fat pastes(b)	NR	NR	C	A	B	B	C	B	C
Wax-base pastes(b)	B	B	B	A	B	B	C	B	A
Heavy-duty emulsions(c)	B	NR	B	A	B	B	NR	A	B
Dry film (wax, or soap plus borax)	B	B	B	NR	B	A	B	NR	A
Pigmented pastes(b)(d)	B	NR	A	B	A	C	NR	NR	NR
Sulfurized or sulfochlori- nated oils(e)	A	A	B+	A	C	NR	A	B	A
Chlorinated oils or waxes(f)									
High-viscosity types(g)	A(h)	NR	A	NR	A	NR	A(i)	A	NR
Low-viscosity types(j)	B+	A	A	A	B	NR	A(i)	A	A
Graphite or molybdenum disulfide(k)	NR	(l)	(l)	NR	(l)	NR	(l)	NR	NR

(a) Vegetable or animal types; mineral oil is used for blending. (b) May be diluted with water. (c) Water emulsions of soluble oils; contain a high concentration of extreme-pressure sulfur or chlorine compounds. (d) Chalk (whiting) is commonest pigment: others sometimes used. (e) Extreme-pressure types; may contain some mineral or fatty oil. (f) Extreme-pressure chlorinated mineral oils or waxes; may contain emulsifiers for ease of removal in water-base cleaners. (g) Viscosity of 4000 to 20,000 SUS (Saybolt Universal seconds, see ASTM D 2161 for more detailed information). (h) For heavy plate. (i) For cold forming only. (j) Viscosity (200 to 1000 SUS) is influenced by base oil or wax, degree of chlorination, and additions of mineral oil. (k) Solid lubricant applied from dispersions in oil, solvent, or water. (l) For hot-forming applications only

8.6 Machining

Conventional machining operations remove metal by means of a cutting edge or surface made of hardened steel, carbide, diamond, or possibly ceramic.

Table 8.2 Relative suitability of stainless steels for various methods of forming

Suitability ratings are based on comparison of the steels within any one class; therefore, it should not be inferred that a ferritic steel with an A rating is more formable than an austenitic steel with a C rating for a particular method. A, excellent; B, good; C, fair; D, not generally recommended

Steel	6.89 MPa (1 ksi)	Blanking	Piercing	0.2% yield strength, Suitability for: brake forming	Deep drawing	Spinning	Roll forming	Coining	Embossing
Austenitic steels									
201	55	B	C	B	A-B	C-D	B	B-C	B-C
202	55	B	B	A	A	B-C	A	B	B
301	40	B	C	B	A-B	C-D	B	B-C	B-C
302	37	B	B	A	A	B-C	A	B	B
302B	40	B	B	B	B-C	C	...	C	B-C
303, 303(Se)	35	B	B	D(a)	D	D	D	C-D	C
304	35	B	B	A	A	B	A	B	B
304L	30	B	B	A	A	B	A	B	B
305	37	B	B	A	B	A	A	A-B	A-B
308	35	B	...	B(a)	D	D	...	D	D
309, 309S	40	B	B	A(a)	B	C	B	B	B
310, 310S	40	B	B	A(a)	B	B	A	B	B
314	50	B	B	A(a)	B-C	C	B	B	B-C
316	35	B	B	A(a)	B	B	A	B	B
316L	30	B	B	A(a)	B	B	A	B	B
317	40	B	B	A(a)	B	B-C	B	B	B
321, 347, 348	35	B	B	A	B	B-C	B	B	B
Martensitic steels									
403, 410	40	A	A-B	A	A	A	A	A	A
414	95	A	B	A(a)	B	C	C	B	C
416, 416(Se)	40	B	A-B	C(a)	D	D	D	D	C
420	50	B	B-C	C(a)	C-D	D	C-D	C-D	C
431	95	C-D	C-D	C(a)	C-D	D	C-D	C-D	C-D
440A	60	B-C	...	C(a)	C-D	D	C-D	D	C
440B	62	...	...	...	...	D	...	D	D
440C	65	...	...	...	...	D	...	D	D
Ferritic steels									
405	40	A	A-B	A(a)	A	A	A	A	A
409	38	A	A-B	A(a)	A	A	A	A	A
430	45	A	A-B	A(a)	A-B	A	A	A	A
430F, 430F(Se)	55	B	A-B	B-C(a)	D	D	D	C-D	C
442	...	A	A-B	A(a)	B	B-C	A	B	B
446	50	A	B	A(a)	B-C	C	B	B	B

(a) Severe sharp bends should be avoided.

This section is concerned with the ways in which the metallurgy of stainless steels affects this sort of machining. However, many other specialized techniques are available and have critical, albeit somewhat limited, applications. Abrasive water-jet machining generates no heat and does not affect the constitution of the steel. Chemical and electrochemical processes as well as electric discharge grinding have special applicability in intricate shaping. Electron beam and laser beam machining offer great precision; the cut of a plasma arc (described in an earlier section) is used in turning tough metals. We can only nod our acknowledgment while moving to the more commonly applied methods. In these, the term "machinability" has an omnibus concern for tool life, finish, and productivity, as well as how easily a piece is turned, drilled, milled, threaded, and so on.

The major categories of stainless steel are available in free-machining grades, most of which include either sulfur or selenium in their chemistry. While the presence of refractory oxides can cause tool abrasion, oxides of lower melting temperature can help to promote chip breaking. Lead is nowadays rarely added. Phosphorus can have a marginal effect in austenitic steels containing sulfur or selenium. Neither the precipitation-hardening nor the duplex grades have free-machining members of the family in UNS or AISI designations. However, more machinable precipitation-hardening grades are available as commercial brands. The non-free machining stainless steels are more difficult to machine than plain carbon steels and are tougher and gummier. They tend to seize or gall. The purpose of the machinability additives is to reduce these aggravations. However, in all grades, toughness, cold and hot formability, weldability, and corrosion resistance are generally adversely affected by elements that are added to improve machinability.

We do not deal here with tool technology. However, the shape of the tool, what it's made of, and possibly its coating must be considered in conjunction with the selection of a machinable grade of steel.

8.6.1 Martensitic Stainless Steels

We begin with these not only because they are the easiest to machine (unless they are in the fully hardened condition) but because they offer a yardstick against which the machinability of other alloys can be measured (Fig. 8.12).

The presence of carbides avoids the stickiness experienced in cutting other stainless alloys, and machinability is further improved in AISI 416Se.

Of course, if the alloy is hard, tool wear is appreciable, but the martensitic grades are usually machined in their annealed condition with only fine work done after the ultimate heat treatment.

8.6.2 Ferritic Stainless Steels

The free-machining grades are easiest at the lower chromium levels. At high levels (AISI 446, for example, which contains 23 to 27% chromium), gumminess and stringy chips can present problems.

8.6.3 Austenitic Stainless Steels

Austenitic stainless steels are more difficult to machine—but don't let that put you off, for many people are doing it well and profitably. The austenitics

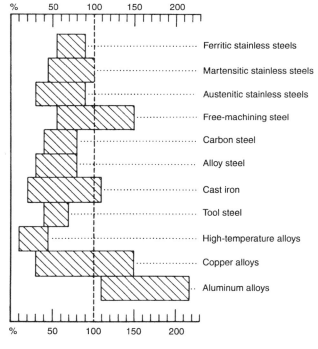

Fig. 8.12 Comparative machinability of common metals. 100% type 416 stainless steel. Courtesy of Specialty Steel Industry of North America

are tough, and they work harden during machining. Chips tend to be stringy, tools run hotter, the assembly chatters, and, unless a determined cut is made, the work-hardened surface progressively resists the cutting tool. The nitrogen-containing austenitics, because of their higher rates of work hardening, present more difficulties.

There is a general view that the machinability of the non-free-machining austenitics is improved by prior cold work. Probably differences of opinion arise depending upon the nature of the machining operation and other variables.

8.6.4 Precipitation-Hardening Stainless Steels

To avoid unnecessary heat treatment, the martensitic grades are generally machined in the solution-treated condition. They may be brought to strength by heat treatment at aging temperature. Because there is very little dimensional change or discoloration, subsequent work is minimized. Alternatively, the martensitic grades may be machined in their fully aged condition in which case no further work at all is required.

The austenitic and semi-austenitic precipitation hardening steels are more difficult. If worst comes to worst, they may be machined in an overaged condition, then put through a complete heat treatment cycle of solution-treatment and aging. Subsequent machining to tolerance is then required.

8.6.5 Duplex Stainless Steels

Duplex stainless steels have high strength and hardness even when annealed, and they are not easily machinable. Circumstances being equal, they are more difficult to deal with than the 18-8 varieties of austenitics but less frustrating than the manganese-nitrogen grades.

Obviously, we cannot deal with all the particulars about machining stainless steels. However, it is advisable that, first of all, the machinist know the condition of the received material—annealed, hardened, aged, etc. Then, with the steel in its most machinable condition, the operator must determine by advice from the supplier, handbook, or experience the optimal set of variables (tool material and design, cutting speed, lubricant, etc.) that best suit the work in hand.

8.7 Surface Finishing and Surface Treatments

These fall into three categories: (a) the surfaces designated as finishes and available from the mill or resulting from hot-working, cold-working, or surface cleaning during fabrication; (b) surface hardening processes; and (c) surface protection by the application of coatings.

8.7.1 Finishes

The fabricator may specify one of several finishes to the material supplied by the mill, whether the material is in the form of sheet, strip, plate, bar, wire, or pipe. Table 8.3 gives a description of standard finishes for sheet, of which No. 4 is the most popular, general-purpose finish. Not all finishes are available in every grade.

Table 8.3 Standard mechanical sheet finishes

Finish	Description
Unpolished or rolled finishes	
No. 1	A rough, dull surface that results from hot rolling to the specified thickness followed by annealing and descaling
No. 2D	A dull finish that results from cold rolling followed by annealing and descaling, and may perhaps get a final light roll pass through unpolished rolls. A 2D finish is used where appearance is of no concern.
No. 2B	A bright, cold-rolled finish resulting in the same manner as No. 2D finish, except that the annealed and descaled sheet receives a final light roll pass through polished rolls. This is the general-purpose cold-rolled finish that can be used as is, or as a preliminary step to polishing.
Polished finishes	
No. 3	An intermediate polished surface obtained by finishing with a 100-grit abrasive. Generally used where a semifinished polished surface is required. A No. 3 finish usually receives additional polishing during fabrication.
No. 4	A polished surface obtained by finishing with a 120 to 150-mesh abrasive, following initial grinding with coarser abrasives. This is a general-purpose bright finish with a visible "grain" that prevents mirror reflection.
No. 6	A dull satin finish having lower reflectivity than No. 4 finish. It is produced by tampico brushing the No. 4 finish in a medium of abrasive and oil. It is used for architectural applications and ornamentation where a high luster is undesirable, and to contrast with brighter finishes.
No. 7	A highly reflective finish that is obtained by buffing finely ground surfaces but not to the extent of completely removing the grit lines. It is used chiefly for architectural and ornamental purposes.
No. 8	The most reflective surface, obtained by polishing with successively finer abrasives and buffing extensively until all grit lines from preliminary grinding operations are removed. It is used for applications such as mirrors and reflectors.

Plate has similar finishes, but, in addition, can be supplied in several hot-rolled conditions where the surface is not highly polished but has been cleaned by abrasive methods or pickling. Strip is narrower than sheet and has fewer available finishes. Like plate, bar can be supplied as rolled or cold finished for highly polished surfaces. If tubular goods are made by hot, seamless processes, their surface finishes are similar to those of hot-rolled bars. Welded pipe and tube made from sheet and strip retain their finer surface qualities; the weld bead is trimmed and the tube may go through a further cold-working operation.

It is important that the fabricator preserve the mill finish ordered and paid for. It is critical that stainless steel not be contaminated during storage and handling by oil, grease, dirt, marking pencils, or finger prints.

Obviously, some fabrication processes (for example, pressing and drawing) do not disturb the mill finish; others (for example, hot processing and welding) inevitably will disturb the finish. The fabricator then has to present the purchaser with the required finish.

8.7.2 Descaling

Descaling removes oxides that result from hot forming. A hot nitric/hydrofluoric acid bath not only does the trick, but also it passivates the steel by encouraging the formation of the oxide film. Ferritic grades may require a preliminary abrasive treatment by sand or grit but not by carbon steel shot! Descaling in salt baths (based upon molten sodium hydroxide) offers the advantages of avoiding any preliminary abrasive cleaning and not attacking the metal itself.

Since the time of earlier editions of this book, people have thankfully become more concerned for the environment; consequently the disposal of noxious chemicals such as pickle liquor and caustic salts has become a greater public issue with consequent legal requirements. Metal fabricators have to bear this in mind as they contemplate the economics of their processes.

8.7.3 Grinding and Polishing

This is necessary in cleaning up welds, removing flash from forgings and castings, and dressing rough cut edges. In addition to the usual precautions observed in grinding, particular respect should be paid to the low thermal conductivity of stainless; distortion, heat-tinting, and deterioration of mechanical and corrosion-resistant properties will occur through overheating.

Following grinding, which itself may be preceded by careful work with a chisel, a succession of increasingly fine abrasives applied by wheel or belt brings the stainless to the degree of polish required. Again, local heating, which can occur too easily, must be avoided (just imagine it is your tooth being polished), and the wheels and belts used for stainless must not be used for other purposes.

8.7.4 Electropolishing

Electropolishing generally is geared to the production line but can be locally applied. The stainless is made anode in an electrochemical cell. Figure 8.13 illustrates how the process may be used for localized polishing.

8.8 Surface Hardening

The surface finishes we have dealt with so far largely have been concerned with smoothness, which can improve corrosion resistance and certainly enhances appearance. On the other hand, surface hardening is to improve resistance to wear and galling (see section 7.8). Many surface hardening treatments adversely affect corrosion resistance because the hardening constituents that form at the surface grab and tie up chromium atoms, which are then no longer available to form the protective oxide layer.

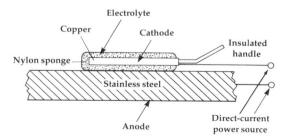

Fig. 8.13 Simple tool for localized electrocleaning of heat tint from the surface of stainless steel

An exception, which we mention only in passing, is where hard-facing alloys present a new surface on a stainless substrate. The use of cobalt-containing austenitic stainless overlays to resist cavitation erosion is a case in point.

Methods of surface hardening stainless steels by heat treatment are the same as those used for low alloy steels. Gas, plasma, and liquid nitriding present surfaces whose hardnesses are due to nitrides rich in chromium. These processes are best applied to martensitic stainlesses, whose cores can withstand the high load that might be expected of a surface hardened component. Prior to nitriding, the surface must be freed of chromium oxides.

Making a generalization, which is pressed upon us because a long review of surface hardening would be out of the way, nitriding in a salt bath is often the best bet. It doesn't require a high temperature and the surface produced is not only wear resistant but improves fatigue properties and apparently is not too deleterious to corrosion resistance.

However, if life should depend upon it, do not forget to consider flame-hardening, carburizing, and boriding, which were mentioned (albeit superficially) in section 3.3.

8.9 Resin Coatings

Although the idea of applying a coating to stainless steel can appear to be a case of gilding the lily, there are sufficient architectural applications of resin-coated stainless steels to warrant mention. Decorative panels on stainless steel bathtubs produced by silk-screen and photo etching have become a hot (and, presumably, a cold) market item. But, of more utilitarian concern, since about 1975 and especially in Japan, resin coated stainless has been increasingly used for building surfaces. This is not only because a tinted finish (appealing to some architectural tastes) can be obtained, but also because the protection of the coating increases the durability of walls and roofs in severe atmospheric environments.

Resin coatings are generally applied to steels of the 18-8 variety. Good bonding requires that the sheet is soft tempered and given a final pass through shot-blasted rolls. The sheet is electrolytically etched in phosphoric acid, coated with epoxy resin, and then coated with anti-weathering resin. Compared to galvanized sheet or copper, durability and strength are superior.

Seams between roofing sheets usually are made by double folding and are fastened by seam welding. Formerly, a protective coating was applied after welding. More recently, however, electrically conducting resins impregnated with about 20 wt% of stainless steel powder have been introduced, obviating that postweld treatment.

8.10 Hot Forming

While most stainless steel fabricators can shape a product by bending, pressing, or drawing, hot forming is much more specialized and consequently touches a comparatively small number of practitioners. It is required if a heavy piece cannot be economically shaped by casting and/or machining or joining, or if (for example) a part can be more readily formed by hot-upsetting a slug cut from a bar than by cold drawing sheet. Such a case is illustrated in Fig. 8.14, where a type 310 stainless (approximately 25Cr, 20Ni) is shaped into a fairly tight ring about 2.5 mm thick.

All stainless steels can be hot formed but with increasing difficulty as the alloy content increases. In all cases, forming pressures are higher than for low-alloy steels. After all, the stainless grades have a reputation for strength at high temperature. Ferritic and austenitic stainless steels do not enjoy a phase transformation on cooling; consequently working temperature should be as low as practicably possible. Because of their comparatively low thermal conductivity, stainless grades take more time to soak than plain carbon and low alloy steels. Martensitic steels in the hardened condition must be cautiously taken to temperature to avoid cracking.

8.10.1 Ferritic Stainless Steels

Ferritic stainless steels are generally worked down to a low finishing temperature of approximately 725 °C (1335 °F) to induce grain refinement. An exception is AISI 405, which may develop grain boundary weakness through the formation of austenite. Stress relief at approximately 300 °C (570 °F) mitigates forging stresses.

8.10.2 Martensitic Stainless Steels

Martensitic stainless steels usually are heated slowly to approximately 800 °C (1470 °F) to attain a uniform temperature across the piece, which minimizes thermal and transformation stresses. The steels are formed at approximately 850 °C (1560 °F) and never below their transformation temperature. To avoid subsequent hardening, a very slow cooling (slower than air-cooling) is necessary.

8.10.3 Austenitic Stainless Steels

The hot strength of austenitic stainless steels requires higher working temperatures than those for ferritic and martensitic grades. To minimize sensitization (with the exception of the stabilized and extra-low carbon

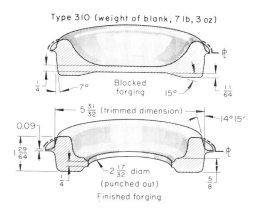

Sequence of operation

1. Upset on flat portion of die to approximatelly 115 mm (4½ in.) in diameter. 2. Forge in blocker impression. 3. Forge in finisher impression. 4. Hot trim (900 to 925 °C, or 1650 to 1700 °F) and punch out center. 5. Air cool. 6. Clean (shot blast)

Processing conditions

Blank preparation	Cold sawing
Stock size	90 mm (3½ in.) in diameter
Blank weight	3.25 kg (7 lb, 3 oz)
Heating method	Gas-fired, slot-front box furnace
Heating time	1 h
Atmosphere	Slightly oxidizing
Die material	6G at 388–429 HB (a)
Die life, total	507–2067 forgings(b)
Die lubricant	Graphite-oil
Production rate	50 forgings per hour(c)

(a) Inserts at this hardness were used in die blocks of the same material, but softer (341–375 HB). (b) Average life was 1004 forgings. Life to rework and total life were the same, because worn die inserts were not reworked. (c) Based on a 50 min working hour

Fig. 8.14 Typical procedure for forging a ringlike part from an austenitic stainless steel. Dimensions given in inches

grades), finishing temperatures above 875 °C (1610 °F) must be followed by rapid cooling. Following hot working, the austenitics are usually soaked between 1000 and 1125 °C (1830 and 2055 °F) and cooled rapidly.

8.10.4 Precipitation-Hardening Stainless Steels

Because precipitation-hardening stainless steels have the least plasticity, they require the most closely controlled forging schedule. The martensitic and semi-austenitic grades are susceptible to cracking and delta-ferrite formation. Their cooling must be carefully controlled.

8.10.5 Duplex Stainless Steels

Duplex stainless steels are more difficult to hot work than any other grades because the ferrite is much more easily deformed than austenite is, and the ratio of the phases changes with temperature. Modest deformation rates are necessary to avoid cracks and tearing.

8.11 Fabrication by Powder Metallurgy

There was a time when the only purposes for parts made from powder depended upon their porosity; they were used as filters, sound attenuators, or, very importantly, as bearings, because they retained lubricant. These are still significant applications for 18-8 type stainless steels. As powder metallurgical techniques have improved, however, and as higher densities (approaching 100%) have been attained, parts made from powder have moved into new markets.

The technique has obvious advantages; a part can be formed, forged, and sintered to dimensional requirements. When a forging is made from a powder blank, there is less loss from flashings; small parts need no subsequent machining.

Although the increase in powder metallurgy parts has been substantial, the total tonnage in stainless commodities is still small, in the order of ten thousand tons annually worldwide. But that small tonnage is mainly represented by millions of little components—gears, sprockets, and levers—for business machines and domestic equipment. A recent innovation is automotive exhaust manifold flanges, replacing a stamped and welded assembly. Examples are seen in Fig. 8.15.

Powder may be made by several processes, but stainless powder is generally made by atomization. Gas atomization produces spherical powders that are used for high density jobs; more commonly, powders are made by water atomization whose product shape is irregular. (See Fig. 8.16 and 8.17.) Powder must be coated with a lubricant so that its green strength allows it to be handled and so that it will eject from the mold. At the same time, its density generally is required to be as high as possible, and, no small point this, the lubricant must burn off during subsequent sintering in whatever atmosphere is used.

The rapid cooling rate in gas atomization produces a powder with a very fine microstructure and with less compositional segregation than would occur in a casting whose segregation is retained to some extent in a rolled product. Consequently, when a powder part is made by techniques producing densities reaching 100%, superior mechanical properties can be attained. Such examples are found among the duplex stainless steels.

The decision about the manufacturing route is almost entirely based on economics. The question remains (for we are interested in stainless steels whose priority has to do with corrosion resistance) whether the powder product matches up to the others.

It well may. But the process by which it has been produced and fabricated can affect its chemistry. Not to go too deeply into this, but we have to ask,

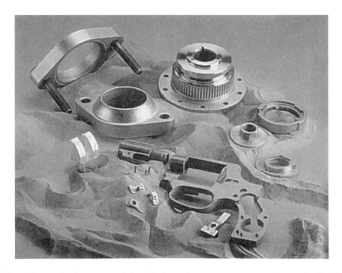

Fig. 8.15 Left to right, foreground: latchbolt and seven gun parts. Left to right, background: exhaust manifold flanges, turbine hub, and a power tool ratchet wheel set, which includes the wheel, flange, and thrust ring

for example, whether a furnace atmosphere has increased its nitrogen content and whether lubricants can become contaminants. If these considerations are put aside and products of equal density are compared, then corrosion resistance is the same.

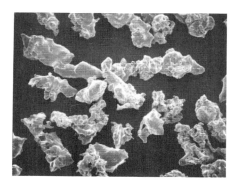

Fig. 8.16 Scanning electron micrograph of water-atomized type 304L stainless steel (–100 mesh). 150×

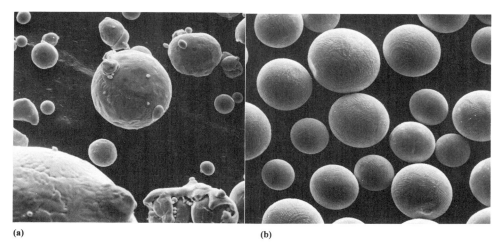

(a)　　　　　　　　　　　　　　　　　　(b)

Fig. 8.17 Scanning electron micrographs of gas-atomized stainless steel powders. (a) Type 316 stainless steel powder produced by conventional gas atomization. Note attached satellites. 700×. (b) Type 316L stainless steel powder produced by the rotating electrode process. Shown are nearly perfect spheres with absence of satellite formation. 200×

We mention in passing that a high chromium surface applied by cementation to a sintered product of less than 100% density shows extremely good corrosion resistance.

8.12 Heat Treating

As mentioned in the introduction to this chapter, the elements of heat treatment and the metallurgy and resulting properties of heat treated stainless steels have been described in section 3.3. A review of a few of the practical aspects of heat treatment follows.

Contamination must be avoided; cleanliness of the steel part is essential. Furnace fixtures generally are made of stainless or heat-resisting nickel alloy.

There are many heating processes. For the field heat treatment of weldments, there is probably no alternative to the open flame of the gas torch. If the weld is part of a production line operation (as, for instance, in the manufacture of seam-welded tube and pipe), induction heating is often used. However, the heat treatment of parts is usually effected in furnaces or salt baths. Where the heat treatment is for annealing or stress-relief, especially for large batches or production line runs, furnaces are used. While salt baths are perfectly satisfactory, they are more often restricted to small batches and particularly to the heat treatment of martensitic and precipitation-hardening grades.

8.12.1 Furnace Heating

Furnaces can be heated by gas burners where the charge is in contact with the combustion products or indirectly heated. If gas is used, the charge is separated from the combustion products either by using muffle furnaces or radiant tube heating. In this case, as in heating by electric resistance, the atmosphere is completely controllable; electric heating has the further advantage that temperature is more easily regulated.

Stainless steels are commonly heat treated in an air atmosphere. Where direct combustion is used, the air-fuel ratio is controlled to maintain sufficient free oxygen to avoid carburization. Descaling is then required (see section 8.7.2).

Where an inert atmosphere is needed, argon or helium is used, but the cost can rarely be justified. Consequently, for bright annealing, dissociated ammonia atmospheres are common. The ammonia is dissociated at a high temperature to avoid nitriding the steel, and it must be dry.

Some hydrogen pickup may occur during the heat treatment of martensitic steels, but it is expelled during slow cooling or during the subsequent tempering process.

8.12.2 Salt Baths

Salt baths used for stainless parts should not be used for any other materials. The salt is usually barium chloride, but we suggest that the supplier's advice be sought about the most appropriate salt to use for a particular purpose. Needless to say, prompt and thorough cleaning following salt bath treatment is vital.

Cast Stainless Steels

9.1 Introduction

The shortness of this chapter should not be mistaken for underestimation of the importance of cast stainless even though the tonnage is small compared to the amount of wrought material used. Most of what is written in this book about wrought alloys also applies to castings.

The Alloy Casting Institute (ACI) originated the system for specifying cast stainless steels. Although the institute has been superseded by The High Alloy Product Group of the Steel Founders' Society of America (whose name gives an impression of a superior metallurgical order), the appointments of the alloys have mercifully remained unaffected.

We mentioned this in section 1.4.10, but having done so, we now have to recognize the different intentions of the designations for wrought alloys (numerous as they are) and cast alloys. The wrought alloys fall into the groups ferritic, martensitic, etc., which are reflected by their AISI and related UNS numbers. But the cast alloys (while they are austenitic or ferritic or whatever) are specified according to whether they are primarily intended for corrosion-resistant service (and given the letter C) or for high temperature service (and given the letter H). There is something about the simplicity of this sort of designation that tells of the traditional practicality of the foundryman.

Tables 9.1 and 9.2 give the compositions of the common cast stainless steels, their correlation with wrought alloys (where possible), and their ASTM specifications, which also prescribe testing procedures, mechanical properties, and heat treatments. While we do not expect every reader to commit all this to memory, a few significant features are pointed out:

- The corrosion-resistant alloys contain less carbon than the heat-resistant alloys contain. Consequently when CK-20, which is in the table of

Table 9.1 (continued)

ACI type	Wrought alloy type(a)	ASTM specifications	Most common end-use microstructure	Composition(b), %					
				C	Si	Mn	Cr	Ni	Others(c)
Chromium-nickel steels (continued)									
CF-12M	316	...	Ferrite in austenite or austenite	0.12	2.00	1.50	18.0–21.0	9.0–12.0	2.0–3.0Mo
CF-16F	303	A 743	Austenite	0.16	2.00	1.50	18.0–21.0	9.0–12.0	1.50Mo max; 0.20–0.35Se
CF-20	302	A 743	Austenite	0.20	2.00	1.50	18.0–21.0	8.0–11.0	...
CG-6MMN	...	A 351, A 743	Ferrite in austenite	0.06	1.00	4.00–6.00	20.5–23.5	11.5–13.5	1.50–3.00Mo; 0.10–0.30Nb; 0.10–30V; 0.20–40N
CG-8M	317	A 351, A 743, A 744	Ferrite in austenite	0.08	1.50	1.50	18.0–21.0	9.0–13.0	3.0–4.0Mo
CG-12	...	A 743	Ferrite in austenite	0.12	2.00	1.50	20.0–23.0	10.0–13.0	...
CH-8	...	A 351	Ferrite in austenite	0.08	1.50	1.50	22.0–26.0	12.0–15.0	...
CH-10	...	A 351	Ferrite in austenite	0.04–0.10	2.00	1.50	22.0–26.0	12.0–15.0	...
CH-20	309	A 351, A 743	Austenite	0.20	2.00	1.50	22.0–26.0	12.0–15.0	...
CK-3MCuN	...	A 351, A 743, A 744	Ferrite in austenite	0.025	1.00	1.20	19.5–20.5	17.5–19.5	6.0–7.0V: 0.18–0.24N; 0.50–1.00Cu
CK-20	310	A 743	Austenite	0.20	2.00	2.00	23.0–27.0	19.0–22.0	...
Nickel-chromium steel									
CN-3M	...	A 743	Austenite	0.03	1.00	2.00	20.0–22.0	23.0–27.0	4.5–5.5Mo
CN-7M	...	A 351, A 743, A 744	Austenite	0.07	1.50	1.50	19.0–22.0	27.5–30.5	2.0–3.0Mo: 3.0–4.0Cu
CN-7MS	...	A 743, A 744	Austenite	0.07	3.50(g)	1.50	18.0–20.0	22.0–25.0	2.5–3.0Mo: 1.5–2.0Cu
CT-15C	...	A 351	Austenite	0.05–0.15	0.50–1.50	0.15–1.50	19.0–21.0	31.0–34.0	0.5–1.5V

(a) Type numbers of wrought alloys are listed only for nominal identification of corresponding wrought and cast grades. Composition ranges of cast alloys are not the same as for corresponding wrought alloys; cast alloy designations should be used for castings only. (b) Maximum unless a range is given. The balance of all compositions is iron. (c) Sulfur content is 0.04% in all grades except: CG-6MMN, 0.030% S (max); CF-10SMnN, 0.030% S (max); CT-15C, 0.03% S (max); CK-3MCuN, 0.010% S (max); CN-3M, 0.030% S (max), CA-6N, 0.020% S (max); CA-28MWV, 0.030% S (max); CA-40F, 0.20–0.40% S; CB-7Cu-1 and -2, 0.03% S (max). Phosphorus content is 0.04% (max) in all grades except: CF-16F, 0.17% P (max); CF-10SMnN, 0.060% P (max); CT-15C, 0.030% P (max); CK-3MCuN, 0.045% P (max); CN-3M, 0.030% P (max); CA-6N, 0.020% P (max); CA-28MWV, 0.030% P (max); CB-7Cu-1 and -2, 0.035% P (max). (d) Molybdenum not intentionally added. (e) CF-3A, CF-3MA, and CF-8A have the same composition ranges as CF-3, CF-3M, and CF-8, respectively, but have balanced compositions so that ferrite contents are at levels that permit higher mechanical property specifications than those for related grades. They are covered by ASTM A 351. (f) Nb, 8 × %C min (1.0% max); or Nb + Ta × %C (1.1% max). (g) For CN-7MS, silicon ranges from 2.50 to 3.50%.

Table 9.1 Compositions and typical microstructures of corrosion-resistant cast steels

ACI type	Wrought alloy type(a)	ASTM specifications	Most common end-use microstructure	Composition(b), %					
				C	Mn	Si	Cr	Ni	Others(c)
Chromium steels									
CA-15	410	A 743, A 217, A 487	Martensite	0.15	1.00	1.50	11.5–14.0	1.0	0.50Mo(d)
CA-15M	...	A 743	Martensite	0.15	1.00	0.65	11.5–14.0	1.0	0.15–1.00Mo
CA-40	420	A 743	Martensite	0.40	1.00	1.50	11.5–14.0	1.0	0.5Mo(d)
CA-40F	...	A 743	Martensite	0.2–0.4	1.00	1.50	11.5–14.0	1.0	...
CB-30	431, 442	A 743	Ferrite and carbides	0.30	1.00	1.50	18.0–22.0	2.0	...
CC-50	446	A 743	Ferrite and carbides	0.30	1.00	1.50	26.0–30.0	4.0	...
Chromium-nickel steels									
CA-6N	...	A 743	Martensite	0.06	0.50	1.00	10.5–12.5	6.0–8.0	...
CA-6NM	...	A 743, A 487	Martensite	0.06	1.00	1.00	11.5–14.0	3.5–4.5	0.4–1.0Mo
CA-28MWV	...	A 743	Martensite	0.20–0.28	0.50–1.00	1.00	11.0–12.5	0.50–1.00	0.9–1.25Mo; 0.9–1.25W; 0.2–0.3V
CB-7Cu-1	...	A 747	Martensite, age hardenable	0.07	0.70	1.00	15.5–17.7	3.6–4.6	2.5–3.2Cu; 0.20–0.35Nb; 0.05N max
CB-7Cu-2	...	A 747	Martensite, age hardenable	0.07	0.70	1.00	14.0–15.5	4.5–5.5	2.5–3.2Cu; 0.20–0.35 Nb; 0.05N max
CD-4MCu	...	A 351, A 743, A 744, A 890	Austenite in ferrite, age hardenable	0.04	1.00	1.00	25.0–26.5	4.75–6.0	1.75–2.25Mo; 2.75–3.25Cu
CE-30	312	A 743	Ferrite in austenite	0.30	1.50	2.00	26.0–30.0	8.0–11.0	...
CF-3(e)	304L	A 351, A 743, A 744	Ferrite in austenite	0.03	1.50	2.00	17.0–21.0	8.0–12.0	...
CF-3M(e)	316L	A 351, A 743, A 744	Ferrite in austenite	0.03	1.50	2.00	17.0–21.0	8.0–12.0	2.0–3.0 Mo
CF-3MN	...	A 743	Ferrite in austenite	0.03	1.50	1.50	17.0–21.0	9.0–13.0	2.0–3.0Mo; 0.10–0.20N
CF-8(e)	304	A 351, A 743, A 744	Ferrite in austenite	0.08	1.50	2.00	18.0–21.0	8.0–11.0	...
CF-8C	347	A 351, A 743, A 744	Ferrite in austenite	0.08	1.50	2.00	18.0–21.0	9.0–12.0	Nb(f)
CF-8M	316	A 351, A 743, A 744	Ferrite in austenite	0.08	1.50	2.00	18.0–21.0	9.0–12.0	2.0–3.0Mo
CF-10	...	A 351	Ferrite in austenite	0.04–0.10	1.50	2.00	18.0–21.0	8.0–11.0	...
CF-10M	...	A 351	Ferrite in austenite	0.04–0.10	1.50	1.50	18.0–21.0	9.0–12.0	2.0–3.0Mo
CF-10MC	...	A 351	Ferrite in austenite	0.10	1.50	1.50	15.0–18.0	13.0–16.0	1.75–2.25Mo
CF-10SMnN	...	A 351, A 743	Ferrite in austenite	0.10	7.00–9.00	3.50–4.50	16.0–18.0	8.0–9.0	0.08–0.18N

(continued)

corrosion-resistant alloys with a wrought equivalent of 310, appears among the heat-resistant alloys as HK (with the same wrought equivalent, 310), carbon content is the significant compositional difference.

- Most of the corrosion-resistant castings, the C series, fall into the classes described for wrought alloys (ferritic, martensitic, etc.), and many have similar compositions to the wrought series.
- Few of the heat-resistant casting alloys have composition equivalents to the wrought series. Where similarities are found, the casting alloys not only have a higher carbon content, but they are generally at the high end of nickel and chromium ranges.
- For otherwise roughly equivalent compositions, the casting alloys contain more silicon. This not only improves fluidity in casting but enhances resistance to stress-corrosion cracking (SCC).
- Grades whose approximate equivalents in wrought categories would be fully austenitic usually contain some ferrite (high temperature delta ferrite, formed on solidification). Figures 9.1 and 9.2 illustrate this in an alloy whose nearest wrought equivalent, AISI 304L, would be completely austenitic.

9.2 Corrosion-Resistant Cast Stainless Steels

The most used of these are in the austenitic class. The approximate amount of ferrite they contain can be determined from the Schoefer diagram

Table 9.2 Composition of heat-resistant stainless steel casting alloys

	Designation			Composition, %			
ACI type	UNS	Wrought alloy type	ASTM Specifications	C	Cr	Ni	Si
HA			A217	0.20 max	8–10	...	1.0
HC	J92605		A297, A608	0.50 max	26–30	4 max	2.0
HD	J93005		A297, A608	0.50 max	26–30	4–7	2.0
HE	J93403		A297, A608	0.2–0.5	26–30	8–11	2.0
HF	J92603	302B	A297, A608	0.2–0.4	19–23	9–12	2.0
HH	J93503	309	A297, A608, A447	0.2–0.5	24–28	11–14	2.0
HI	J94003		A297, A567, A608	0.2–0.5	26–30	14–18	2.0
HK	J94224	310	A297, A351, A567, A608	0.2–0.6	24–28	18–22	2.0
HK30			A351	0.25–0.35	23–27	19–22	1.75
HK40			A351	0.35–0.45	23–27	19–22	1.75
HL	J94604		A297, A608	0.2–0.6	28–32	18–22	2.0
HN	J94213		A297, A608	0.2–0.5	19–23	23–27	2.0
HP			A297	0.35–0.75	24–28	33–37	2.0

(Fig. 9.3). Do not get these fellows Shoefer and Schaeffler (already referred to) confused even though the Schoefer diagram is derived from Schaeffler's! Percentage nickel and chromium equivalents are calculated from the following equations:

$$Cr = Cr + 1.5(Si) + 1.4(Mo) + Nb - 4.99$$

$$Ni = Ni + 30(C) + 0.5(Mn) + 26(N-0.02) + 2.77$$

While these are the generally accepted equations, in view of the evident scatter (shown in Fig. 9.3), the last components of the equations can be rounded to two significant figures, 5.0 and 2.8 respectively, without damaging their integrity.

In general terms, the grades with higher nickel and carbon contents designated austenitic in Table 9.1 will be sensibly free of ferrite. The other grades may be compared to the duplex class of the wrought alloys and similarly, at higher ferrite contents, better resist SCC and intergranular corrosion. The ferrite content of these alloys, which, by the way, are magnetic, improves strength and weldability but reduces toughness.

The inevitable sensitization through chromium depletion can be mitigated by solution treatment, stabilizers, and reduced carbon content or by a composition change to increase the ferrite content.

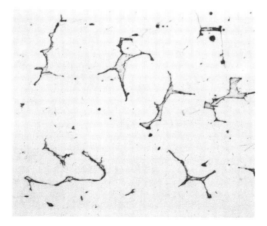

Fig. 9.1 CF-3 alloy, as cast, showing dispersed islands of ferrite and grain boundary carbide particles in an austenite matrix. 100×

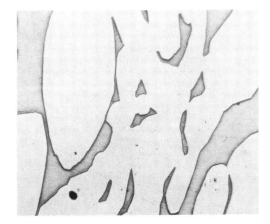

Fig. 9.2 As in Fig. 9.1 but solution treated at 1120 °C (2050 °F) and water quenched. Elongated pools of ferrite in an austenite matrix (light). 250×

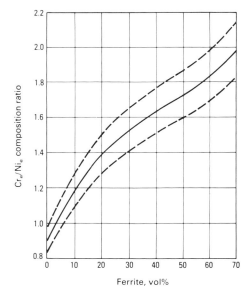

Fig. 9.3 Schoefer diagram for estimating the ferrite content of steel castings in the composition range of 16 to 26% Cr, 6 to 14% Ni (max), 4% Mo (max), 1% Nb (max), 0.2% C (max), 0.19% N (max), 2% Mn (max), and 2% Si (max). Dashed lines denote scatter bands caused by the uncertainty of the chemical analysis of individual elements. See text for equations used to calculate Cr_e and Ni_e.

A homogenization treatment at approximately 1100 °C (2010 °F) is common, especially in large sections, to reduce the unavoidable heterogeneity of a cast material. A slightly higher temperature up to approximately 1200 °C (2190 °F) ensures that the carbides are taken into solution. Rapid cooling from that temperature through the sensitizing range, 870 to 540 °C (1600 to 1010 °F), avoids their subsequent precipitation.

A few general remarks follow about the chemical composition of the corrosion-resistant steels of the austenitic class: carbon is held to low values and nickel additions improve ductility, toughness, and general corrosion resistance. As in the wrought alloys, molybdenum is added to resist pitting and improve passivity where the environment is not highly oxidizing. The active agent in the age-hardenable alloys is copper, which also improves resistance to sulfuric acid corrosion.

As seen in Table 9.1, some corrosion-resistant stainless steel castings are heat treatable. After quenching, they are usually tempered between 540 and 750 °C (1010 and 1380 °F); and their properties can be additionally enhanced by precipitation hardening. Again, copper is the active agent. The forfeit of ductility, toughness, and corrosion-resistance as strength is increased by quenching and tempering resembles that of the wrought alloys.

Notice, too, in Table 9.1 two ferritic grades, CB-30 and CC-50. When the nickel content is increased for purposes of corrosion-resistance, the chromium content must be supplemented. They have particular but limited applications where their chromium content resists attack in oxidizing acids and where additional alloying elements are not called upon for particular mechanical or corrosion-resistant properties. Room-temperature mechanical properties of corrosion-resistant stainless steel castings are given in Table 9.3.

9.3 Heat-Resistant Cast Stainless Steels

With the exception of HA, HC, and HD in Table 9.2, these alloys are austenitic. HA is modestly heat-treatable. Following air-quenching and tempering, it has good oxidation resistance up to 650 °C (1200 °F) although creep resistance is inferior (as shown in the lower graph in Fig. 9.4).

HC is ferritic and used at temperatures not exceeding 650 °C (1200 °F). Notice that the prescribed nickel content is a maximum controlled to lower levels when the alloy is to be used in high sulfur atmospheres where the possible formation of a nickel-rich eutectic can lead to catastrophic failure. Nickel content is also limited where its presence might lead to catalytic cracking of hydrocarbons.

At slightly higher nickel levels, alloy HD has better high-temperature strength. The ferritic structure will contain amounts of austenite depending upon the precise composition within permissible ranges. Sigma phase formation can cause room temperature brittleness if the alloys are held for long periods at temperatures between approximately 700 to 900 °C (1290 to 1650 °F).

The remaining alloys in Table 9.2 are austenitic, and HH is the most common. Depending upon the composition within the permissible ranges, it can be partially ferritic (HH1) or wholly austenitic (HH2). Because of the contained ferrite, HH1 is more forgiving of temperature and stress fluctuations. Although sigma embrittlement and carbide precipitation are expected

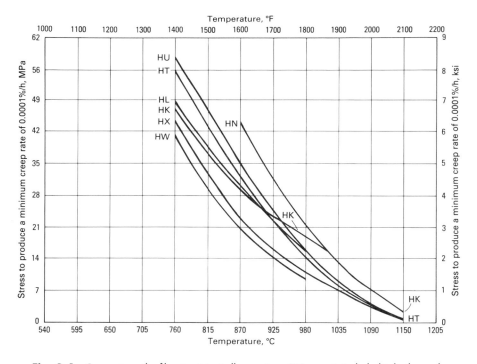

Fig. 9.4 Creep strength of heat-resistant alloy castings (HT curve is included in both graphs for ease of comparison)

between 700 and 900 °C (1290 and 1650 °F), service conditions might tolerate them. They are avoided at higher temperatures; that is, up to the maximum useful working temperature of approximately 1100 °C (2010 °F) where strength is very low (see Fig. 9.4) although oxidation resistance is satisfactory. HH2 demands a carefully balanced chemistry to assure that its microstructure is wholly austenitic and appropriate to the operating temperature. Its high temperature strength is far superior to that of HH1.

Other alloys in the series contain more or less chromium and nickel with consequent effects upon their constitution and high temperature properties. Figure 9.4 shows their creep behavior. Generally, higher chromium contents improve high-temperature oxidation resistance.

As nickel overtakes the chromium content, the alloys (completely austenitic) are freer from embrittling effects, and their precise composition is less critical than it is with the chromium-rich alloys. They are more resistant to

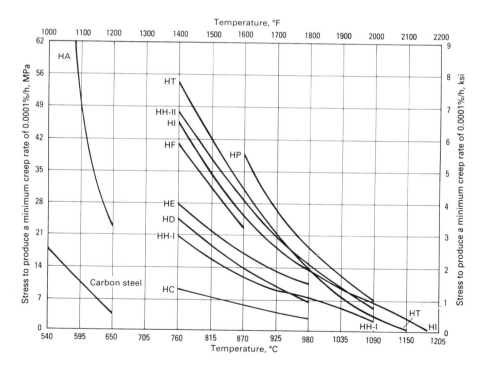

Fig. 9.4 (continued)

Table 9.3 Room-temperature mechanical properties of cast corrosion-resistant alloys

Alloy	Heat treatment(a)	Tensile strength MPa	ksi	Yield strength (0.2% offset) MPa	ksi	Elongation in 50 mm (2 in.), %	Reduction in area, %	Hardness, HB	Charpy impact energy J	ft·lb	Specimens
CA-6NM	>955 °C (1750 °F), AC, T	827	120	689	100	24	60	269	94.9	70	V-notch
CA-15	980 °C (1800 °F), AC, T	793	115	689	100	22	55	225	27.1	20	Keyhole notch
CA-40	980 °C (1800 °F), AC, T	1034	150	862	125	10	30	310	2.7	2	Keyhole notch
CB-7Cu	1040 °C (1900 °F), OQ, A	1310	190	1172	170	14	54	400	33.9	25	V-notch
CB-30	790 °C (1450 °F), AC	655	95	414	60	15	...	195	2.7	2	Keyhole notch
CC-50	1040 °C (1900 °F), AC	669	97	448	65	18	...	210	...	...	...
CD-4MCu	1120 °C (2050 °F), FC to 1040°C (1900 °F), WQ	745	108	558	81	25	...	253	74.6	55	V-notch
	1120 °C (2050 °F), FC to 1040 °C (1900 °F), A	896	130	634	92	20	...	305	35.3	26	V-notch
CE-30	1095 °C (2000 °F), WQ	669	97	434	63	18	...	190	9.5	7	Keyhole notch
CF-3	>1040 °C (1900 °F), WQ	531	77	248	36	60	...	140	149.2	110	V-notch
CF-3A	>1040 °C (1900 °F),WQ	600	87	290	42	50	...	160	135.6	100	V-notch
CF-8	>1040 °C (1900 °F), WQ	531	77	255	37	55	...	140	100.3	74	Keyhole notch
CF-8A	>1040 °C (1900 °F), WQ	586	85	310	45	50	...	156	94.9	70	Keyhole notch
CF-20	>1095 °C (2000 °F), WQ	531	77	248	36	50	...	163	81.4	60	Keyhole notch
CF-3M	>1040 °C (1900 °F), WQ	552	80	262	38	55	...	150	162.7	120	V-notch
CF-3MA	>1040 °C (1900 °F), WQ	621	90	310	45	45	...	170	135.6	100	V-notch
CF-8M	>1065 °C (1950 °F), WQ	552	80	290	42	50	...	170	94.9	70	Keyhole notch
CF-8C	>1065 °C (1950 °F), WQ	531	77	262	38	39	...	149	40.7	30	Keyhole notch
CF-16F	>1095 °C (2000 °F), WQ	531	77	276	40	52	...	150	101.7	75	Keyhole notch
CG-8M	>1040 °C (1900 °F), WQ	565	82	303	44	45	...	176	108.5	80	V-notch
CH-20	>1095 °C (2000 °F), WQ	607	88	345	50	38	...	190	40.7	30	Keyhole notch
CK-20	1150 °C (2100 °F), WQ	524	76	262	38	37	...	144	67.8	50	Izod V-notch
CN-7M	1120 °C (2050 °F), WQ	476	69	214	31	48	...	130	94.9	70	Keyhole notch

(a) AC, air cool; FC, furnace cool; OQ, oil quench; WQ, water quench; T, temper; A, age

Table 9.4 Typical room-temperature properties of heat-resistant casting alloys

Alloy	Condition	Tensile strength MPa	ksi	Yield strength MPa	ksi	Elongation, %	Hardness, HB
HC	As-cast	760	110	515	75	19	223
	Aged(a)	790	115	550	80	18	...
HD	As-cast	585	85	330	48	16	90
HE	As-cast	655	95	310	45	20	200
	Aged(a)	620	90	380	55	10	270
HF	As-cast	635	92	310	45	38	165
	Aged(a)	690	100	345	50	25	190
HH, type 1	As-cast	585	85	345	50	25	185
	Aged(a)	595	86	380	55	11	200
HH, type 2	As-cast	550	80	275	40	15	180
	Aged(a)	635	92	310	45	8	200
HI	As-cast	550	80	310	45	12	180
	Aged(a)	620	90	450	65	6	200
HK	As-cast	515	75	345	50	17	170
	Aged(b)	585	85	345	50	10	190
HL	As-cast	565	82	360	52	19	192
HN	As-cast	470	68	260	38	13	160
HP	As-cast	490	71	275	40	11	170
HT	As-cast	485	70	275	40	10	180
	Aged(b)	515	75	310	45	5	200

(a) Aging treatment: 24 h at 760 °C (1400 °F), furnace cool. (b) Aging treatment: 24 h at 760 °C (1400 °F), air cool.

carburizing and nitriding atmospheres, and their resistance to thermal shock improves with increased nickel content. Short-term elevated-temperature mechanical properties for representative alloys are given in Table 9.4.

Corrosion Resistance of Stainless Steels

10.1 Particular Susceptibilities

At the end of Chapter 4, which concerns the principles of corrosion, specific types of corrosive attack are discussed. Some are more than an eating away of metal; they induce catastrophic failure. Given the wrong circumstances, most metals and alloys meet their nemesis, and this proves a fascinating general study. However, our concern is for the particular circumstances that afflict stainless steels. This chapter begins with a section about those circumstances so that their hazards will be kept in mind throughout subsequent sections that deal more generally with corrosion resistance in common environments.

10.1.1 Stress Corrosion Cracking (SCC)

This heads the danger list. The required circumstances are a tensile stress, which can be applied or residual, and a specifically effective corrosive environment. Figures 4.7 and 4.8 show microstructures of characteristic fracture paths. The most intensively documented cases involve the austenitic class in chloride environments. However, ferritic stainless steels are not immune to chloride SCC. Rather, they are generally (but not always) resistant to boiling magnesium or sodium chloride solutions, which forms the basis of tests wherein austenitic stainless steels are prone to failure.

Even in these conventional chloride tests, ferritic stainless steels can be victim to SCC if they have been sensitized during fabrication or heat treatment. The immunity of the superferritics, which are frequently and successfully used in chloride environments, is endangered by nickel and other alloying elements independently or in concert. This points up the observation that slight changes in composition can substantially affect the resistance of an alloy to SCC.

While nickel is detrimental to the behavior of ferritic stainless steels, it is highly beneficial to the austenitics, as Fig. 10.1 shows. Even though such high nickel contents as the figure suggests have been contested, there is no doubt that a substantial amount (around 40%) is required to avert SCC. Tests have shown that other elements are beneficial, but far less so than nickel is. The available data are confusing in that a particular element may show positive or negative effects depending upon its concentration, the presence of other elements, and the testing environment. It is safe to con-

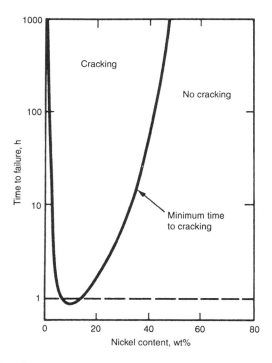

Fig. 10.1 Effect of nickel content on susceptibility to SCC of stainless steel wires containing 18 to 20% chromium in a magnesium chloride solution boiling at 154 °C. Reprinted with permission from A.J. Sedriks, *Corrosion of Stainless Steels*, John Wiley & Sons, Inc., 1996

clude, however, that in environments where SCC can be anticipated, the beneficial effect of nickel in the austenitic class is overwhelming. Even so, as suppliers caution, any austenitic stainless steel may be a candidate.

The susceptibility of duplex stainless steels lies between that of the ferritic and austenitic classes. While no data are available for the effects of individual alloying elements, generally it appears that the more the better; as the total chromium, nickel, molybdenum, and nitrogen is increased, so is resistance to SCC in laboratory tests.

Inhibitors in a chloride environment reduce SCC susceptibility. There are many, including carbonates, nitrates, phosphates, and silicates. The choice depends upon circumstances that include, of course, the distinct possibility that the very nature of the process in contact with the stainless prohibits any addition at all. Then cathodic protection can be considered. It has been successfully applied in desalination plants, but most of the extensive data originate from laboratory research.

Among other candidate environments for SCC, two specially concern the stainless steel user. One, polythionic acids, is touched upon in section 11.2.5, and we add nothing here. The other is caustic soda. At very high concentrations, pure nickel is the preferred metal. At concentrations less than 50% and at moderate temperatures, austenitic stainless steels are commonly used. However, high concentrations of caustic soda can arise in what might at first appear benign waters at heat-transfer surfaces. The phenomenon of caustic cracking in plain carbon steels long has been known but was unanticipated in stainless usage. Where a high concentration of caustic occurs, there is a danger of SCC in austenitic stainless at temperatures above 100 °C (212 °F). With more nickel, cracking resistance increases markedly. Boiler waters, unlike many environments, allow the addition of inhibitors of which phosphates are the most common.

10.1.2 Hydrogen Embrittlement

High strength steels, martensitic or precipitation hardening, are susceptible to brittle failure in specific corrodents by a mechanism currently ascribed to hydrogen embrittlement. This is a phenomenon that all high strength steels can suffer, and the higher their yield strengths are, the more likely they are to crack up. Whether the initiation and propagation of a brittle fracture in a corrosive environment should be ascribed to a hydrogen-induced process or to a dissolution process (in which, of course, hydrogen is part of the reaction) is, as they say, left as an exercise for the reader.

While many environments, gaseous or liquid, provide an opportunity for hydrogen embrittlement in high-strength steels, most attention has been paid to sulfides, particularly hydrogen sulfide. Interest in this environment was enlivened by the increasing production of sour oil and gas. (What was once confidently described as sulfide stress-corrosion cracking is probably a hydrogen embrittlement phenomenon, implying a similarity of failure mechanisms.) Research provides an unsurprising generalization: for a given applied stress there is a minimum hardness below which cracking will not occur, and this hardness increases with decreasing hydrogen sulfide concentration in the environment. A specific finding that can be more useful is that at any sulfide concentration, any high-strength stainless steel with a yield strength above 690 MPa is susceptible to hydrogen embrittlement.

10.1.3 Corrosion Fatigue

As we pointed out in section 4.4.7, a corrosive environment encourages the initiation of a fatigue crack and its propagation. The conditions are not as specific as they are in SCC because any corrosion will worsen fatigue properties. However, if the environment is conducive to SCC, fatigue life is further reduced. At very low frequencies of stress alternation, differentiation between the phenomena is difficult and possibly not of vital importance to the practically minded.

Figure 10.2 shows how the fatigue life of an austenitic stainless steel is reduced in chloride solution and in dilute sulfuric acid. Interestingly, while one might expect results in the saline solution to be worse (because of initial pitting) the effect of sulfuric acid, which does not cause localized corrosion, is more pronounced, suggesting, perhaps, an embrittlement phenomenon in crack propagation. In any event, there is a substantial reduction in the number of cycles to failure at low stresses both in chloride and in sulfuric acid.

The results of similar experiments on a ferritic stainless steel in sodium chloride solution are shown in Fig. 10.3, where not only is the reduction in fatigue strength less pronounced, but also there is, indeed, a fatigue limit. The curve levels off, showing that stresses about 300 MPa can be tolerated. The same effect is reported for duplex steels.

In regular fatigue and in many cases of corrosion fatigue, failure can be attributed to the tensile component of the alternating stress. In stainless steels, however, where a protective, passive film is broken by applied stress, compression is also active. The substantial lowering or even the disappearance of an endurance limit is associated with this double whammy.

10.1.4 Sensitization

Including the subject here completes the index of particular susceptibilities. It has been discussed in sections 7.2.4 (regarding ferritic stainless steels), 7.4.2 (austenitics) and 8.4.3 (welding austenitics).

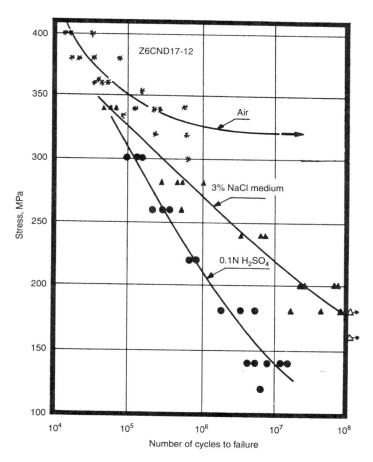

Fig. 10.2 Influence of a corrosive medium on the fatigue life of a 17Cr-12Ni austenitic stainless steel. Courtesy of *Stainless Steels*, P. Lacombe, B. Baroux, and G. Béranger, Ed., Les Editions de Physique Les Ulis

10.2 General and Localized Corrosion

10.2.1 Atmospheric and Aqueous Corrosion

In dry atmospheric conditions at humanly tolerable temperatures, iron and its alloys do not rust. However, the air surrounding us and (more importantly in this context) surrounding our structures is generally moist and often contaminated. Plain-carbon and low alloy steels corrode under such

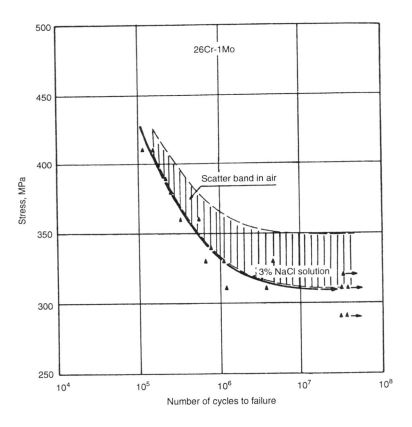

Fig. 10.3 Influence of a corrosive medium on the fatigue life of a 26Cr-1 Mo ferritic stainless steel. Courtesy of *Stainless Steels*, P. Lacombe, B. Baroux, and G. Béranger, Ed., Les Editions de Physique Les Ulis

circumstances, but stainless steels are resistant. In clean air free of soot and chlorides, all grades of stainless remain rust-free even in the most hot and humid conditions.

As contamination increases and if water with its dissolved salts condenses on the steel, a more careful choice is required. The graphs of Fig. 10.4 show atmospheric corrosion resistance as a function of chromium content. Two conclusions are evident: in the moderately aggressive atmospheres of semi-rural and industrial environments, a chromium content about 11 to 12% effectively combats corrosion; however, in marine environments almost 20% chromium content is required. Notice that in Fig. 10.4 the extent of corrosion is indicated by average penetration, which indicates that we are concerned for resistance to pitting corrosion, which stainless steels are susceptible to in marine environments and many industrial atmospheres, since these contain chlorides.

Figure 10.4 properly implies that the superferritics with their high chromium content offer more protection. Among other alloying additions that are beneficial to them, molybdenum is outstanding and becomes more effective as chromium content is increased. Both common interstitial elements, carbon and nitrogen, reduce pitting resistance, but experiments have shown that their effect can be offset to some extent by titanium additions. However, because steelmaking techniques currently can limit both carbon and nitrogen to low values, the circumstance and its remedy now are more academic than practical.

Signaling to us that pitting mechanisms differ in different crystal structures, the effect of titanium and nitrogen in austenitic grades is opposite to their influence in ferritics; titanium is detrimental while nitrogen is helpful. Beneficially high nitrogen levels can be attained through the addition of manganese.

Data abound for the performance of austenitic stainless steels in industrial and marine sites. Tables 10.1 and 10.2 are typical and present the generally favorable results of long-term exposure.

Whatever the class of stainless steel, special attention should be given to surfaces in sheltered or stagnant environments. Corrosion resistance stems from passivity. Passivity is threatened by a speck of soot or, worse, a particle of iron settling on the steel, which consequently becomes insulated from an oxygen-bearing atmosphere. Usually, wind and rain look after this. If they do not, the surfaces should be regularly hosed down.

Where stainless steels appear to fall victim to corrosive attack in the atmosphere, the cause generally lies not with a poor selection of steel but with inadequate attention to design. We have just mentioned the case where stagnation prevents the surface from having a fair chance to retain passivity. More severe circumstances arise where oxygen depletion initiates crevice

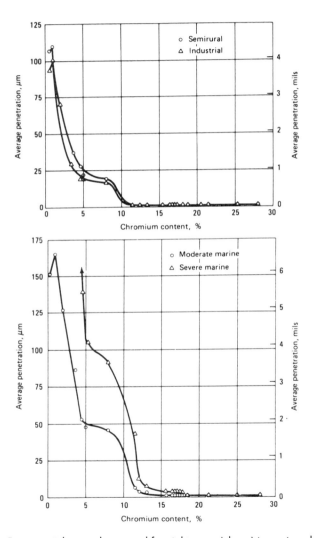

Fig. 10.4 Ferritic stainless steels exposed for eight years (above) in semi-rural and industrial atmospheres and (below) in moderate and severe marine atmospheres

corrosion, which we introduced in section 4.4.3.

In all circumstances and for all the stainless grades, resistance to crevice corrosion is improved as the amounts of major alloying elements are increased. This does not excuse thoughtless design but is a generalization worth remembering. In the austenitic class, molybdenum is particularly significant, and in its presence, nitrogen is beneficial.

Section 11.2.7 further discusses stainless steels in building construction where resistance to atmospheric corrosion is a principal concern.

Table 10.1 Atmospheric corrosion of austenitic stainless steels at two industrial sites

	New York City (industrial)		Niagara Falls (industrial-chemical)	
Type(a)	Exposure time, years	Specimen surface evaluation	Exposure time, years	Specimen surface evaluation
302	5	Free from rust stains	$< \frac{2}{3}$	Rust stains
302	26	Free from rust stains	...	...
304	26	Free from rust stains	< 1	Rust stains
304	...	...	6	Covered with rust spots and pitted
347	26	Free from rust stains	...	...
316	23	Free from rust stains	$< \frac{2}{3}$	Slight stains
316	...	...	6	Slight rust spots, slightly pitted
317	...	...	$< \frac{2}{3}$	Slight stains
317	...	...	6	Slight stains
310	...	...	< 1	Rust stains
310	...	...	6	Rust spots; pitted

(a) Solution-annealed sheet, 1.6 mm ($\frac{1}{16}$ in.) thick

Table 10.2 Corrosion of AISI 300-series stainless steels in a marine atmosphere
Based on 15-year exposures 250 m (800 ft) from the ocean at Kure Beach, NC

AISI	Average corrosion rate		Average depth of pits		
type	mm/yr	mils/yr	mm	mils	Appearance(a)
301	$< 2.5 \times 10^{-5}$	< 0.001	0.04	1.6	Light rust and rust stain on 20% of surface
302	$< 2.5 \times 10^{-5}$	< 0.001	0.03	1.2	Spotted with rust stain on 10% of surface
304	$< 2.5 \times 10^{-5}$	< 0.001	0.028	1.1	Spotted with slight rust stain on 15% of surface
321	$< 2.5 \times 10^{-5}$	< 0.001	0.067	2.6	Spotted with slight rust stain on 15% of surface
347	$< 2.5 \times 10^{-5}$	0.001	0.086	3.4	Spotted with moderate rust stain on 20% of surface
316	$< 2.5 \times 10^{-5}$	< 0.01	0.025	1.0	Extremely slight rust stain on 15% of surface
317	$< 2.5 \times 10^{-5}$	< 0.001	0.028	1.1	Extremely slight rust stain on 20% of surface
308	$< 2.5 \times 10^{-5}$	< 0.001	0.04	1.6	Spotted by rust stain on 25% of surface
309	$< 2.5 \times 10^{-5}$	< 0.001	0.028	1.1	Spotted by slight rust stain on 25% of surface
310	$< 2.5 \times 10^{-5}$	< 0.001	0.01	0.4	Spotted by slight rust stain on 20% of surface

(a) All stains easily removed to reveal bright surface.

As we move on to aqueous corrosion, we have to recognize a fuzzy dividing line, for we have already spoken of damp atmospheres and wet weather. Now attempting to make a distinction, we imagine stainless steels that are not in the air but immersed in water or made into pipe and tube through which water flows. Water! What sorts of water? Waters navigated in the next few paragraphs range from ones so exquisitely distilled and purified that while soap lathers, no thirst is satisfied, to barely potable waters, brackish waters, mine waters, and sea-waters.

Surely enough has been said about chlorides that no repetition is needed except a reminder that tap water is usually chlorinated. This may not concern domestic plumbing but must be considered in, for example, boiler installations, water treatment plants, and desalination plants where the variety of potential corrodents reads like a mail order catalogue. A further problem can arise through deposits of solids that can be calcareous or of an organic origin; both choke passivity. The calcareous deposits present opportunity for pitting and crevice corrosion. Bacterial attack, which occurs wherever water is allowed to stagnate, is more complicated.

Bacterial corrosion looks like any other pitting attack and its true cause will be undetected if the water or corrosion products are not carefully analyzed. Of the principal bacterial groups, two—the aerobic iron-oxidizing and manganese-oxidizing bacteria, and the iron-oxidizing and sulfur-oxidizing bacteria—generate cathodic reaction products, which encourage and accelerate pitting attack. Anaerobic sulfate-reducing bacteria also can be active. Mitigation requires avoidance of stagnant water (which is easily overlooked, for instance, after hydraulic testing of pipe, tube, and pressure vessels) or treatments that kill the bacteria.

Tests have shown that pitting corrosion is more marked in natural seawater than in artificial seawater, which is attributable to biochemical attack. Where seawater is used for cooling, it must be heavily chlorinated to kill bacteria. This, in turn encourages—but you've guessed—substantial pitting, crevice corrosion, or SCC. Whether or not high nickel alloys rather than stainless steels should be used is a matter for economic appraisal.

In seawater applications, cathodic protection is worth investigating. This can take the form of connected metallic anodes (iron, aluminum, or zinc) which, in practice, may be naturally offered by the surrounding structure. Alternatively an electric current can be impressed. At first, it can seem perverse that cathodic protection, which makes the stainless steel the cathode in a galvanic cell, should be at all attractive. After all, generally people strive to maintain passivity on the stainless steel surface, and passivity is created by the oxidizing conditions at the anode. Indeed, as mentioned in the next section, anodic protection can be applied to stimulate this process. However, where there are chloride ions at work at the anode to the extent that the protective oxide layer is unstable, passivity is out of the question. Consequently, anodic reactions are best suppressed.

Soils present a vehicle for aqueous corrosion. If soil is dry, it is usually benign. However, it generally carries water that contains such a variety of salts and organic material that we offer no single prescription about the choice of material. Indeed, underground piping is often of plain-carbon steel, probably coated and possibly cathodically protected; alloys of aluminum and copper commonly are used; and ceramics (in sewers) and plastics (all over the place) find their applications. We include soil corrosion as an aqueous corrosion category one should be aware of and for which stainless steels should be considered.

The 18-8 family of stainless steels resists most mine-water environments. In the presence of highly oxidizing materials—sulfates and sulfuric acid— type 304 is satisfactory. Where oxidation is less intensive, type 316 or even more highly alloyed grades are used.

10.2.2 Common Acids and Alkalis

Most cases in the following section deal with "general" corrosion; there is no pitting or crevice corrosion, to which we alluded earlier, and the metal is eaten away fairly evenly. Consequently, thickness allowances ensure safety during the anticipated life of the vessel or structure.

Corrosion rates of several stainless steels in sulfuric acid are shown in Fig. 10.5. Figure 10.6 illustrates temperature and concentration dependence. Because no universal measure of corrosion loss appears to be agreed on, Table 10.3 can be helpful.

Table 10.3 Multipliers to convert other units to mils per year

Unit to be converted	Multiplier
Inches per year	1.000
Inches per month	12,000
Millimeters per year	39.4
Micrometers per year	0.039
Milligrams per square decimeter per day	1.44/D
Grams per square meter per day	14.4/D

D = density in grams per cubic centimeter. Note: The following approximate relationship is often useful in cursory comparisons of corrosion rates of stainless steels: 10 g/m^2/d = 100 mdd ≈ 20 mpy ≈ 0.5 mm/y. Source: A.J. Sedriks, *Corrosion of Stainless Steels*, John Wiley & Sons, Inc., 1996

Nickel, molybdenum, and copper in austenitic steels improve corrosion performance substantially. However, Fig. 10.5 and 10.6 show that as temperature and acid concentration increase, stainless steels of all compositions become more susceptible. At very high concentrations (see Fig. 10.7), passivity is induced, and corrosion rates in austenitic stainless diminish.

In those intermediate concentrations where corrosion is appreciable, one approach to mitigation is to add a strong oxidizing agent such as nitric acid to the sulfuric acid. Figure 10.8 shows the improvement with small additions. But such a remedy is not always practicable. Anodic protection (in-

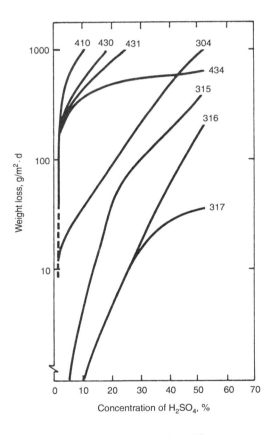

Fig. 10.5 Corrosion rates of various stainless steels in different concentrations of underaerated sulfuric acid at 20 °C. Reprinted with permission from A.J. Sedriks, *Corrosion of Stainless Steels*, John Wiley & Sons, Inc., 1996

creasing the passivity by applying an electric current to make the steel more strongly anodic) has been shown effective. If all this fails, then the use of alloys of very high nickel content might be necessary.

In section 11.2.3 where the use of stainless steel in chemical plants is discussed briefly, we point out that small changes to the composition of sulfuric acid at any concentration can substantially effect performance. We emphasize the point here.

In nitric acid, a strong oxidizing agent, the preferred stainless is the low carbon grade austenitic 304L. The low carbon content provides substantial immunity to intergranular corrosion caused by sensitization in the heat-affected zone of welds. Unlike its effect in sulfuric acid corrosion, molybdenum is harmful here; it dissolves to produce a soluble compound. Another detrimental constituent is hexavalent chromium, Cr^{6+}, inevitably formed as

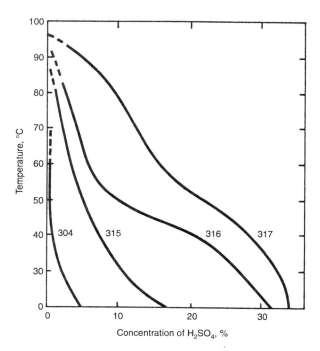

Fig. 10.6   Concentrations and temperatures of sulfuric acid solutions required to give a corrosion rate of 25 g/m^2 · d for various stainless steels. Reprinted with permission from A.J. Sedriks, *Corrosion of Stainless Steels,* John Wiley & Sons, Inc., 1996

a corrosion product. Figure 10.9 clearly indicates that an accumulation, which can arise through recirculation of the acid, should be avoided if at all possible.

The corrosion resistance of high silicon cast iron has been known for at least half a century. Only more recently, high silicon austenitic stainless steels have been made. Containing 4 to 6% silicon, these have remarkably good resistance to concentrated nitric acid (Fig. 10.10).

Experience shows that of the stainless steels the austenitics are by far the most resistant to phosphoric acid. Their performance is improved by molybdenum and much improved by small additions of copper, as Fig. 10.11 demonstrates.

Figure 10.12 shows that except at very low concentrations, hydrochloric acid is a vicious corrodent. The polarization curve is represented by Fig. 10.13; there is no active-passive transition. The presence of oxidants is deleterious (contrary to their effect in sulfuric acid) because their only function here is to increase the anodic corrosion rate. Because there is no passive potential, anodic protection is out of the question.

Formic acid is the most highly ionized and therefore the most corrosive of the organic acids. Type 304 is a satisfactory material of containment at

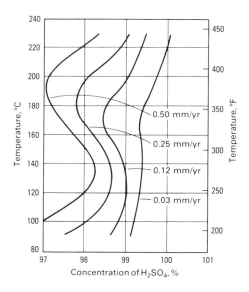

Fig. 10.7 Isocorrosion diagram for type 304 stainless steel in highly concentrated H_2SO_4

ambient temperatures, but at elevated temperatures higher alloy compositions are the safest bet. A low carbon grade is important, especially where
acetic acid is involved, in order to avoid intergranular corrosion through
weld decay.

In alkali environments of caustic soda, we have to be on guard against the
possibilities of caustic SCC, which we mentioned earlier. At temperatures
less than 50 °C (120 °F), ferritic and austenitic grades are resistant to
general corrosion in caustic soda at any concentration. (Remember, however, that local concentrations can far exceed the measured concentration of
the solution!) At higher temperatures up to 100 °C (270 °F), the austenitic

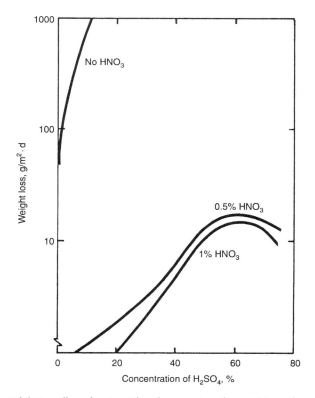

Fig. 10.8 Inhibiting effect of nitric acid on the corrosion of type 304 stainless steel in sulfuric acid solutions at 100 °C. Reprinted with permission from A.J. Sedriks, *Corrosion of Stainless Steels,* John Wiley & Sons, Inc., 1996

steel 304L performs better. More chromium and more nickel in both austenitic and duplex grades enhance resistance to general corrosion as temperatures increase. However, when either residual or applied stresses are foreseen, designers frequently play safely by specifying a very high nickel alloy or pure nickel.

10.3 Molten Metals and Salts

The containment of liquid metals has become more important with the development of the nuclear industries. Here the problem is not only one of resisting corrosive attack of all kinds but also of maintaining a clean surface so that heat transfer is not impeded. Although high alloy austenitics have been used in contact with lithium and sodium, more exotic alloys are generally in service. In all cases where liquid metals are concerned, the possible

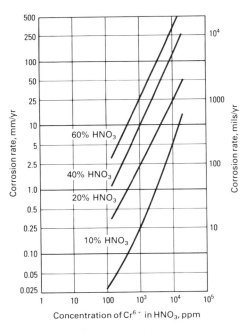

Fig. 10.9 Effect of hexavalent Cr^{6+} contamination on the corrosion rate of type 304 in HNO_3. Test duration: 40 h

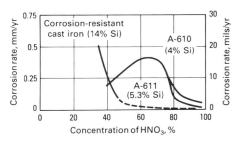

Fig. 10.10 Effect of silicon content on the corrosion of iron and iron-chromium-nickel alloys in boiling HNO_3

reactions are complex, and field experience is not as extensive and prolonged as it is with corrosion in aqueous solutions. Embrittlement is a particular hazard underlined in a topic whose specialization is outside the scope of this text.

Molten salts are another matter! While they also are used for heat transfer, a longer history is to be found in tool and die shops where steels are heat treated. To some extent, the corrosion principles that relate to a metal surrounded by molten salt are similar to those described in aqueous corrosion; there is a movement of ions, reduction at the cathode, and oxidation at the anode.

The situation is more interesting because molten salts not only conduct ions (as is the case in aqueous electrolytes), but they also conduct electrons. Consequently, reduction reactions are not restricted to a cathodic metal surface; they can take place in the molten salt, increasing the reaction rate beyond that expected in an aqueous cell. What is more, at the invigorating temperatures of molten salts, reactions are rapid.

Selective attack of one element or another is a common characteristic of molten salt corrosion. For example, in stainless steels, chromium can be reactive at the metal surface and a chromium compound is formed with a

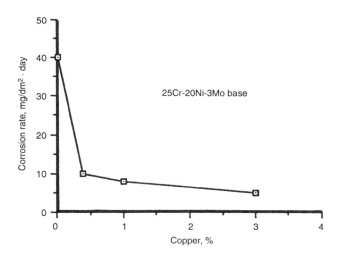

Fig. 10.11   Influence of pure copper on the corrosion resistance of the 25Cr-20Ni-3Mo stainless steel in pure 85% H_3PO_4 phosphoric acid at 150 °C. Courtesy of *Stainless Steels*, P. Lacombe, B. Baroux, and G. Béranger, Ed., Les Editions de Physique Les Ulis

consequent surface depletion. Then chromium ions diffuse to the surface from the body of the metal, causing internal vacancies that agglomerate. The vacancies generally get together at such active sites as grain boundaries where they cause intergranular weakness and failure.

A common molten salt bath in tool and die shops largely contains nitrates. To temperatures of approximately 500 °C (930 °F), plain carbon and low-alloy

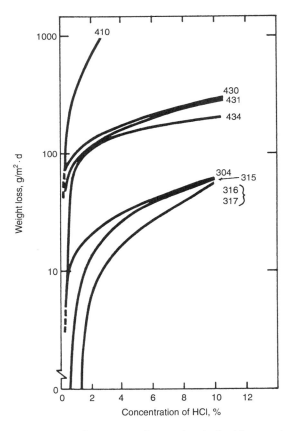

Fig. 10.12 Corrosion rates of various stainless steels in hydrochloric acid solutions at 20 °C. Reprinted with permission from A.J. Sedriks, *Corrosion of Stainless Steels,* John Wiley & Sons, Inc., 1996

steels work well enough as salt pots. The corrosion rate is much reduced in ferritic and (more so) in austenitic stainless steels, which are generally used at higher temperatures.

Other common molten salts that must be contained are carbonates, where austenitic stainless is satisfactory up to 500 °C (930 °F), beyond which superalloys and ceramics are used. In molten hydroxides, chromium is preferentially oxidized. And at this point, there is no need to suggest that better performances are expected in molten chlorides as chromium and nickel contents are increased beyond the range where iron is the principal element, no longer constituting stainless steels.

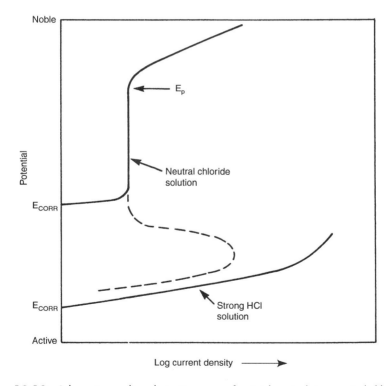

Fig. 10.13 Schematic anodic polarization curves for stainless steels in a neutral chloride solution and a strong hydrochloric acid solution. Reprinted with permission from A.J. Sedriks, *Corrosion of Stainless Steels,* John Wiley & Sons, Inc., 1996

10.4 Corrosion in Gases at Elevated Temperatures

At normal atmospheric temperatures and where the gas is dry, general corrosion is immeasurably small. But the presence of moisture allows galvanic attack whose severity is influenced by the ions absorbed into what is now an aqueous electrolyte. If the gas remains dry, it becomes a corrodent as temperature is increased. For stainless steels in dry gases that are nonoxidizing, especially the halogens fluorine and chlorine, the threshold temperature at which general corrosion may be troublesome is surprisingly low. We will come to that.

10.4.1 Oxidation

Oxidation is the most significant of high-temperature corrosion processes. On one hand, oxidation can be the cause of ultimate failure through metal removal; on the other hand, oxygen produces a surface layer that inhibits attack by more malevolent elements.

That surface layer is, initially, of chromic oxide, whose persistence is important to the continued well being of the underlying metal. It resists the flow of oxygen and metal ions. However, depending on the composition of the environment, its temperature, and the constitution of the steel, the scale can become physically and chemically changed, presenting an inner layer of an iron-chromium oxide (the spinel $FeCr_2O_4$) and an outer layer of ferric oxide. This is not nearly as impervious as chromic oxide, and cracking and spalling, which reveal fresh metal for attack, can aggravate the situation. At those temperatures at which stainless steel is not generally used in continuous service (say, above 1000 °C, or 1830 °F), chromic oxide can volatilize and the corrosion rate accelerates beyond practical tolerance.

Obviously best performance occurs when the chromic oxide film is maintained. It will, of course, grow slowly, and at all but very modest temperatures, eventual metal loss calls for replacement.

While a hefty chromium content is a first requirement for oxidation resistance as the temperatures increase, tests have shown that for the same chromium content, nickel additions are beneficial. Perhaps the adhesion of the scale is improved, the rate of ionic diffusion is reduced, or the transformation of chromic oxide to the less resistant ferric-chromic oxide is impeded. Figure 10.14 illustrates the effect of increasing nickel and chromium.

Several theories (but not the ones that pertain to nickel) are available to rationalize the beneficial effect of silicon. Figure 7.20 compares the influence of 3% silicon (AISI 302B) on the composition of 302 (a straight 18-8)

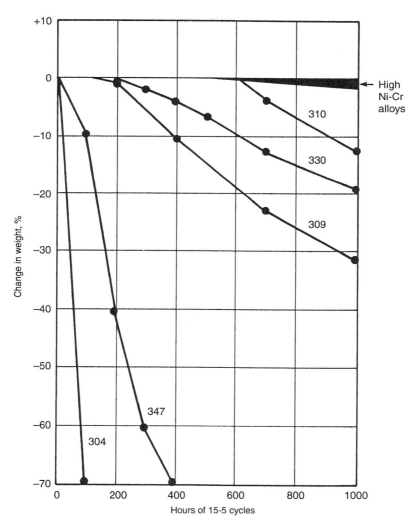

Fig. 10.14 Scaling resistance of some Fe-Cr-Ni alloys in air at 980 °C. The test employed cyclic exposures with each cycle consisting of 15 min at 980 °C and 5 min of cooling. Reprinted with permission from A.J. Sedriks, *Corrosion of Stainless Steels,* John Wiley & Sons, Inc., 1996

with the performance of AISI 310 (25-20). Higher silicon contents reportedly close the gap. Aluminum can play a similar role, but it is more difficult to introduce into commercial steelmaking processes.

As a selection is made for service at high temperature, long-term strength must be considered as well as corrosion resistance. Consequently, ferritic stainless steels are restricted in their use above 650 °C (1200 °F). This is not because of oxidation resistance but because creep resistance is unsatisfactory. Section 7.2.2 showed that ferritic steels suffer 475 °C (885 °F) embrittlement.

A common oxidizing atmosphere is engine exhaust gases, which gain increasing attention as emission control becomes more important because it involves not only the exhaust composition but its temperature. The use of stainless in exhaust systems is described in section 11.3.1 where the generalization is reported that up to temperatures of 800 °C (1470 °F), most stainless steels show little attack. Beyond that, richer stainless alloys are needed, and above 1200 °C (2190 °F), no iron base alloy is satisfactory.

Catastrophic oxidation was first reported in the late 1940s. Alloys that normally withstand higher temperatures in flowing air-rich atmospheres fail miserably in circumstances where oxide mixtures with low melting temperatures apparently are formed at the metal surface. This may simply arise as a result of a static atmosphere, or it may be associated with contaminants.

10.4.2 Sulfur-Containing Atmospheres

In sulfur containing atmospheres, the most likely aspirants are sulfur dioxide (or possibly trioxide) and hydrogen sulfide. All can occur in flue gases as well as in many processing industries.

Dry sulfur dioxide is more corrosive than dry air, but high chromium steels, in practical terms, are resistant up to temperatures about 900 °C (1650 °F). Specific service temperatures are suggested in Table 10.4. Water vapor, which is usually present in flue gases, accelerates the attack. Generally, however, the same sorts of considerations apply to the selection of stainless steels in the presence of gaseous sulfur oxides as in air. We rely on the formation of a chromium rich oxidic protection enhanced by the presence of those other elements found in the commercially available stainless steel classes. After all, that is why the alloys were developed.

Hydrogen sulfide presents a quite different situation. No longer is the formation of an oxidic protective surface a safeguard. Where sulfur dominates in the atmosphere, low melting-point phases form at the metal surface. While none of these compounds and their eutectics is attractive, nickel is

Table 10.4   Generally accepted maximum service temperature in sulfur dioxide for selected stainless steels

Material	Temperature, °C
304	800
321	800
347	800
310	1050
410	700
430	800
446	1025

Source: A.J. Sedriks, *Corrosion of Stainless Steels,* John Wiley & Sons, Inc., 1996

particularly deleterious. Aluminum, however, is a useful addition. Perhaps this is because even under very low oxygen partial pressures, alumina can form and provide protection, or perhaps the stability of aluminum sulfide helps. When high chromium stainless steels are inadequate, designers generally turn to cobalt-base alloys.

10.4.3 Halogens

Halogens constitute a depressing note on which to end the chapter, but it must be done, and our comments will not surprise those who have stayed so far. Operating temperatures above 300 °C (570 °F) in atmospheres of dry chlorine or hydrogen chloride confound most stainless steels. Because nickel chloride is among the least volatile of the scales that form, the high nickel alloys work best. Dry fluorine is more aggressive. One must turn to more exotic materials.

Applications of Stainless Steels

11.1 Introduction

Section 1.7 touched on the applications of stainless steel and threatens a more complete survey. That threat is fulfilled here. A review of several noteworthy commercial uses precedes discussion of three specific applications, each illustrating an important use and collectively telling of the versatility of stainless.

A principal factor in selecting a stainless steel is corrosion resistance. In some environments, particular susceptibilities to corrosion processes must be guarded against. These are only briefly mentioned in this section because they have been dealt with more comprehensively in Chapter 10.

11.2 General Applications

11.2.1 Cutlery

Cutlery by no means comprises a great tonnage but represents the earliest significant use of stainless steel, that is, for knives, which were first made about 1913 or 1914. With a composition approximately 13% chromium and 0.25% carbon, these blades were rustless compared to other tableware and kitchenware, and they could be heat treated to provide a good cutting edge. At first, there existed a prejudice against them that stainless more quickly lost its sharpness, but experience won out. Rustless knives became accepted, and they contributed to a realization that hygienic conditions in the kitchen were no less important than sterile instruments in the hospital operating room. Indeed, the observation of the former conditions might avoid the necessity of the latter requirement.

Many—perhaps most—early knives were made by steelmakers in Sheffield, England, and even today many knives with still shiny blades bear the stamp "Firth Stainless" or "Firth-Brearley Stainless" as shown in Fig. 11.1. Firth was one of the earliest steelmakers to make stainless blades; Brearley (as mentioned in Chapter 2) was one of the metallurgists responsible for the development of stainless steel.

Although opulent dining tables can be laid with silver flatware (and pretentious ones with silver plate), most cutlery made today is stainless steel. Evidence to substantiate assertions about the ubiquity of stainless steel cutlery includes a contemporary advertisement, "Special Offer: $520.00 Stainless Service for 8. A 40-piece set. Now only $297. [Canadian] All Dishwasher Safe." This is not a bad price for a long-term investment.

You may want to surreptitiously check out your own flatware. If it is silver, that will be obvious enough. It is heavy, and family will guard it. Then test the rest with a magnet. Knife blades should be magnetic because they are martensitic stainless, grades 410 or 420. Spoons and forks are often found to be nonmagnetic because they are made of an austenitic grade, probably 301, or they can be magnetic and probably a ferritic stainless. As

Fig. 11.1   An old Firth Stainless knifeblade

to being "dishwasher safe," the softer stainlesses (the spoons and forks) may scuff, but unlike the silverware they do not require polishing by a butler's staff.

11.2.2 Food Processing

From those early cutlery applications, stainless steel usage quickly extended into many aspects of food processing from farm to factory. Although plows are more commonly made of plain-carbon or low-alloy steel, hardenable stainless steels (type 410, for example) have been used where soils are particularly corrosive and abrasive. Still on the farm, hardenable stainless steels can be used for planting machines, and ferritic or (more commonly) austenitic stainless steels can be used for tanks carrying liquid fertilizers.

Those gleaming trucks transporting milk and other liquid food products on the highway are made of stainless (generally type 304) that is as nonmagnetic as (but much more economical than) the celebrated silver churn of W.S. Gilbert's lyric in *Patience*. Storage and processing vessels for milk, beer, wine, and fruit juices are almost always made of stainless steel. This is usually 18-8 or a near relative.

A point to remember about these vessels in service is the susceptibility of austenitic stainless steel to corrosive attack by the chloride ion, a topic discussed in sections 4.2.4 and 10.1.1 and to which we refer too frequently perhaps. The ion is present in hypochlorite solution, which is commonly used to disinfect and sterilize. Hypochlorite cleansing is followed by a water rinse. The thoroughness of this rinse is vital; otherwise traces of hypochlorite remaining in low spots of the vessel will concentrate through evaporation and cause pitting and possibly cracking. Also note a special sort of attack not tolerated in the manufacture of bourbon whiskey where even the smallest amounts of iron will blacken that good, golden liquid. For that reason the austenitic stainless steel fermenting tanks are passivated by hot, dilute nitric acid (followed, needless to say, by a thorough neutralizing and rinsing cycle) before use. This may come as a surprise because stainless steel forms its own passive surface layer. However, in certain instances (of which the manufacture of bourbon appears to be one) the very slightest traces of surface iron present, perhaps, as a result of forming and machining operations are injurious and call for this additional precaution.

Most metal parts of food processing equipment in the kitchen, store, and factory are made of stainless steel. Some of them (cutters, sinks, counters, and trays, for example) may not be subjected to particularly corrosive environments or to high temperatures, but they must be scrupulously and easily cleansed. Other applications, such as the processing of fruits and pickles, demand a special corrosion resistance. Others (for instance, autoclaves and moving belts through bakery ovens) must work at elevated temperatures.

The thermal conductivity of stainless steels is much lower than that of plain carbon steels; ferritic and martensitic alloys are about one-half as conductive while austenitic steels have values about one-third. Comparisons are shown in Fig. 11.2. Consequently, to take advantage of the corrosion and abrasion resistance of stainless steel without forfeiting uniform heat distribution, cooking utensils can be made of clad materials.

Of all the places where stainless steel is used, those that involve getting food to our bellies are the most evident. An engaging exercise is to keep a tally for a day or so (or to ask one's children to) of those myriad instances.

11.2.3 Chemical Industry

Austenitic stainless steels are a standard material of construction in much of the chemical industry as in the production of acids and alkalis, ammonia, fertilizers, organic acids, and plastics. Stainless steels are not used in the production of hydrochloric acid because they pit (and worse). Austenitic grades are susceptible to stress corrosion cracking, and while many ferritic

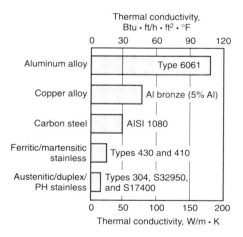

Fig. 11.2 Comparison of thermal conductivity for carbon steel, copper alloy, aluminum, and stainless steels

grades are not affected by the chloride ion this way, their resistance is not universal. In short, stainless steels are given a wide berth as far as hydrochloric acid is concerned, and where chloride ion is present in any condition a selection should be cautious and judicious.

Not suprisingly, we cannot cover all places where stainless steels serve the chemical industry, but we will try to give useful examples.

Sulfuric acid lies at the heart of the chemical industry. While stainless steels usually are resistant to sulfuric acid, such a generalization must be hedged. And we are by no means the first to warn that although published corrosion data are a good guide, what seem to be minor variants in specific conditions in fact can be disastrous.

In sulfuric acid environments, austenitic grades are by far the most common and are substantially corrosion-free where the acid at room temperature is above 93% concentration. (This of course relates to the passivation of the steel.) At lower concentrations, corrosion occurs if the acid is not aerated. Circumstances may demand that the stainless is purposely made anodic by impressing an electric current on it to develop and maintain passivity.

While superalloys must be used in some sulfuric acid environments in chemical plants, austenitic stainless grades are very common. Weldability, especially of the very low carbon grades, is a particular point in their favor.

Handling nitric acid up to 95% concentration presents no particular corrosion problems for austenitic stainless steel. Storage and transportation are usually in vessels and pipe of type 304. (At higher concentrations, an aluminum alloy is used.) The actual production of the acid (usually by the oxidation of ammonia) involves high temperatures. Consequently mechanical properties are a first consideration.

Caustic soda, the most common alkali, is an active reagent in the manufacture of soap and paper and in the textile and tanning industries. It is made concurrently with chlorine by the electrolysis of sodium chloride solution, brine. Although nickel exhibits superior corrosion resistance, austenitic stainless steels generally contain and transport caustic soda. They are perfectly satisfactory for caustic concentrations up to 50% and at temperatures below 95 °C (205 °F), conditions that accommodate most requirements. While ferritic materials are more susceptible to caustic stress-corrosion cracking, the phenomenon does occur with the austenitic stainless steels at high temperatures and concentrations (see section 10.2.2).

Ammonia, used in the manufacture of alkalis, fertilizers, and nitric acid and in liquid form as a commercial refrigerant is made predominantly from natural gas whose principal constituent is methane. The process is complicated.

Briefly, following desulfurization, catalytic steam reforming at high temperature produces a mixture of hydrogen and carbon dioxide. The carbon dioxide is removed, and the hydrogen is then catalytically combined with nitrogen from the air (high temperatures again) to produce ammonia. During these steps, the vessels and associated equipment are exposed to sulfides, chlorides, and combusted burner gases, as well as oxygen, nitrogen, hydrogen, and carbon dioxide at elevated temperatures. Consequently, they are potentially subject to hydrogen embrittlement, nitriding, corrosion from sulfides, chlorides, and carbonic acid. They must be oxidation resistant and capable of high-temperature operation.

In such demanding environments, several stainless steels are called into service. AISI 304, 321, and 316 are used in desulfurization tanks, and 310 is used for pipe and tube for which 430 and 304 are used to protect the external thermal insulation. Tie rods and tube supports are of 304 and 321. Heat exchanger tubes are made of 430.

Austenitic stainless steels are used where ammonia is contained or carried as gas or as ammonia in water (which is commonly, but not altogether correctly, called ammonium hydroxide). Liquid ammonia (like most condensed gases at subzero temperatures) is accommodated by austenitic stainless. The increase in strength at lowered temperatures is greater with the 200 series, which is gaining popularity in cryogenic applications.

11.2.4 Heat Exchangers

Because heat is money, its conservation through heat exchangers is an important economic aspect of manufacture and power generation. Heat exchangers are of many designs, but a common type is the shell-and-tube heat exchanger illustrated in Fig. 11.3 in which heat is transferred (in this case) from steam circulating in the shell to water passing through the tube bundle.

An exercise in life cycle costing (LCC, section 1.6) may be especially appropriate here to assess the most economical material for heat exchanger tubing, shell, and plates. The answer can be a stainless steel (ferritic or austenitic). It will hold strength at operating temperature and maintain heat-transfer properties because insulating deposits do not accumulate. If such attributes show prominently on the savings side of the ledger, the question of which grade to use remains. For example, chloride pitting is a common heat exchanger problem greatly affected by operating conditions but mitigated by the choice of a higher alloy or a duplex grade. Many possibilities

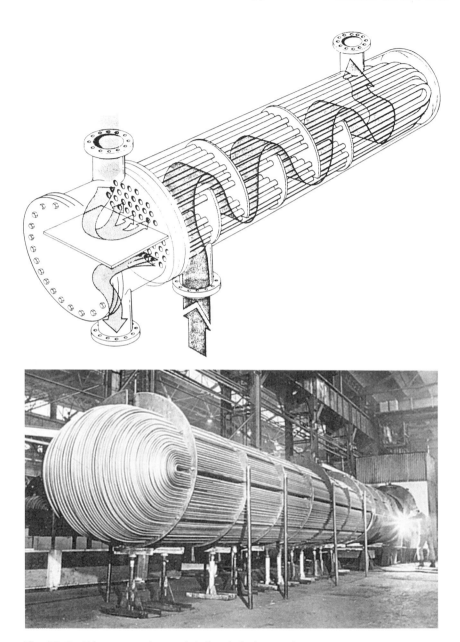

Fig. 11.3　Tubing in stainless steel shell-and-tube heat exchanger

would be included in the LCC exercise, for example, adjustments to operating conditions, water treatment, barrier coatings or other surface treatments, and anodic protection.

11.2.5 Petroleum Refineries

Before refineries had to process sour crude, that is, oil containing hydrogen sulfide, stainless steel was not used very much. However, as sour wells were brought in, stainless steel became a common construction material. Pressed by the thirst of the automobile for gasoline, what began as a fairly straightforward fractional distillation process had already been supplemented by catalytic cracking so more gasoline could be made from the heavier fractions. Through this and other developments, the major products of a petroleum refinery, fuels, solvents, lubricating oils, and waxes, to name a few, became supplemented by literally hundreds of petrochemicals. The substantially increased range of products together with the requirement to treat sour crude brought stainless steel in quantity into the petroleum refineries.

Again, economic compromises were made, because no affordable material could be guaranteed permanency. Here we consider only sulfide attack. This takes two forms. The first is, sulfidation, which at high temperatures in atmospheres containing hydrogen sulfide creates a loose, friable scale that reduces metal thickness. Such a circumstance arises in the hydrodesulfurization of petroleum liquids. Higher chromium contents and added nickel can stem but not stanch the corrosion.

The second challenge presented by hydrogen sulfide is the more pernicious phenomenon of stress corrosion cracking, which as we suggested in section 10.1.1 is difficult to differentiate from hydrogen embrittlement. Such failure is common in hardened plain-carbon and low-alloy steels in a hydrogen sulfide environment, but hydrogen sulfide had not been thought to be a treatment specific to austenitic stainless steels. The evil agent appears to be a polythionic acid, $H_2S_4O_6$, which forms during shutdowns when aqueous condensation occurs. If the stainless has become sensitized during operation, grain boundaries are attacked and failure results. The usual mitigation applies including the minimization of grain boundary depletion by using very low carbon steel containing titanium or niobium carbide formers (321 or 347), which should be heat treated at 900 to 925 °C (1650 to 1700 °F) before service to ensure the maximum precipitation of titanium or niobium carbide. If the steel is to be used at operating temperatures below 400 °C (750 °F), practice has shown that the use of a low carbon austenitic steel is sufficient.

These metallurgical prescriptions are supplemented by two fairly obvious procedural precautions: preventing water condensation and maintaining alkalinity.

Probably because chloride SCC in stainless steels is transgranular while polythionic SCC, which we have just reviewed, is intergranular, there is sometimes a reluctance to describe it categorically as "stress corrosion cracking," and it is referred to as "accelerated intergranular corrosion." Until the mechanisms of stress corrosion cracking are better understood, we shall not take sides.

11.2.6 Pulp and Paper Industry

The start of papermaking requires that cleaned wood chips be converted to a pulp by cooking them in one of several hot, aggressive solutions. In the craft process (the sulfate process), sodium sulfide is first made by the furnace reduction of sulfate with carbonaceous material. Mixed with sodium hydroxide solution, this is the liquor that cooks the wood chips in a digester, commonly cylindrical, about 3 m diameter and 15 m high.

Most digesters are made of mild steel with a corrosion allowance. Once that amount has corroded, the digester is repaired by applying an austenitic stainless steel weld overlay to maintain the pressure rating of the digester. In the late 1970s, many mills reported unexpected corrosive attack of the overlay. This appeared to be due to either dilution of chromium and nickel in the weld bead or to a nonuniformity of overlay composition caused by excessive deposition speeds.

Corrosion was also observed, not surprisingly, where the overlay beads did not form a complete surface, allowing galvanic attack to occur.

To mitigate these problems the application of stainless overlays to deteriorated mild steel plate in digesters now conforms to requirements of structural uniformity, chemical composition, and thickness of overlay as established by the Technical Association of the Pulp and Paper Industry.

The pulp and paper industry began to use stainless steels as early as the 1920s. Not only are there intensive corrosion conditions in evaporators, reheaters, and bleaching operations, but in blander environments, a polished surface finish has to be maintained. This is not only a requirement of screens, rolls, cylinders, calender and blades but also in locations where the flow of pulp must not be impeded by rough surfaces.

Pulp bleach plants, which produce white paper, present critical corrosion problems. AISI 317L was satisfactory for a long time. However, conditions have become more demanding as environmental regulations have called for a reduction in effluent. Among the possible choices, which also include titanium alloys and nickel-base alloys, three groups of stainless should be included in any LCC. Table 11.1 summarizes their characteristics.

11.2.7 Architecture, Building, and Construction

Because of its excellent corrosion resistance in atmospheric environments, stainless steel is ideal for externally exposed parts of buildings. Within buildings too its resistance to light abrasion makes it useful as railings and banisters, on escalators, and for elevator trim and floor plate. Its high-temperature strength makes it an attractive material for safety ladders where there may be fire hazards; examples abound. Despite earlier reports of failures, stainless steel has regained a reputation in swimming pools in both construction and pool equipment. More recently, stainless has been used for that mundane but vital purpose, reinforcing bar.

Table 11.1 Characteristics of three families of stainless steels for bleach plant service

Family	Examples	Characteristics	Comments
Austenitics	316L 317L 904L 254SMO AL-6XN	Tough, ductile, readily welded without loss of corrosion resistance; corrosion resistance related to alloy content	Bleach plant steels traditionally chosen from this group
	Nitronic 50	As above, with better pitting resistance than type 317L	Manganese-substituted austenitic, may be better value than type 317L; not common at present
Ferritics: low-interstitial type	29-4-2 29-4	Not as tough as austenitics, particularly after welding thicke sections. Special precautions needed for welding to avoid N pickup. Corrosion resistance, related to alloy content, can be very good.	Higher alloys have remarkable corrosion resistance. Thin-section (<3 mm, or 0.120 in.) may find applications as corrugated deck or tubing; not common at present. (C + N) ≤ 0.025%
Ferritics: Ti- or Ti + Nb stabilized type	29-4C NYBY MONIT SEA-CURE	0.02% C max versions	Less expensive 0.02% C version of low-interstitial ferritics, for thin-section weldments (≤1.14 mm, or 0.045 in.)
Duplex	2205 Ferralium 255	Tough, ductile, should be weldable without significant loss in corrosion resistance	Combines toughness and corrosion resistance of austenitics and ferritics. Can be made highly resistant to SCC

We cannot deal with all this in detail, but some stainless building applications, which follow, reflect international attention. Well-known landmarks include the Gateway Arch on the bank of the Mississippi River in St. Louis, MO; New York's Chrysler Building (still bright after nearly 70 years); the more recent CN Tower in Canada; the Chunnel terminal in London; and Canary Wharf Tower. The Kansai International Airport terminal in the bay of Osaka, said to be the longest building ever constructed, is clad with stainless steel tile covering a length of 1.7 km. In the Petronas Towers in Kuala Lampur, Malaysia, 4000 tonnes of panels and tubular structurals are used in a building said to observe classic Islamic geometric principles. The long overdue North Terminal of Washington Airport features stainless steel roofing on its 54 vaulted domes.

All these architectural applications and scores more involve austenitic stainless steels for which data on atmospheric corrosion abound. Tables 10.1 and 10.2 offer examples. Often, no doubt, the enhanced corrosion resistance of nickel-bearing stainless has been a consideration in its selection, and all reports of performance have been superlative. There is comparatively little information about manganese-substituted austenitics, which appear to perform well; and less about ferritic stainless steels. In making an appraisal, remember that the 18-8 stainless steels have a longer and richer history and perhaps have enjoyed a more powerful marketing force.

Where stainless is found to rust, the problem usually arises because of either chlorides or foreign particles, particularly iron dust, on the surface. The chlorides may be part of the environment of brisk sea air, or a nearby chemical plant can be the source. Foreign particles and traces of iron, which reduce the passivity of metal by shielding it from oxygen or locally reducing its effective chromium content, might have been deposited during the last stages of fabrication or during the erection of a structure. Nothing can be done to avoid a chloride exposure. In consequence, a more resistant steel must be specified, or coatings must be considered (see section 8.9). The presence of surface scruff can either be avoided by more careful handling or by subsequent cleansing.

Only a few years ago a suggestion that concrete reinforcing bar could be made of stainless steel might have been discounted because of higher initial capital costs. Per pound, austenitic stainless reinforcing bar costs about five times as much as mild steel. However, LCC, referred to in section 1.6, presents attractive results. Stainless steel reinforced concrete has a greater life expectancy because concrete failure is often associated with reinforcing corrosion. But we must use the phrase life expectancy in its fullest sense because few data are available for periods exceeding 20 years, and little if any exist for very low carbon ferritics. However, accelerated tests on austenitics support the contention of considerably longer life.

Most of the materials under test and in use are types 304 and 316. Marine environments, simulated marine environments, and tests in chloride solutions show a surprising tolerance to chlorides, a fact of importance not only in sea breezes but also on reinforced concrete bridges and piles that suffer deicing salts. The resistance to chlorides is probably associated with the fact that hostile environments surrounding the reinforced concrete under test are not those which steel inside the concrete experiences, either through the chemistry of the concrete or by seepage from without. Specifically, it seems that a high alkalinity surrounding the steel and/or created by initial corrosion stifles subsequent reactivity.

Without going into a detailed LCC, it is easy to appreciate that the cost of reinforcing bar is not a large proportion of the bill for the completed structure. For instance, in London, England, the total cost of the new Guildhall building is estimated at approximately $100 million (U.S.). Its consumption of about 140 tonnes of type 304 stainless steel reinforcing bar for external walls costs about $300,000 more than mild steel bar would cost. That is less than one-half a percent. However, the example is biased because the Guildhall is a pricey building in which the proportionate cost increase can be absorbed. Estimates for more commonplace structures such as bridges suggest a marginal cost increase of approximately 15% of total. When this is factored into a longer life expectancy, less maintenance, and greater safety, the proposition of stainless steel reinforcing bar deserves careful examination.

11.2.8 Textile Industry

This section began with an important but low-tonnage item, cutlery. It ends with another low-tonnage, highly specific application, textiles.

Resistance to high temperature oxidation is important when woven stainless steel fabric is used as a separation cloth between glass and mold in the manufacture of bottles and car windows and to reduce heat transfer and vibration in engine assemblies. Here we are more intrigued with the use of stainless steel woven into fabrics to avoid static.

Although the electrical conductivity of stainless steels is far lower than that of many other metals, it is considerably higher than the conductivity of fabrics whose insulating properties cause the buildup of static electricity.

This not only causes people a jolt when they are walking over carpet and touching a door-handle, but also the discharge can ignite fires, especially when tiny dust particles are nearby.

Austenitic stainless steel wire can be woven into the fabric of floor coverings, protective clothing, and dust filters so that the electric charge is carried away. Its conductivity is perfectly adequate for this; it is readily made into fine dimensions and woven with natural or synthetic fibers. Its other properties, particularly strength, corrosion-resistance, and wear-resistance, are attractive.

Although we have not put this to personal test, good authority tells us that clothing containing stainless fiber can be very quickly pulled on (and presumably off) without that frustrating puckering and snagging that happens when you least want it.

We now move to three specific applications.

11.3 Automotive Applications

Although the earliest uses in automobiles were engine parts requiring good strength, hardness, and corrosion-resistance, stainless steel soon became more widely used for exterior components while frequently replacing brass where the particular call was for corrosion resistance. The 1930 Model A Ford (which few readers will have had the pleasure of driving) used stainless in radiator shells, hubcaps, headlamp cases, and tie rods. Later in the 1930s, door handles, bumper bolts, radiator caps, window channels, and a number of other exterior items were of stainless grades.

In 1936, two Ford touring sedans were completely skinned with austenitic stainless steel (supplied by Allegheny) to showcase durability, and in the 1960s stainless steel Thunderbirds and Lincoln Continentals were made as demonstration vehicles. A Delorean specialty car with a stainless steel body made in the late 1970s showed minimal degradation after nearly 20 years.

In 1965 stainless steel consumption averaged 10 kg per car. Current information is not consistent, but we believe it safe to say that the figure has trebled largely due to the shift to stainless in exhaust systems. By 1990, about 75% of cars and trucks so utilized stainless steels, and by 1994 this had increased to 95%. This represents about 200,000 tonnes annual consumption for cars and much the same amount for light trucks. General Motors is now the largest single consumer of stainless steel in the United States.

Other stainless applications in automobiles include engine valves, seat belt anchors, water pump seals, thermostats, fuel filters, air injection tubes, trim, air bag components, and output shaft wear sleeves. While these do not represent large tonnages, each calls on a special combination of properties best answered by stainless steel. We will deal with two examples, which seem to be not only demonstrative of characteristic properties but also to call into play developments in manufacturing processes. The first of these is the big consumer, exhaust systems, and the second involves a much smaller consumption but the most exacting requirements, engine valves.

11.3.1 Automotive Exhaust Systems

The earliest stainless steel mufflers of ferritic grades were introduced in 1961 to combat corrosion in the newly popular dual exhaust systems, which took longer to warm up than the single muffler and tailpipe did. Consequently acidic condensate was formed from the exhaust gases and muffler perforation occurred. Worse, it occurred during the warranty period. The situation was aggravated by salt-water corrosion externally as salt became more liberally applied to roads.

Aluminized mild steel exhaust systems can be expected to last about 30 months, an improvement over the 18 months expected of mild steel. Stainless steel lasts for four or five years, and the objective for the year 2000 is a life of ten years with less than a 1% failure rate. (80% of failures are due to corrosion; most of the remainder are through fatigue.)

Not surprisingly, an early obstacle to be overcome was price. The nickel-bearing austenitic steels, though attractively formable and weldable, were too expensive, and a minimum effective chromium content in the ferritic grades required very low carbon and nitrogen values, which also enhance fabricability. Initially these were not always consistently attained, but improved manufacturing techniques such as argon oxygen decarburization (AOD) followed by continuous casting reliably reduced carbon and nitrogen values to less than 0.015 and 0.02% respectively.

But even at these low levels, ferritic stabilizers (titanium and possibly niobium and zirconium, too) are generally added to improve formability and weldability. All will also prevent intergranular corrosion; niobium improves creep resistance and toughness while zirconium enhances high temperature oxidation resistance.

The rolling and annealing schedule for ferritic stainless steels can be controlled to give an anisotropy (high normal, near zero planar) suitable for forming.

AISI 409 can be used for the entire cold end of the system (see Fig. 11.4). At the hot end, before the days of catalytic converters, 409 was capable of handling operating temperatures that did not exceed 700 °C (1290 °F). However, the converter operates about 900 °C (1650 °F). So while its shell may be made of 409, the substrate is made of higher chromium alloys, frequently proprietary brands. The operating temperature of the converter is necessarily influenced by its design. It must be reliable; legislation and replacement cost see to that! And the backpressure it creates must not overly detract from engine power.

If, generally as a result of the converter, temperatures in any parts of the hot end of the system exceed the tolerance of 409, the higher chromium AISI 439 can be substituted—at a price, of course. If flexible couplings are used at the hot end between the manifold exit and the catalytic converter, these are generally austenitic. The manifold itself is often of cast iron, which has good noise and vibration suppression, but it is bulky and therefore heavy. A high chromium ferritic steel such as 439 is sometimes used for a lighter but more expensive unit.

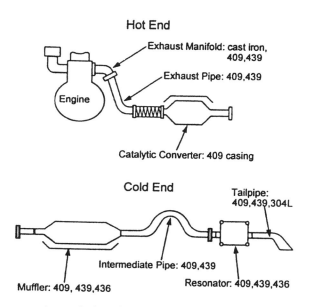

Fig. 11.4 Frequently specified stainless steels for automotive exhaust systems

11.3.2 Automotive Engine Valves

The mechanical requirements here are much more demanding than those in the previous example, requiring creep and fatigue resistance; resistance to abrasion and galling; tight dimensional tolerances; and the possibility of taking surface coatings.

Valves open and close more than 60 times per second with accelerations up to 1500 g and at operating temperatures of 800 °C (1470 °F) near the head of exhaust valve stems. (This temperature is lower in sodium-filled valves because of the enhanced heat transfer along the stem.)

Martensitic stainless steels were used for exhaust valves in the 1920s but as engine temperatures increased, their properties could not be sustained. They are now almost universally used for intake valves in gasoline and diesel engines.

Their manufacture generally involves two-step forging following induction heating. Hardening is by airblast from the forging temperature, with subsequent tempering to a hardness between 32 and 40 Rockwell C. Wearing surfaces, tip face, collet, and seat face can be subsequently induction hardened. Abrasion resistance can be improved by chrome plating, stellite deposition, or nitriding.

While austenitic stainless steels cannot be hardened to the level enjoyed by martensitic grades, their properties persist at exhaust valve temperatures. The most widely used austenitics for exhaust valves are of the manganese-nitrogen family. Compositions and mechanical properties are summarized in Table 11.2 for two of these, both developed by Armco. The austenitic 21-4N, always the more popular in Japan, has now overtaken 21-2N in North American engines, probably because of its greater austenite stability and better galling resistance. The nitrogen content of both alloys makes them susceptible to precipitation hardening following quenching from 1160 to 1190 °C (2120 to 2170 °F). Because the aging temperature coincides with engine operating temperature, hardening can be allowed to take place during

Table 11.2 Properties of two exhaust valve stainless steels

| Steel type | Composition, % | | | | | | Properties at 760 °C | | | Stress for 1% strain |
	C	Cr	Mn	N	Ni	Si	Ultimate tensile strength, MPa	0.2% yield Elongation, MPa	in 100,000 h, %	MPa
21-2N	0.55	21	9	0.3	2	0.25	...	...	...	...
21-4N	0.45–0.6	20–23	7–10	0.3–0.5	3–5	0.25	427	255	18	25 at 732 °C 227 at 538 °C

the initial engine operation. Further alloying additions to reduce lead corrosion, now no longer necessary where leaded fuels are illegal, brought vanadium and niobium or tungsten into the composition. Tungsten enhances hot strength and reduces pitting corrosion, thus eliminating initiation points for fatigue.

There are not only variants to compositions, but to the manufacturing process previously outlined. For instance, the steelmaking process can involve vacuum degassing; hard surfacing can be applied by plasma arc transfer; valve head and stem can be separately fabricated and processed in order to attain optimal performance properties in each, and then the two components can be friction welded. Some valves are now made by gas atomization and cold isostatic pressing followed by heating and extrusion. Such processing eliminates directionality in mechanical properties (which may not be an advantage), and, by the avoidance of segregation, the valves may reasonably be expected to have improved corrosion resistance.

11.4 Surgical Implants

Not uncommonly people in their sixties complain that they have been told they are too young to have a knee implant. Probably the surgeon is making the best estimate she can on the basis of the life-expectancy of the patient to avoid the eventual necessity of a second implant.

Implants are most commonly of austenitic stainless steel. This is not simply because stainless has a good track record, but it is because its track has been longer, the first successful implant having been performed in the late 1920s. In 1974 (the most recent year for which we could find records) nearly 2 million stainless steel implants of all types were made in the United States of which more than half were bone screw implants.

However, a stainless implant like its bearer is not immortal. If the stainless prosthetic is scrupulously fabricated (we will deal with this in a moment), the cause of its eventual failure is usually associated with design or with the way in which the implant has been attached. The matter of designing prosthetics is a subject in itself; we can't begin to describe it. However, problems arising from the way in which the piece is actually implanted involve familiar metallurgical principles.

The most common cause of failure is fatigue, especially corrosion fatigue (section 10.1.3) that is initiated through crevice corrosion (section 4.4.3) which arises at interfaces, for example, between the mating surfaces of a screw and plate. An opportunity for body fluids to seep in here initiates pitting corrosion from which a crack can develop. The joint must, therefore, be tight; and where appropriate, sealing gaskets must be inserted. The inevitable alternation of stresses accentuated by any freedom of movement between the two surfaces is the ingredient promoting corrosion fatigue. In passing, note that although a passive film can be maintained by body fluids, these contain about 1% of sodium chloride, which can be catastrophically active at a pH of 7.4 (just alkaline) and at body temperature about 37 °C.

Grade 316L is most commonly used for implants (see Fig. 11.5). It is important that the steel be fully austenitic with fine grain size to enhance formability and mechanical properties. Inclusions must, of course, be minimal, a requirement best met by vacuum degassing. Although molybdenum is present to enhance corrosion resistance, it should not exceed the range 2 to 4% for fear of inducing sigma phase embrittlement (see section 7.2.3) whose presence encourages crevice corrosion but whose likelihood is reduced by ensuring that the steel is fully austenitic. This, in turn, points to

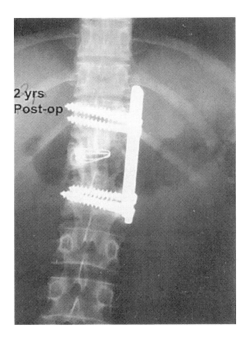

Fig. 11.5 X-ray of an implanted 316L spinal fixture plate and fasteners. Courtesy of Terray Corp.

nickel at the high end of the range and raises a warning should the prosthetic be cast, because here there is a likelihood of segregation, ferrite pools, and sigma.

The surface of the implant must be meticulously finished with no tool marks, nicks, scratches, or embedded foreign matter. Frequently surfaces are electropolished for this not only removes any embedded contaminants but reduces the potential area available to corrodents because of a finer finish.

Metal ions are released to some extent, however miniscule, through inevitable corrosion reactions. Chromium and nickel in the tissue surrounding the implant increases measurably, and evidence exists of specific metal buildup in the liver, kidney, and spleen. Reassuringly, these are small, and studies show that stainless has a low toxicity (see Appendix 2). Metal does not appear to be related to the very small number of tumors that have occurred at implant sites, for these have been otherwise accounted for, with initial tissue damage during implantation among the diagnoses.

Stainless is not used as much for hip implants, which have a high susceptibility to fatigue, since stresses on the implant can be very large (and alternating). Standing on one leg creates, on the implant, a load equivalent of 1.5 times the body weight. Titanium alloys and cobalt-base alloys (which have a better wear-resistance) are commonly used.

Our survey of the literature (which is substantial) and conversations with colleagues who are closer to the business lead us to believe that, with the exception of hip implants, stainless is a good bet. The metallurgical requirements and surface finish must be rigorously observed. That having been done, it remains for the designers and surgeons to recognize and avoid as far as they can the circumstances within their ambits that may lead to catastrophic failure.

11.5 Turbines

One of the turning points (and how appropriate is the phrase!) of technological invention was a realization that the rotation of an electric generator was best served by an engine which itself presented rotatory rather than reciprocating energy. With difficulty we avoid weaving a colorful historical fabric but must recall that first rotary jet engine, which is ascribed to Heron of Alexandria in approximately A.D. 300.

Heron's reaction turbine could not be harnessed to drive machines. Subsequent turbines (depending on a different principle in which the rotor was turned by the force of water directed onto its buckets or blades) were efficiently coupled as in the old overshot waterwheel. Contemporary water turbines engage both impulse and reaction principles as do steam turbines, which are at the heart of most electrical power generation in North America whether the source of heat is coal, oil, gas, or nuclear fuel.

High pressure, superheated steam enters the steam turbine at temperatures which bring the blades on the first stage to red heat. The blades, nozzles, and wheels on which they are mounted must sustain this temperature continuously under stresses created by the centrifugal force of the entire rotor assembly.

The gas turbine works on similar principles but at higher temperatures. However, while steam is easily compressed within its generator, the gas turbine requires a compressor, a rotary unit, which compresses air prior to combustion consuming a significant proportion of the energy of the turbine. The pressure of the combustion products and their heat transfer drives the turbine.

Turbines then present us with ranges of operating conditions to be sustained.

11.5.1 The Water Turbine

The water turbine offers no problems regarding operating temperature, but cavitation-erosion, which we mentioned in passing in section 7.4.3, is troublesome. It is a mechanical problem which arises through the collapse of air (or gas) bubbles formed at the metal surface, producing such high stress concentrations that fatigue cracks occur and metal can even be torn away. A highly work-hardenable surface mitigates this effect, and as mentioned in section 7.4.3, AISI 301 is best among the standard grades. However, a much higher work-hardening rate is achieved with a cobalt-containing manganese-nitrogen austenitic stainless whose nominal composition is given in Table 11.3. The alloy and its compatible welding electrodes are patented.

Table 11.3 Composition of austenitic stainless steel developed to resist cavitation corrosion

Element	Composition, wt%
Carbon	0.2
Chromium	17
Manganese	9.5
Silicon	2.5
Cobalt	9
Nitrogen	0.2
Iron	bal

Once again, however, the relationship between design and materials comes into play. A change in the flow pattern of water impinging on and moving through the turbine can substantially reduce the cavitation problem.

11.5.2 Steam Turbines

For a given difference between the temperature of source and sink, the efficiency of any heat engine improves as the source temperature increases. During the 20th century, higher operating temperatures raised the efficiency of steam turbines and contributed to a tenfold drop in coal consumption per unit of electrical energy generated. Those higher operating temperatures were associated with the availability of tolerant metal, notably the stainless steels.

Martensitic stainless was and still is used for rotors. Types 410 and 403 can be used to temperatures about 490 °C (910 °F). Where creep resistance is less important, these grades may be used to 540 °C (1000 °F). Modifications producing types 422 and 431 allow operating temperatures about 100 °C (212 °F) higher.

Although austenitic grades have a higher temperature capability, their lower thermal conductivity leads to failures where frequent start-ups and shutdowns induce thermal stresses. Operating conditions therefore determine the grade of stainless to be selected for maximum efficiency.

Ferritic stainless steels have been specially developed for turbine blading. Initially based on 12% chromium with additions to encourage the formation of strengthening carbide precipitates, more recent variants have pushed up the temperature of useful application. Noteworthy among them (and typical of the group) is an alloy based on iron with 11% chromium, whose additions of niobium, vanadium, and tungsten (while nitrogen and carbon are carefully controlled) are expected to give useful creep properties up to 650 °C (1200 °F).

11.5.3 Gas Turbines

The stainless steels used in steam turbines find applications in gas turbines as long as the temperatures are much the same. But the advantage of the gas turbine is its ability to use a higher temperature heat source than steam will provide. Consequently the turbine blading demands more than stainless is able to give if the principle of good heat engine design is to be exploited. Initially stainless was used, and it still is used where lower temperature conditions prevail. And there were occasions, reportedly in early jet fighter planes of World War II, where a very limited life of the turbine blades was acknowledged as they were pushed to higher temperatures, and the risk was taken that they would not last through the mission.

Older gas turbines made in the 1950s and 1960s relied extensively on stainless steel components, and many are still in operation, particularly stationary engines, whose components embody the precipitation-hardening grades.

A survey of components used in the GE CF6 aircraft engine, which was introduced about 1970 and is still widely used on many commercial airlines, illustrates the persistence of stainless steel for compressor blades where its creep resistance was, at the time, superior to any of the available titanium alloys. The higher pressure ratios of newer engines and the correspondingly high temperatures of the final compressor stages still favor precipitation-hardenable stainless over more recent titanium alloys.

Accruing to the advantage of stainless is its comparative fire resistance. On occasions when rotating blades of titanium alloy have rubbed against their housing, sparks have ignited the entire compressor section when it all consists of titanium. However, by replacing the titanium stationary vanes with stainless steel, fire propagation is avoided. Although the engine is severely damaged through blade rubs, some engine power is maintained.

We are reassured that blade rubs only occur when an engine is driven beyond its anticipated capacity and the creep of the blading exceeds the design tolerances. This can occur in high performance fighter jets whose specifications include stainless for the high-pressure compressor vane stages.

During the early development of gas turbine blade materials to provide better resistance to creep and oxidation at very high temperatures, the high nickel-iron alloys Nimonic, Inconel, and others appeared. These were complemented by chromium-base and cobalt-base alloys whose exotic compositions lie far beyond the range of stainless steels. And so we take our leave.

Identification of
Stainless Steels in Service

When stainless steels must be identified during service for purposes of quality control or inspection, the procedure must be nondestructive and not effect the fitness of the component for its application. Similar tests are used for identification as a preliminary step in failure analysis where, of course, the integrity of the piece is less important.

In addition to these purposes, the grade must be known when stainless enters the recycling stream because most stainless steels are recycled to produce a similar grade whenever possible. Clearly fast and efficient procedures for identification are necessary in all these cases. A summary of some of the available techniques follows.

Magnetic Testing

Typically, the first step in determining grade is to see if the steel is magnetic. The 400 series is, and the 300 and 200 series are nonmagnetic or only slightly so. Any simple magnet can be used; try it out on household cutlery as suggested in section 11.2.1.

Spark Testing

(Spark testing is not for the cutlery!) With experience, 200, 300, and 400 grades can be separated. Sparks are generated by using a powered grinding wheel of alumina or carborundum with a tangential speed at least 23 m/s. The sparks are best identified in a spark cabinet, a chamber with flat black walls and no natural light, into which the sparks are directed. The sparks generated have the characteristics listed in Table Appendix 1.1. This is a useful technique, but cautions are necessary: accuracy depends on the skill of the operator, protective glasses must be worn, and the sparks must be thrown clear of personnel. Obviously, if the piece is to remain in service, its shape and dimensional tolerances must be respected.

Spot Chemical Testing

When drops of specific chemicals are placed on the surfaces of stainless steels, the resulting reactions cause color changes that depend on the stainless grade. The tests involve placing a few drops of test solution on the surface of the metal to be identified, sometimes with a small piece of filter paper.

Spot testing with sulfuric acid or phosphoric acid can distinguish molybdenum-containing grades (316 and 317) from non-molybdenum grades (302 or 304), while testing with hydrochloric acid can differentiate low chromium 400 series grades (403, 410, and 416) from high chromium grades (430, 431, 440, and 446). Spot chemical testing does create a small surface imperfection, which may not be acceptable where surface finish is important.

Commercial spot chemical kits are available from:

- Koslow Scientific Company
  75 Gorge Road
  Edgewater, NJ 07020
  Telephone: 201-941-4484 Fax: 201-941-4485

Table Appendix 1.1   Spark characteristics of stainless steels compared to plain carbon steel

Material	Spark characteristics
Plain carbon steels	Heavy, dense sparks 45–60 cm (18–24 in.) long that travel completely around the grinding wheel. Sparks are white to straw color with bursts whose intensity and profusion increases with carbon content.
400 series stainless steels	Sparks, which are fewer and less dense than those from plain carbon steels, are 34–45 cm (14–18 in.) long, and travel completely around the grinding wheel. They are straw to orange color, giving some burst and ending with forked tongue.
300 series stainless steels	Similar to the 400 series but with slightly shorter sparks. They end in a straight line, with a few, if any, bursts.
310 series austenitic stainless steels	A thin, short spark stream, 10–15 cm (4–6 in.) long. Sparks, which are orange to red, do not travel around the grinding wheel and have no bursts.

- Technicorp
  646 Eyster Boulevard
  Rockledge, FL 32955
  Telephone: 407-631-6817 Fax: 407-631-6824
- Walker Scientific Inc.
  Rockdale Street
  Worcester, MA 01606
  Telephone: 508-852-3674 Fax: 508-856-9931

Thermoelectric Testing

This testing utilizes the same physical principle that makes thermocouples work, the Seebeck effect. A heated junction of dissimilar metals is created between a heated probe and the sample. The voltage generated by this junction is characteristic of the metal being tested. When appropriately calibrated, thermoelectric testing can distinguish stainless steel grades including 201, 301, 303, 304, 316, 321, and 347. It is fast and does not mar the product surface. The localized heating (about 160 °C, or 320 °F) is too low to cause property changes. Units are available from Koslow Scientific Company and Technicorp.

Optical Spectroscopy

A very small volume of the metal surface is vaporized and heated to luminescence by an electrical discharge. The light produced is analyzed and compared to the characteristic spectrum of individual elements. Although a quantitative analysis is not possible, the presence or absence of elements is established. Hence this technique can distinguish between 200, 300, and 400 grades and detect the presence of molybdenum in austenitic grades.

This is a sophisticated technique requiring considerable skill. Portable spectrometers are available, one supplier being:

- Metorex Inc.
  Princeton Crossroads Corporate Center
  P.O. Box 3540
  Princeton, NJ
  08543-3540
  Tel: 609-406-9000 Fax: 609-530-9055

X-Ray Analysis

X-ray analysis is also useful for determining the presence of particular elements within an alloy. In contrast to optical spectroscopy, it can quantify the amounts present. The sample is bombarded with x-rays, which in turn radiate a spectrum unique to the sample composition. Again, this is a sophisticated technique requiring considerable training. Nevertheless, portable x-ray spectrometers are extensively used for identification of scrap stainless. Such units are available from Metorex Inc.

Magnetic Permeability Testing

While the grade of a stainless steel cannot be determined by testing its magnetic permeability, this test is useful for measuring the ferrite content of austenitic and duplex grades. As we have pointed out, ferrite content has a significant effect on mechanical and corrosion properties of austenitic and duplex stainless steels. While it can be measured by metallographic techniques, these are time consuming and generally require that samples be cut from the component. Magnetic testing is accurately quantitative and nondestructive.

Portable probes developed specifically for this purpose can measure ferrite contents between 0 and 80%. One supplier is:

- Fischer Technology, Inc.
  750 Marshall Phelps Road
  Windsor, CT 06095-2199
  Telephone: 860-683-0781 Fax: 860-688-8496

The names and addresses of equipment suppliers identified in this appendix are provided only for the convenience of the readers. Neither authors nor publisher endorses any product.

APPENDIX 2

Toxicity of Stainless Steel

Two groups are concerned, the users and the manufacturers. At the outset and to avoid unnecessary alarm, we must point out that the user is not at risk, and the manufacturer should observe those precautions which, in general, ought to be observed in all metal-making and fabricating plants.

The Users

Contamination of foodstuffs from containers and cooking utensils has been recognized for a long while. This is not restricted to metal cooking pots and pans; a lead glaze on earthenware may be a culprit, and we recall exaggerated claims that the fall of the Roman Empire was due to lead poisoning from cold water pipes. However, back to the subject of stainless steels! Concerns expressed around 1990 led to intensified research on the possible pickup of chromium and nickel at unacceptable levels. (As far as we can discover, similar concerns were not expressed about iron, whose use in cauldrons, pots, and frying pans has a much longer history.)

Chromium, nickel, and many other metallic elements are believed to be essential ingredients of a normal diet and present in the human body. Not surprisingly, we can only infer from experiments on animals in what ways humans would suffer should these elements be completely absent, but the inference is that they are needed, and some authorities have recommended minimal daily intakes.

Hence the question is whether the use of stainless cooking utensils increases the levels of chromium and nickel to an unacceptable degree. That question is made more difficult because we do not know with certainty what the acceptable average levels might be. In any case, few of us are average, and none of us would admit to it even if we were.

With these provisos, we can say that actual tests, that is, tests in which real foods are cooked in off-the-shelf pots and pans, have set our own minds at ease. First, however, we must acknowledge that chromium in the hexavalent state is toxic. But little, if any, chromium is released in that state during the cooking of even the most corrosive foods and that which can be released (we are told) would not survive in the high acidity of our gastrointestinal tracts.

As to nickel, no detectable pickup has been noted except when rhubarb or apricots were cooked in brand new vessels. (Interestingly, when pots that had been used a few times were scoured, there was no measurable increase.) The amount of nickel at first use, however, is within a normal dietary intake unless one is a rhubarbaholic.

The only caution that we can discern in a great deal of literature on the subject is that if a person already has a hand eczema caused by contact with nickel or its compounds, the affliction may be aggravated by ingesting nickel. While this can occur by overeating stewed rhubarb cooked in a new pot, the cause can, no less, be an indulgence in too much chocolate. A similar assertion about chromium-related dermatitis has been made but is in contention.

In the preceding paragraphs, we have written about stainless steel in cooking utensils. We would be remiss not to remind you of references already made in this book to the uses of stainless steel where cleanliness is of utmost importance: in hospitals, food containment and transportation, surgical instruments, and kitchen sinks and counters. Their reliability has been shown to be not only due to the initial asepsis of the stainless surface but also to the effectiveness of subsequent cleansing in removing bacteria.

The Manufacturers

In many parts of the world where stainless steel is made or fabricated, legislation ensures or at least recognizes decent levels of industrial safety. These laws, for the most part, are general; that is to say they apply to all melt shops or to all processing facilities. Some are more specific and relate to particular metals or operations. This part of the appendix does not attempt to review or summarize these regulations. Rather, it touches upon those hazards that exist.

Almost two-thirds of the world production of nickel is consumed by stainless steel. Whether a person works in a nickel smelter or a stainless steel heat treat shop, the principal exposure to nickel is through inhalation. However, while one might at first believe that exposure would be greater in the smelter than in the heat treat shop, the range in each situation is so wide that no generalization can be made. And, in any case, it is quite possible, though improbable, that a normal diet can account for a greater intake of nickel than is breathed in at the smelter. Next to inhalation, skin contact presents the second important route of nickel absorption (probably not a very close second).

Most chromium is manufactured in the form of ferrochrome, almost all of which is used in stainless steel. Not unnaturally, worries about lung cancer and respiratory diseases associated with either nickel or chromium have topped the list of concerns. Here, in studies about both nickel and chromium, analyses have been skewed by tobacco smoking. However, a study involving lung function tests and radiographic examinations of workers who had spent on average 18 years in ferrochromium and stainless steel production detected no respiratory changes. Equally, tests relating to the effects of metallic nickel have shown no such association.

In this short appendix, we have necessarily tried to summarize a great deal of information which, while not conflicting, does not permit a hard, quantitative synthesis. Consequently, we recommend that persons with concerns direct them to the two organizations whose extensive publications we have used to provide this summary, The Nickel Development Institute and the International Chromium Development Association. Needless to say, we (not they) are responsible for any misinterpretations of the data they have published.

APPENDIX 3

Table of
Equivalent Designations

Table Appendix 3.1 lists stainless steel equivalent grades for the most widely used designation systems. Caution is required. Many grades are not represented in several of the systems, and more importantly, there is not always a precise correlation. For example, the last two digits of the U.K. designation identify the product form (bar, plate, sheet, etc.), and therefore several U.K. designations can correspond to one UNS designation. The identifiers under "Europe" are, for the most part, the EURONORM designations; however, there are several unique systems within Europe, many of which are very similar. The user of any of these designations should check specifications carefully against the steel composition, form, and condition required.

Table Appendix 3.1 Stainless steel equivalent grades for the most widely used designation systems

AISI	UNS	U.K.	Germany DIN	Europe	Russia	China	France AFNOR	Common name
Mn austenitic grades								
201	S20100	...	...	...	...	...	Z12CMN17-07 Az	...
...	S20161	...	...	...	...	...	...	
202	S20200	284S16	1.4371 X3 CrMnNiN 18 8 7	...	12Ch17G9AN4	1Cr18Mn8Ni5N	Z10CMN18.09	Gall-Tough(a)
...	S20300	...	...	...	...	...	...	...
205	S20500	...	...	...	...	...	...	203EZ(b)
...								Croloy 299
...	S20910	...	1.4565	X3 CrNiMnMoNbN 23 17 5 3	...	...	...	22-13-5(a), Nitronic 50(c)
...	S21000	...	...	...	...	...	...	SCF19(a), Sea-Fast
...	S21400	...	...	...	...	...	...	Tenelon
...	S21460	...	...	...	...	...	...	Cryogenic Tenelon
...	S21500	...	...	...	...	...	...	Esshete 1250
...	S21800	...	...	...	...	...	...	Nitronic 60(c)
...	S21900	...	...	...	...	...	...	Nitronic 40(c), 21-6-9(a)
...	S24000	...	...	...	...	...	...	Nitronic 33(c), 18-3Mn(c)
...	S24100	...	...	...	...	...	...	Nitronic 32(c), 18-2-12(a)
...	S28200	...	...	...	...	...	...	18-18 Plus(a)
...	...	...	1.4875	X55 CrMnNiN 20 8	...	...	...	
...	...	...	1.4871	X53 CrMnNiN 21 9	...	...	...	21-4N
...	...	...	1.4882	X50 CrMnNiNbN 21 9	...	...	...	21-43
Austenitic grades								
301	S30100	301S21	1.4310	X12 CrNi 17 7	...	...	Z11CN17-07	...
302	S30200	302S25	1.4300	X10 CrNiS 18 9	12Ch18N9	...	Z12CN18-09	...
302B	S30215		1.4330	...				
303	S30300	303S31	1.4305	X10 CrNi 18 9	...	1Cr18Ni9	Z10CNF18-9	...
	S30310							
303Se	S30323	303S42			12Ch18N10E			303 Plus X(d)
304	S30400	304S15	1.4301	X6 CrNi 1810KD	08Ch18N10	0Cr18Ni9	Z7CN18-09	
304Cu	S30430	394S17	1.4567					18-8, Pyromet350
304L	S30403	304S12	1.4306	X2 CrNi 1810KD	0Ch18N11	00Cr18Ni9	Z3CN18-10	...
304H	S30409	304S49	1.4948	...				...

(continued)

Table Appendix 3.1 (continued)

Austenitic grades (continued)

AISI	UNS	U.K.	Germany DIN	Europe	Russia	China	France AFNOR	Common name
	S30431	...	...	...	...	...	...	...
304N	S30451	304S65	...	X5CrNiN189KT	...	...	...	302HQ-FM(a)
304LN	S30453	304S62	1.4311	X2CrNiN1810KD	...	...	Z3CN18-10Az	...
305	S30500	305S19	...	X8CrNi1812KD	O6Ch18N11	...	Z8CN18-12	...
	S30600	...	...	...	...	...	...	Cronifer18-15LCSi
308	S30800	...	1.4303	...	...	...	Z6CN20-10	...
309	S30900	309S24	1.4829	X15CrNi2313	20Ch23N13	...	Z20CN24-13	...
309S	S30908	309S16	1.4833	X6CrNi2213	...	...	...	...
310	S31000	310S24	1.4841	X15CrNiSi2520	Ch25N20	...	...	...
310S	S31008	310S16	1.4845	X6CrNi2520	...	...	Z8CN25-20	...
314	S31400	...	1.4841	...	20Ch25N2052	1Cr25Ni20Si2	Z12CNS25.20	...
316	S31600	316S16	1.4401	X6CrNiMo1712KD	...	...	Z7CND17-11-02	...
316L	S31603	316S11	1.4404	X2CrNiMo18133KD	...	OOCr17Ni14Mo2	Z3CND17-11-02	...
316H	S31609	...	1.4919	X6CrNiMo1713	...	...	...	...
316Ti	S31635	...	1.4571	X6CrNiMoTi17122	O8Ch17N13M2T	OCr18Ni12Mo2Ti	Z6CDDT17.12	Type316Ti
316Nb (316Cb)	S31640	318S96	1.4580	X6CrNiMoNb17122	O8Ch16N13M2B	...	Z6CNDNb17-12	...
316N	S31651	316S66	1.3952	X6CrNiMoN17122	...	...	...	...
316LN	S31653	316S62	1.4406	X2CrNiMoN17133	...	...	Z3CND17-12Az	...
317	S31700	317S16	1.4449	X2CrNiMo18164	...	...	...	Type317LM
317L	S31703	317S12	1.4438	...	...	...	...	Type317LN
	S31725	...	...	...	...	...	...	...
	S31753	...	...	...	...	...	...	...
321	S32100	321S12	1.4541	X6CrNiTi1810	...	...	Z6CNT18-10	...
321H	S32109	...	1.4941	X8CrNiTi1810	...	...	...	...
330	N08330	...	1.4864	...	...	...	...	...
347	S34700	347S17	1.4550	X8CrNiNb1811	O8Ch18N12B	...	Z6CNNb18-10	...
348	S34800	...	1.4878	...	...	...	...	...
	...	...	1.4873	X45CrNiW189	...	...	...	...
384	S38400	...	1.4321	...	...	...	...	...

(continued)

Table Appendix 3.1 (continued)

AISI	UNS	U.K.	Germany DIN	Europe	Russia	China	France AFNOR	Common name
Super austenitic grades								
...	N08028	...	1.4563	X1 NiCrMoCuN 31 27 4	...	...	...	Sanicro 28
...	N08800	...	1.4876	X10 NiCr AlTi 32 20	...	...	...	Type 332
...	N08904	...	1.4539	X1 NiCrMoCuN 25 20 5	...	...	...	904L
...	N08367	...	1.4529	X1 NiCrMoCuN 25 20 6	...	...	...	AL-6XN(e)
...	N08925	...	1.4529	X1 NiCrMoCuN 25 20 6	...	...	...	Cronifer 1925 hMo, 25-6Mo
...	N08926	...	1.4529	X1 NiCrMoCuN 25 20 6	...	...	...	20Mo-6(a)
Duplex grades								
...	S31803	...	1.4462	X2 CrNiMoN 22 5 3	...	...	...	2205, 233 FAL, SAF2205
...	S32304	...	1.4362	X2 CrNiN 23 4	...	...	...	2304, UR 35N
...	S32550	...	1.4507	X2 CrNiMoCuN 25 6 3	...	...	...	Ferralium 255, UR 52N
329	S32900	...	1.4460	X4 CrNiMoN 27 5 2	...	...	...	7-Mo
...	S32950	...	...	...	...	...	...	7-Mo Plus(a)
Ferritic grades								
405	S40500	405S17	1.4002	X6 CrAl13	...	...	Z8CA12	...
409	S40900	409S19	1.4512	X6 CrTi12	...	...	Z3CT12	...
429	S42900	...	...	...	...	...	...	
430	S43000	430S15	1.406	X6 Cr 17	12Ch17	1Cr17	Z8C17	...
430F	S43020	...	...	X10 CrS17	...	...	Z10CF17	...
430FSe	S43023	...	...	...	...	...	...	...
430Ti	S43036	...	1.4502	...	...	1Cr17Ti	Z4CT17	Type 430Ti
434	S43400	434S19	1.4113	...	O8Ch17Ti	Z8CD17-1	...	...
439	S43035	...	1.4510	...	O8Ch17Ti	0Cr17Ti	...	
442	S44200	442S19	...	...	...	...	...	
444	S44400	...	1.4523	...	...	1Cr17Mo2Ti	...	18Cr-2Mo, AL 29-4-C(e)
...	S44800	...	...	...	...	...	...	E-Brite(e), AL 29-4-2(e)
446	S44660	...	1.40083	...	15 Ch28	1Cr25Ti	Z10C24	SEA-CURE(f), SC-1
...	S44635	...	...	...	...	...	...	MONIT

(continued)

Table Appendix 3.1 (continued)

AISI	UNS	U.K.	Germany DIN	Europe	Russia	China	France AFNOR	Common name
Martensitic grades								
403	S40300	410S21	1.4006	...	...	1Cr13	Z6C13	...
410	S41000	410S21	1.4006	X12 Cr13KD	12Ch13	...	Z13C13	...
410S	S41008	403S17	1.4000	...	08Ch13	0Cr13	Z8C12	...
414	S41400	...	...	...	...	2Cr13Ni2	...	...
415	S41500	...	1.4313	X4 CrNi 13 4	...	...	...	CA6NM, 410NiMo
416	S41600	416S21	1.4005	...	...	Cr14S	Z12 CF 13	...
416Se	S41610	...	...	...	...	...	...	416 Plus X(d)
...	S41623	416S41	...	...	...	...	...	...
420	S42000	420S29	1.4021	...	20X13	2Cr13	Z20 C13	Trim Rite(a)
...	S42010	...	...	...	...	...	...	...
420F	S42020	...	...	...	...	...	...	...
422	S42200	...	...	...	15Ch12WNMF	...	...	Lapelloy, 619
...	S42300	...	...	...	...	...	...	...
431	S43100	431S29	1.4057	X19 CrNi 17 2	14Ch17N2	1Cr17Ni2	...	...
440A	S44002	...	1.4109	...	...	...	Z60 CD 17	...
440B	S44003	...	1.4112	...	9Ch18MoV	...	780 CD 17	...
440C	S44004	...	1.4125	...	95Ch18	9Cr18	Z100 CD 17	...
...		...	1.4718	X45 CrSi 9 3	...	...	...	...
...		...	1.4731	X40 CrSiMo 10 2	...	...	...	...
...		...	1.4748	X85 CrMoV 18 2	...	...	...	...
Precipitation hardenable grades								
...	S13800	...	...	...	...	...	...	PH13-8Mo(c)
...	S15500	...	...	...	...	...	...	15-5PH(c)
632	S15700	...	1.4540	...	...	OCr17NiMo2Al	Z10 CNDA 15-7	15-7PH(c), PH15-7 Mo
630	S17400	...	1.4542	X5 CrNiCuNb 17 4	...	OCr17Ni4Cu4Nb	Z25 CNU 17-04	17-4PH(c)
...	S17600	...	...	...	...	...	...	Stainless W
631	S17700	...	1.4568	...	O9Ch17N7Jul	OCr17Ni7Al	Z9 CNA 17-7	PH 17-7(c)
...	S45000	...	...	...	...	...	...	Custom 450(a)

(continued)

Table Appendix 3.1 (continued)

AISI	UNS	U.K.	Germany DIN	Europe	Russia	China	France AFNOR	Common name
Precipitation hardenable grades (continued)								
...	S45500	...	...	...	...	...	...	Custom 455(a)

(a) Tradename of Carpenter Technology Corp. (b) Tradename of Al-Tech Corp. (c) Tradename of Armco Inc. (d) Trademark of Crucible Inc. (e) Trademark of Allegheny Ludlum Steel Co. (f) Trademark of Trent Tube

Subject Index

A

O

P

Z

Alloy Index